Anne-Marie Newland's

SUN POWER YOGA

SHALA

A Personal Journey through the Theory, Philosophy and
everyday Practice of Yoga, as both a Student and Teacher.

" I defy anyone *not* to turn the next page! "

Laura McGregor
Principal Lecturer in Photography and Video
at De Montfort University, Leicester

Secret Recipe

Without that special ingredient *inspiration*, this book would not exist. Cathlene Kidston-Fitt was heaven-sent to me as that special flavour that only she could provide, and it's called the Essence of Love, Laughter, Colour and Endless cups of tea!

Secret Ingredients

My love and salutations to **The Models** Magda Szarota, Nicola Ongaro, Terry Williams RIP, Mymuna Ali, Charlotte Walsh, Ryan James-Ludlam, Shola Arewa, Melissa Newland, Jamie Newland, Talitha Hepple-Newland, Sam Hadcock, Rita Osborne, Tomasz Geborys, Brendan Murphy, Aziz Alajaji and Sandra Laznik.

My heart-felt thanks and deepest respect to **The Artists** Lala Meredith-Vula, Sylvia Reitzema, Talitha Hepple-Newland, Lucy Archer, Silvia Occhionorel and Bob Spencer for their original artwork and photography.

Secret Agents

The people who kept me going were Jamie, Liam & Melissa Newland, Talitha Hepple-Newland, Chris Hepple, Shereen Khachik, Shola Arewa, Rita Osborne, Laura McGregor, Lala Meredith-Vula, Joy Campbell, Teresa Saliba, Karen Logan, John McKeogh, Camilla Moselund Toft, Massi Caneli, Helen Ingall, Bipin and Jyoti Mistry, Sherraine Morris, Ellen Bianchini, Ariane Thompson Van de Vyver, Annette Jarvis, Samir Khachik, Rachel McDonald, Annie Vincent, Andrew Tomlinson, Kajoli Gokarn, Kailash Mistry, Bob Spencer and my coffee support team, Stephen, Savanah, Mukhtar & Laura at Costa, Queens Rd Leicester.

Dedication

For my parents Joan and Abdulahad Khachik who were always sitting with me throughout this endeavour.

My Father's parents Yousef and Khatoun were illiterate Armenian peasants who,
God knows how, managed to get my father educated and to study in Leicester, England.
My Mother's father was self-educated, reading everything he could lay his eyes on. Sunday
lunch could only be eaten after we correctly answered his 3 general knowledge questions!

My Mother always revered knowledge no matter where or how it was obtained or stumbled upon.

"Knowledge is the food of the mind and no knowledge that comes your way is not
of use. If it comes, treasure it, you never know when you may need it."

Saraswati

The Goddess of Knowledge

Saraswati is a Sanskrit fusion word of Sara which means 'essence', and
Sva which means 'oneself', the fused word meaning 'essence of oneself', and
Saraswati, meaning 'one who leads to essence of Self knowledge'.

Oh Mother Goddess, remove my mental dullness!

Contents

Foreword by Toyah Wilcox..15

OPENING PRAYER 17

ABOUT THIS BOOK 19

How to use this Book 20

Introducing Yoga..22

About Anne-Marie 29

A Conversation with Anne-Marie 34

YOGA SHALA 41

Sun Power Yoga Shala..42

SACRED SPACES 47

THE TRADITION 55

AT THE FEET OF THE GURU 57

Why are the Guru's feet called 'Lotus Feet'?

Gurukula...62

What are the Vedas?

The Teachers 64

The Guru 66

My Guru..72

Indra Devi: Yoga's First Lady 76
Founder of Sai Yoga

Swami Sivananda Radha 80

IS YOGA A RELIGION?.. **85**
Yoga is not a Religion 86

Nataraj 87

Prayer 87
Is praying religious?

Yoga Philosophy made easier......................................92

Reincarnation..94

YOGA THEORY **99**
Practicing Ahimsa, on which Yoga Psychology is based 100
Tuning into our Grooves, our Samskaras

A Map for a Successful Life.. 106
So what is Hatha Yoga?
What is Astanga Vinyasa Yoga?
Yoga Sutras of Patanjali

The Four Paths of Yoga... 109
Karma Yoga
Bhakti Yoga
Raja Yoga
Jnana Yoga
Vedanta
The Upanishads

The Art of Sacred Geometry 124
What is Tantra?
Yantra: the Tantric Symbol of Cosmic Unity
What is the Sri Yantra?

Mandala

Yantra Mandalas and their Power

The Gunas 132

What are the Three Gunas and why do Yogis live by them?

The Three **Gunas**, in all areas of life

The Mind's Relationship with Food 136

Food and Mood

Some tips for a Loving Body and Healthy Mind

THE ASHRAM 147

What is an Ashram? 148

Satsang 150

A Gathering of Like-Minded People

Mauna 153

What is Mauna?

Mauna Vratham, the Vow of Silence

Mahabharata 156

Ramayana 157

The Bhagavad Gita 158

What was the purpose of the Bhagavad Gita?

The Purpose of Mauna 161

THE PURPOSE 171

RITUALS FOR FAITH AND HOPE 173

In Yoga Practice, why do we do ...? 174

Why do we perform certain Rituals?

What is Pradakshina? 176

Why is it practised?

What is its meaning and purpose?

Lighting a candle or oil lamp 178

What is the Purpose of an Altar or Sacred Space?.................. 181

Why do we do Namaste?... 182

Why do we Prostrate?... 186
   The different ways of showing respect

Why we never touch people, books or papers with the feet... 188

Why do we consider the Lotus Flower as Auspicious? 190

Why fast? 192
   Anna Yoga
   Fasting and Mental Clarity

Why do we chant OM?... 196

SYMBOLS OF PROTECTION 201
   Ganesha, the Elephant God
   Hand of Fatima
   The Evil Eye
   Dream Catcher
   The Cross
   Isis – Angel Wings and Heart

THE PRACTICE 221

Yoga Nidra 222
   The Yoga of Conscious sleep in Savasana
   Achieving Savasana

Breathing for Life and Peace of Mind 224
   Pranayama
   1. Breath-Awareness.
   Taking notice of the action of breathing.
   2. Yogic Breathing – Abdominal Breathing
   3. Ujjayi – Victorious Breath

Kapalabhati
Dynamic Diaphragmatic Breathing

Balance the Breath

Anuloma Viloma
Alternate Nostril Breathing

Mudras: Yoga for the Hands 238

What is a Mudra?

Chin Mudra – Conscious Breath Gesture

Tse Mudra – The Secret Gesture

Shankh Mudra – Indian term for Conch

Prana Mudra – Invocation of the Life-force energy

Rude-ras!

News Flash!

The Chakras: What are they anyway? 246

An introduction to the function, the purpose
and the history

Double Helix and The Nadis 281

The Body Prayer 286

Hatha Yoga 290

The Hatha Yoga Pradipika

The Art of True Practice 294

Thought before Practice

SURYA NAMASKA 297

Surya Namaska – Classical... 298

Your Body is the first place to begin your Prayer

What is the Sun Salutation about?

Sun Power Series... 306

A Journey from Earth to the Sun

A DAILY PRACTICE 321

How to fit some Yoga into your busy schedule

Taking steps to get on your mat

A Yoga Home Class Plan

YOGA FOR HARD TIMES 345

Your body is your calling card, it says who you are

Yoga for when you've overdone it!

Yoga for stressful real – life drama

Yoga in the Work place – Home or away

Yoga for a near-functional family Life

Yoga in your home space

The Four Agreements

DEPRESSION 379

Depression: The Human Kind 380

In my own experience

Zen Buddhist Meditation 391

How I ultimately overcame my own depression

GOOD VIBRATIONS 397

The Power of Light 398

MEDITATION 403

What are the benefits of Meditating? 404

Where and how do I start?

Why do we use incense, inspirational objects and candles?

Starting Your Meditation Practice 412

Why meditate anyway?

Preparing your Body 415

Start By 'Acting out' the Positive

Abstract Brain changes in Meditation 418
   Brain Training: Activating the Amygdala
   The Pineal Gland, what an eye-opener!
   Change your Mind

Three Easy and Sustainable Meditation Practices 427
   Prepare to Meditate
   Candle Gazing – Tratak
   How to Practice Tratak
   Breath Awareness Meditation
   Japa Meditation

VISUALISATIONS 443

Visualisations for Heart and Soul 444
   The Rose–Heart: A Story about Love and Forgiveness.
   The Chakra Garden: A Place for Us
    A Visualisation for Children and vulnerable Young People

SACRED SOUNDS 459

Kirtan: Chanting of Sacred Sounds 460
   The Theory and Practice
   What is the Subtle Vibration we experience in Kirtan?

Om Namah Shivaya 467

LIVING A LIFE 469

Affirmation 470
   We, The Lotus Bud of Perfection

Lifestyles 472
   Which one do you fit into?

NATURAL YOU 477

FROM LUMINOUS BIRTH TO GOLDEN YEARS 483

Heart to Heart Resuscitation

What is 'being' young and what is 'being' old?

The secret of Youth is Yoga

ASK ANNE-MARIE 493

. . . about establishing breathing techniques........................... 494

. . . about Surya Namaskar, Sun Salutations 500

. . . about Adho Mukha Svanasana, Down Dog 504

. . . about Warrior I & II and the Triangle................................ 508

. . . about Balances 516

. . . about Twists 522

. . . about Forward and Back Bends.. 530

. . . about Inversions: Headstand, Shoulder stand, Plough and Legs up the Wall pose... 538

. . . about Matsyasana, The Fish Pose............................. 544

. . . about Anatomy Basics 548

. . . about Sanskrit Terminology and Philosophy..................... 566

What are the Sanskrit names and translations of the basic Yoga postures that we use in a Sun Power Yoga class?

YOUR KNOWLEDGE LIBRARY 580

How to access what you have learned

Method of Loci: The Mind Palace

Creating your own Mind Palace

CLOSING PRAYER 589

My Favourite Books... and other resources

Index

Credits

Foreword by Toyah Wilcox

TV Presenter, Actress, Singer and Speaker

Life is a constant journey of growth and enlightenment for all of us and this is what I love about Anne-Marie Newland's *Sun Power Yoga Shala*.

Within this beautifully illustrated book, not only has Anne-Marie mapped the journey of a fulfilled, creative life but she has also managed to contain within its pages the wisdom of Yoga and the possibility of a step-by-step journey into a more enlightened lifestyle for the reader.

It tackles serious subjects such as depression, how to get a daily practice established with a family and work as well as why we light candles and incense.

I am particularly pleased to see 'chair -Yoga' as I am not made for sitting crossed legged.... therefore no more excuses for me! Yoga is available to everyone and you don't need me to tell you Yoga prolongs life and helps everyone have an active life whatever age you are.

As an international teacher of Yoga Anne-Marie has clearly mapped the culture, the beliefs and the art of Yoga in a way that will open doors of understanding to those who may not otherwise have considered the spiritual side of this health giving art form.

Toyah Wilcox

Already punks, Toyah and Anne-Marie met in 1977 in Crouch End London. She lived over the chip shop and Anne-Marie in a left wing socialist commune! Their mutual love of music and anything 'off the wall' threw them full on into the Punk era that transformed both their lives in diverse and remarkable ways.

Toyah formed a band called The Maneaters with Anne-Marie as her drummer. They filmed Jubilee with Derek Jarman and Adam Ant and it is now seen as a 'cult film' of its time.

Toyah became one of the faces of the Punk revolution, a singer with a string of hits and an extraordinary actress. Anne-Marie became a well known Fashion designer, drummer and entrepreneur. Toyah is well known for her health and well-being work and Anne-Marie as an international Yoga teacher and trainer.

Interesting how their paths have crossed yet again!

Opening Prayer

Divine Teacher,

I close my eyes to open them to you.

To see the intricate workings of the Soul's path

leading with its light before me.

I ask that I learn to see this path with my eyes wide open

and to understand those parallel worlds are not separate

but are simply not yet understood.

Divine Student,

I, who take you from Darkness to Light, ask that you be

joyful in the knowledge that you too hold the light for

those around you.

In all things there is an element of wonder, fear and pain

but ultimately, *Enlightenment*.

AMN

about this book

How to use this Book

Some books need to be read cover to cover, others you can dip into, like an Oracle, asking a question and receiving an answer.

This book is a celebration of knowledge and the relationship between a teacher and a student, and is therefore something you could start by reading cover to cover then using it as an Oracle. The teacher is within you, as is the student, for a good teacher is also a good student.

Wear both your hats in all you do.

At the end of each part is a work page with a place for your thoughts to be recorded. This will relate to the section you have just read and is called 'Note to *Self*'.

Consider each section as a step in the right direction. Be brutally honest here and listen to your mental dialogue. Is it your voice you hear, or the ego? In Greek the word Ego means 'I' but it is the small 'i' not the greater Self.

I write as I teach, with Intuition, the Inner-Tutor,
and I hope you may read it in the same way.

Introducing Yoga

You could be one of the thousands of people who have had a secret desire to try Yoga but have not had the courage to join a class yet, or you're simply curious about its philosophy.

For whatever reason you are here reading this now, it really doesn't matter.

I am hoping this book will answer some of your questions, take the mystery out of Yoga, clear up some misconceptions and help you see that Yoga is normal, natural and for everyone.

❖ What is Yoga anyway?

Great question!

I know so many who were never told what Yoga is or what the word means. 'Yoga', loosely translated, comes from the Sanskrit root *Yug*, 'to yoke'. The yoking here is bringing together in

It's not enough to have an active body; try considering your mind's health and how you breathe too and it will make you not just fit but 'Fit for Life'.

When people consider Yoga as an alternative to running, impact exercise or sport because of recurring injuries or a 'change of life' direction, the most common questions I am asked are:

one practice, the Mind, the Body and the Breath. I like to imagine the Breath as the bridge between the Mind and the Body. Without these elements we are not practicing Yoga but are simply exercising the body.

❊   Can I really feel good afterwards for longer than a few hours?

Yes! It's an opportunity to switch off that busy mind and give it one job to do – watching the breath. This is better than sleep when you consider our dreams can be dramas lived out and are often exhausting! Being able to learn the skill of relaxing is your biggest reward because you take it with you when the class ends.

Deep relaxation, *Savasana* (Corpse pose) allows the adrenals to calm down because you lie on the floor, allowing the spine to rest and the organs to release into their natural positions. Tension is created inside the body first then manifests itself on your outer body. Try switching your focus to feeling good!

The awareness of how good we feel when relaxed is the most important aim of this practice, not to focus on when we feel ill-at-ease. This lasts as long as your awareness does.

❊   Do I need to be flexible first?

This is such a common question. No of course you don't have to be flexible first. Part of the bonus of your Yoga practice is that you become flexible. But guess what? It's the Mind that we work on to become flexible first! When you are able to let go of stress in the body, this allows the mind to relax as well. Stress, illness and tightness are mostly due to our mental states.

We become mentally exhausted and in the end our barriers fall down and we are vulnerable to more 'Dis-Ease'. When we are relaxed and able to handle stress then we are more 'At-Ease'.

❋ Am I too old to start Yoga?

No! What is too old anyway? I would say this is the one practice you can start at anytime in your life and it's often when you need it most. That is the best reason for starting. I have people come in at 80 and 8. Yoga is more than the physical; it's a connection to all aspects of the human being. Yoga gives you a sense of self-control when the rest of your life seems out of control. Yoga lets you have time out to switch off from anything; the good, the bad and the ugly in your life right now. So if Yoga sounds interesting and you want to try it then what's stopping you? Your Mind that's all!

❋ I am overweight. Do I have to lose weight first?

This is one of the saddest things I hear. I always feel so upset that Yoga has this awfully wrong illusion for most of us. I am distraught to hear my own daughter say this, "When did you ever see a big girl in a Yoga class Mum?" Ouch!

Well you will in mine! The modern impression of Yoga is a testament to teachers out there who do not include all body types in a class. Maybe they are not even aware that there are souls on the outside of their class simply looking in and not joining in. Yoga is for all...Every Body! Yoga helps to deal with the mind and to learn to accept who we are.

I have the same problem with very thin people who are also disillusioned about their body image and think Yoga will allow them to hide in the class with other skinny people and their problems can hide there too.

I teach a lot of my class with eyes closed. This allows us to not see the outer bodies but to spend time with ourselves. In the end we are not our bodies, we are our minds. Changing our minds helps change how we feel about what we are and to make rational decision's about how we change and what we change.

❖ I want to work deeper in my practice. What does this mean and how do I do it?

When I first stumbled into Yoga, I had no idea what it was…. just a set of movements in silence. I enjoyed this the first time but my mind was not impressed. As a ballet dancer I was used to using my body in a way most other people could not. So I gave it up! Then in 1983, while I was sitting in my shop in Kensington selling my own designs, I took a break. I lit a cigarette and made a very strong cup of tea and sat to talk about the gig I had played at the night before. I was a rock'n'roller and drumming was a great passion. I had been in bands since working with Toyah Wilcox and the Clash in 1977.

I heard a voice in my right ear. "Do Yoga Seriously". I was held in a moment of complete stillness and confusion. "Did you hear that?", I asked my colleague. "Hear what?", "Do Yoga Seriously". I picked up Time Out and started looking at the ads at the back of the magazine, looking for Yoga classes. I rang one, it didn't feel right, I rang another and a man I later learned was Swami Padmananda, told me I had missed the first class on the Monday but today, Wednesday, was the 2nd class of a three-week course and I could join it that night. After I closed my shop, I walked off happily to Notting Hill to the Sivananda Yoga Centre. When I entered the place I had a moment of panic and I nearly ran out. I realized I was about to take the first steps onto my Spiritual life. I had yearned for this for many years, since I felt the pull when I was as young as four in Iraq, going to the Syrian Orthodox church of my birth.

The teacher that night became my husband. Swami Vishnu-devananda blessed us on Swami Sivananda's birthday, 8 September 1983, and we were married in the traditional Yoga tradition on the 10th!

That is the meaning of working deeper. Seeing the door wide open and not running away.

Opportunities to change our lives, directions and our selves are always presenting themselves. It is whether you walk through that open door or not!

This is a lovely story I heard somewhere:

After our death we find ourselves walking toward the 'pearly gates' of Heaven and we ask to come in.

When we enter we are shown to our own apartment.

It's exactly what we always wanted when in our physical body!

In it are many boxes with our name on them, unopened.

"What are these?".

"Ah. These are all the miracles you ordered on earth, they were delivered to you but you never collected them"

Do you recognize
this story?

Is this you?

*If so, go and collect
your miracles now!*

About this book

About Anne-Marie

I need to go back to when life was just a series of images, smells, sounds and feelings. To a time when my head was bigger than my body and all I wanted was love.

It is 19 October 1955; a hot night in Kirkuk, Iraq. I am ready to be born and I am resisting. My mother is ready, the doctors and nurses are ready but still I remain in my dark warm place. I am staying right here. I don't want to come out.

How do I know all this? I know because I was there! My entry into the world was a good one. No trauma, no forceps, no drugs. Why am I resisting then?

My soul entered my body at the time of conception. That is one theory. My soul entered my body at the time I took my first breath; maybe. My soul entered my body the moment I knew I was me, separated from my soul brothers and sisters and the bigger soul of Spirit. Yes, that feels right.

I am separated from the bigger picture and I have an ego now; the 'little me', and yet I have a 'Knowledge of Self' but I am already beginning to forget. Such is the nature of the human being.

And so our journey begins here with a glimmer of a place that we have forgotten and now must journey back to so we can remember.

When I gave birth to my first child I was very aware of the depth of the experience and it seemed to me that I was in three places at one time; in the Past, the Present and the Future. I was in a mud hut with many women and I knew the desert was around me. I was not as I know me now but I was still myself, none the less, in one of my past lives. I was also present in the pain of childbirth, standing as my ancestors may have done. Pain is one of the most profound here-and-now experiences. It is not for running away from, but for diving into.

What I learned was that life is stronger than death and that life will fight to survive.

My child entered this world through the birth canal. Its four inches are the most dangerous four inches a human will travel. Its rotation, spiralling and massaging prepares the skin, the muscles, the bones and the nerves and senses for human life. This first physical stimulus is how we understand love through touch and how the brain is stimulated to open the eyes and receive messages for movement.

The Future was revealed to me in the hardest part of the birth. I knew very clearly that I had no choice from now on. The life that had come through me was out of my hands, my mind and my heart. The cord may still be attached to me but already that life would be my future.

The Moving—Being in its very earliest manifestation is a Ball of Light with no form, and so our body becomes our Divine Robe and shapes us.

AMN

This book has wanted to be written for a long time. Like all of us I had doubts; did I have anything to say worth reading? Was my story interesting? Was I deluded? I have read many Yoga books over the years and the ones that stay in my consciousness are those that have relayed a personal journey. There are books that have not remained in my consciousness. Why not? Because they didn't sound true of seem true and it helped me see I should never look at other books, just let mine come out.

Here you will find an easy way to learn, to remember and to take off from.

But be warned, Yoga is not a panacea for all emotional or physical problems; in fact it can sometimes make things worse before they get better. In other words, be honest and find out what you want Yoga for. It saved me from drugs at a time I thought I was fine. It helped sort out my relationship with my Father. I stopped trying to force things. Though I could make things happen, they were not always for the right reason. I learned to stop still and let things take their own course.

It was such a wonderful feeling to trust that all was well and as it should be.

I needed to put this book together for me but it's been as hard as giving birth! Harder because it has taken so long!

I have had an amazing life so far, diverse, exotic, frightening, courageous, brutal, and it continues to be rich in experience. If there were a choice between standing on the floor and flying, I would fly. If there were a choice between lying down and running, I would run! I also know when to do nothing – what a relief!

It's a practical message because it is simple in essence and useful today, right here, right now; because it will help change your life and you won't even know it until you react and connect differently one day and become the person you knew you were looking for all the time!

I wanted to travel my personal journey with my eyes open this time. Our personal journeys are so personal that often we miss them.

People have a varied view of Yoga. Often it is stereotypical; perfect people, perfect life, and perfect practice; if only that were true. My Yoga has been a painful journey as well as a blissful one.

My travels have led me from
country to person,
from self–belief to
self–doubt and back again.
I have experienced highs that
gave me the truth and
lows that have taken all
my sense of Faith and Self
to recover from.

Yoga is the map I chose to travel with.

A Conversation with Anne-Marie

❋ What were you doing before Yoga?

I was a ballet, contemporary and jazz dancer, having been trained by Arlene Phillips. In 1976 I joined a 9 piece political, left-wing band, after practicing drums for two weeks! I joined the punk revolution and played drums with Toyah Wilcox and Maneaters, for the movie Jubilee, 1977. As a punk drummer I did a tour of the country with a support act during The Clash's 1978 'Sort it Out' tour.

I became a fashion designer, selling my clothes in London at Camden Lock market, with a stall next to Anita Roddick, later to become The Body Shop phenomenon. Sue Clowes, later to become designer to Boy George, suggested I move into Kensington market, and I opened my first vintage clothes shop in 1979.

❋ How did you start Yoga?

My Mother introduced me to her local Yoga class in 1972. I was bored to tears; and then I found Iyengar Yoga in 1976 during an Annus Horribulus! But it did not hold me. It seemed empty for me.

In 1983 Yoga found me in my psychedelic designer clothes shop in Kensington Market, London. At around 2pm I had an epiphany; and the rest is history. I left my rock and roll life behind and walked into the light!

❋ How did it affect your life?

It changed it dramatically! I found I was able to adopt the principles of Yoga by dealing with things a lot better. I had a very hot temper and the meditation and chanting at the Sivananda

centre in Notting Hill was working! People always expected me to fight them. I stopped and I still got what I wanted by with reason and skill. This was powerful stuff!

1978

1977

1970

1983

1982

1979

SWEET CHARITY Swinging London Dollybird wear

About this book 35

What do you enjoy most about teaching Yoga?

I am old school; teaching is a vocation. I was forced into teaching my first jazz dance class in 1974 by a well-known choreographer, Arlene Phillips. I really thought this was the pits! In those days you were either a dancer or, if you didn't make it, a teacher ... but maybe that was my own prejudice because after that very first class I was hooked. I have been teaching some sort of body work ever since. I am passionate about teaching because that day when I was 19 I discovered I could really help people feel good about themselves and give clear instructions as to how they could achieve a dance, an exercise and to put something of themselves into it. Teaching is a Practical Magic!

Tell us about the particular style of Yoga you teach?

After many years of apprenticeship, which included teaching for some years without asking for payment, I built up a solid following. I studied Iyengar with Maxine Tobias, workshops with Iyengar in 1976 in London, Qualified with Swami Vishnu-devananda in Canada, London, Berlin and graduated in India at their Sivananda Vedanta Yoga centre in South India in 1984. I then studied Astanga Vinyasa Yoga with Beryl Bender Birch here in the UK and followed Bryan Kests enigmatic and powerful style. I ran classes in local clubs, pubs and schools, often stepping on cigarette ends and beef burgers left on the floor! All in all I did my homework and by 2001 I had blended all I had learned, by taking elements of all three styles, and Sun Power Yoga was born. I use all the subtle mind and breath work of Sivananda and the technique and alignment taught in Iyengar. As an ex-ballet and contemporary dancer, this was a crucial element to good practice and teaching for me. Astanga Vinyasa Yoga was that missing touch of flow, grace and heat. I began teaching this eclectic mix and style to my classes and it became so popular that students began to ask if they could train to teach it. So in 2003 we opened the Sun Power Yoga School. I started with seven students that year and now train 50 a year from all parts of the world. Apart from my four children, this school is my greatest achievement.

How do you fit your own practice around your teaching work?

What about being a single mother of four – the washing, cleaning, taxing, and being the main breadwinner? I do what I can each day by practising what I preach. Be as kind as you are allowed to be, try to work things out with your children, give them some space and always do a job to your best ability. Make each second matter; don't waste time; use it or be in it ... it's all Yoga! I work 6 days a week and I can get on the mat after I have unloaded the dishwasher!

What do you think makes a great Yoga teacher?

A great Yoga teacher is a person who works from a genuine passion for the work they do. It doesn't matter what you do in life, as long as it makes you feel good about yourself and it's authentic. Don't play at being a Yoga teacher; be it because you genuinely want to do nothing else. That's the same of any job you do but I know I am particularly lucky to have found my purpose so young in life. Purpose has to be the Holy Grail. If it's *only* a job then consider you still haven't found your purpose.

Do you have any favourite or memorable moments from your time on the Yoga mat?

Yoga for me is not about only being on the mat. Yoga is a huge, inclusive concept of theory and life. So when I am on the mat I am able to bring all those elements together. My breath is in time with my mind and my mind in rhythm with my body. Creating Sun Power Yoga came from this union and a moment of intuition and inspiration. I had been thrown out of the Astanga elite crew that morning, by letter, for not being a purist. I smiled to myself and realized that I did not need approval or permission, just the courage to let my Yoga experience take shape, then flight, and it did. Sun Power Yoga was born that day on the mat.

What do you do when you're not teaching or practicing Yoga?

I practice Yoga in all I do or say. I get it wrong, I get it right and some days I am plain horrid, others divine. I run my school, which is very big now, and as Founder and Company Director I am hands-on in all aspects. Saturday I don't open the computer, and spend time with my youngest teenage child. We chill out together. Sundays are our big teaching days, and if I am abroad I am on the job 24/7. I don't do hobbies; I love my work.

What would you say to those that have never tried Yoga before, to encourage them to take their first steps?

I don't encourage anyone unless they have shown interest and asked me about it. The most common statement I hear is, "I am not supple so I can't do Yoga". Dispelling people's idea of Yoga because of images and media is sometimes tough. I never told my children to do Yoga; it was my path but there is no reason it has to be theirs. Having said that, now they are grown they all practice it, apart from my youngest who, at the age of ten told me, "I hate Yoga; it's ruined my life!" However, I did notice her pack her Yoga mat when leaving for university.

Any words of wisdom for your fellow yogis?

Yes. Be honest; allow your weaknesses to show as well as your strengths; admit when you don't know something and be a real person. Pretending to be perfect is so hard to keep up. If you need help, ask or you will always seem to be coping; maybe you are but if you aren't then communicate it to your friends and family. Being human means that we are not meant to be alone. We are aspiring to reach a higher mental attitude but in the end, it's your heart that makes you feel your life.

Why do you think people should practice Yoga?

*I don't think people should practice Yoga.
I think people can find their own path in life and
it just so happens that Yoga is mine.*

The many faces of Yoga

The term Yoga Shala
has more than one meaning.
It is a collection of spaces used for
the absorption, delivery, practice and
accumulation of Knowledge
from Teacher to Student,
for the creation of family and
community and for
Personal Spiritual Growth.

Yoga Shala

Sun Power Yoga Shala

The Sanskrit word *Shala* means 'abode', 'home' or 'school',
and it can also mean a 'Sacred Space'.
This is what my life and school has become, the Sun Power Yoga Shala.
I have been teaching bodywork since 1974 and I always tell my students
'Wherever I lay my mat is my home'.

I may be considered a maverick, yet I am old school; I believe in such things as manners, etiquette, hard honest work, commitment and loyalty; this may seem odd if indeed I am a maverick!

The dictionary definition of 'maverick' is to be unorthodox, independent, do your own thing. The true root of the word however, means being a rebel and not doing what other people do or go along with, and actually comes from the American cattle ranches – a term used to refer to a loose cow that doesn't have a brand. Love this!

What I did when I started my school and 'style' is what so many other adventurers have done; that is to forge a path in a new direction, carrying with you the tools and manuscripts of the past.

So often this path is one you walk alone. It was at a time of great personal hardship that my school was realized. I was breaking away from tradition apparently, but like all traditions, they are things we do each moment, day, month or year. After a while the reason and purpose is forgotten. Getting into grooves with no understanding as to why we are doing it is mindless rather than mindful.

The Relationship between the Yoga Teacher and the Yoga Student is unique in so far as Yoga, in its purest form, is about change. The responsibility laid at the feet of the Teacher or Guru is one of guidance, of leading with a gentle but firm hand, and a way of giving and receiving. A contract that involves 'Energy' involves a two-way flow of those energies. If *Prana* (Life-force, *Qi* or *Chi)* is not allowed to flow then we become sick, either in our body or mind. Both Teacher and Student agree on the terms of that Karmic contract. In itself this is liberating because its about timing. Right time right place – it can never be forced, only found.

I stepped into my present life as Yoga Teacher trainer with both determination and clear vision, a deciding moment that made another profound change in not only my own life but of those I was destined to work with. I had walked away from a life that I loved and worked hard for but, as ever, miracles fall into your lap and if you are awake you will recognize them and act upon them.

I did my apprenticeship after I had finished my initial training with Swami Vishnu-devananda in Canada, and had qualified in India by teaching at the Sivananda Centre in Notting Hill. I was pregnant and was asked to teach a pregnancy class. I was in awe to find that these women were blind and they had no idea what they would look like when they were getting bigger. I was seven months pregnant and they held my belly and oohed and ahhed...it was a lovely moment for me, a realisation that the world could look so different for other people.

I do believe it was then that I saw my teaching, my future mothering and all the nurturing to come as my purpose. My dear students and the teachers I have trained are like my children and when they have a wonderful day teaching others they perpetuate the unique relationship between Teacher and Student and it is so like Parent and Child.

Yoga reached out to me with a quiet voice, a voice that I now call my 'compassionate other', that speaks gently to me when I lose my way, my understanding and my temper!

That day that I got my first clear call to change my life and 'do Yoga seriously' was when I learned that one human being could give up their personal life for the good of others. That person was Swami Vishnu-devananda and of course Swami Sivananda, whose presence is forever with me in my work; in fact I could not and do not work alone.

A Yoga Shala is also a community, a family and a support structure, but it should never be exclusive, excluding other people or other ways. There is a place for all and there cannot be just one way of doing or living. If you never put your leg around the back of your neck or meditated it does not mean you have never practiced Yoga. Yoga is life on all levels of awareness and asks that you live with compassion and *Ahimsa*, non-violence in word, thought or deed. But if on the way you stumble then pick yourself up and carry on.

The Paths are many
but the Truth is One
There are many Paths up the
Mountain no matter what you
believe but in the end there is only
one Summit.

I woke up and looked around.

I felt the Sun on my body and I knew I was born.

My map for life was on the patterns of my skin
and the path under my feet.

As I reached out my small hand to touch the Divine
I touched my Mother and wept.

AMN

Sacred Spaces

Sacred Spaces

Any Sacred Space is the home of Knowledge, the Mother of the Mind and the place we begin. It may be the beginning of a story, a journey or the first step into a place of Self-Discovery.

I have had four children; all different in every way, and that included their births. The births were so intense that I realized that all the Yoga I had been practicing was exactly what I needed to allow the natural process to take place. I chose to have my babies at home for lots of reasons, the most important one being that having a baby was a super-natural urge and therefore something that was beyond reason, more like a season, and my Mother had told me not to worry, I wasn't ill I was having a baby!

Birth is the most mysterious event on Earth.

Where I gave birth to them was very important, so I had them at home in the safe space I had created through intense Yoga and meditation, preparing the ground of my body and the place to offer my children their human incarnation.

I can clearly remember watching my mother give birth to my little sister at home in Iraq, where babies were born every day in simple environments. Hospitals were far away and only used by the English and foreign workers in high positions. I was 5 years old at the time and all the children of the street, our dusty road in Basra, pressed noses up against the shutters of the room leading into the courtyard and could hear the women with my Mother while giving birth. It all seemed very normal and just part of our lives. We laughed as we tried to look through the slats and I still see my mother standing and leaning against the wardrobe as the women knelt down to catch her child. In that instant I knew I was witnessing a moment of Sacred Inspiration, a moment in silent witness to a new life, not just for the child but also for the family.

The most profound of all Sacred Spaces
has to be the womb.

During my years of raising my children I have seen things change, but ultimately we love and we nurture as we have always done, unless our own babyhood was disturbed or disturbing. It's obvious to me that the problems children have these days are no different to those a hundred years ago. No positive role model leads to copying the role the parents have in their own drama. How and when we begin our journey with our child will depend on our own life experiences, some of which we have no conscious memory of.

As my children have grown into uniquely individual people I feel awed at the choices they are making for their lives. You lose your children at some point in their growing up journey, that is inevitable; breaking away from the Mother-Ship is as important as choosing to break the rules at school.

What does this have to do with Scared Space you may be asking? Teaching children, family, loved ones, students and teachers the idea of a Sacred Space is a step towards self-respect. Putting a quality of awareness into what we do and where we do it is a simple building block towards reverence of both Self and Purpose. We behave differently in each part of our life, for instance we are respectful of Silence in a Holy place, of the quiet needed in hospitals for the sake of the ill. Our energy is very different in a dance club or party. However, this in no way means we should have less respect in those busy human spaces.

Sacred Space is about both our personal space and that of others.

As we delve deeper into Yoga Theory and Philosophy we begin to understand that what we develop is an innate respect for all things animate or in-animate. We have begun to realize that the life force, life giver, (*Prana*), is in all. This concept is shared by many cultures, such as the Native American Indian, Australian Aborigines and the lesser-known civilisations of the South American Indigenous peoples.

What is life if not Sacred?
What is the purpose of life if not to respect and to honour?
What is the point of the pain and joy of life if not to rediscover who we are and from where we came?

Where does this Scared Space begin? It must begin with the womb and therefore with education for Mother and Father, the family, the community. Being allowed to be sensitive is the start. But how do we protect our Sacred Space from abuse, horror, pain and dishonour? It must start with us. Meditation, contemplation and awareness are the tools we need, and ultimately all these are triggered and given life from LOVE. Teaching our selves to live with LOVE is the ultimate goal. LOVE is Divine and human but if we are born into violence then how do we know what love is?

As a teacher, on many levels I see my own personal work as a hand to hold. I cannot do the work for my children, family, friends or students but I can certainly show a way.

Take courage, and respect who and what you are and who you may become. Honour your parents and forgive them if its been a painful Sacred Space you were born from and into. Easy to say, hard to do, but not impossible.

Be the person you want to be with,
love and honour all and the rest will come some day.
TRUST.
AMN

Note to Self

the tradition

At the Feet of the Guru

At the Feet of the Guru

The Astanga Invocation:
Vande Gurunam Charanaravinde
Sandarashita Swatma Sukhava Bodhe

In the Sanskrit *Astanga* (Eight Limbs of Yoga) Invocation: *Vande Gurunam Charanaravinde*, the translation is often simply,

I bow to the Lotus feet of the Guru.

A *Guru* (Teacher) is regarded as a person who has great knowledge and wisdom and the position of being able to guide others.

In Sanskrit *Gu*, is your Goo, darkness, limitations and ignorance.

Ru is teacher, light and radiance. So taking a student out of Darkness into light.

Why are the Guru's feet called 'Lotus Feet'?

In many cultures, touching the feet of a wise and knowledgeable person or teacher is a sign of respect and reverence. It is also accepting the many miles that teacher has walked to gain such wisdom. The Lotus flower is a symbol of emerging wisdom, as the petals unfold so too does the knowledge of the Self.

The Guru's Lotus Feet have the connotation of wisdom and unfolding Self-Knowledge.

The word Guru needs to be seen metaphorically, as it is not, in its truest form, a person, but the inner teacher, and the journey our feet follow towards Self-realisation. We are our own inner Guru; but it takes courage to believe that we could have it all right here, right now.

Sanskrit always has a shallow and deeper meaning, for example Hatha. Hatha in its simplest form is 'effort' the first road to the body's Yoga endeavour. We begin with the outer layer, the body, and it is an 'effort' to get it to do what you want it to do. After many years of practice the word Hatha becomes *Ha* (Sun), *Tha* (Moon); the duality of all things and the two halves needed to become whole.

> I travelled the world to find out who I was and in the end I arrived where I began, at the *Shala*, Home.

This is a simplistic explanation of course but a way to understand that Sanskrit develops with the learner's depth of knowledge, like peeling an onion and its many layers to the core.

The second line of the Astanga Invocation, '*Sandarashita Swatma Sukhava Bodhe*', is describing the subject of the previous phrase, the Guru, and is telling us the role the Guru performs and expresses.

In the first part, the word *San* from *Sandarashita* means 'to offer' and *darshita* to 'uncover', so this in essence means the role of the Guru is to uncover or give knowledge. In reality the Guru helps us to discover what we already have within us...uncovering the dust and veil that clouds the truth (*Satya*).

The next word, *Swatma*, is *Atman* (Self), and is what we are uncovering with the help of the Guru and the teachings of Yoga.

Sukha, the opposite of *Dukha,* can be translated as 'good space' or 'soft', which I prefer as it says something about the way in which to approach all spiritual teachings and practices, in my opinion.

The word *Bodhe* comes from the Sanskrit root *bd* that translates as 'to Know'.

So 'we will know a good/soft space'.

Touching the feet of the Guru is a Hindu tradition but many true Gurus and Aspirants (those aspiring to reach Spiritual awareness of the Self) know that the true teacher is to be found within us. It's a long journey from you back to you!

This all seems rather complicated but actually it's expressing what we understand of the nature of The Tradition, The Path and The Vision of Yoga as a whole system for living a good and positive life that is destined to reach both Joy and the Self.

Gurukula

In Ancient India, every subject whether it was Spiritual or academic was seen as Divine and taught by the Guru in the *Gurukula*.

Gurukula means 'the place of the teacher'. *Kula* means 'family', so *Gurukula* means more than just a school, but the place where the student comes to be a part of the family of the guru for some time – to learn the culture and etiquette of the *Vedas*, as well as the knowledge.

If the student recognizes that the teacher and the parent are both to be respected and honoured, and if they feel that the teachers and the parents embrace the same ethos about their education, then their conception of guru and spiritual authority becomes very healthy and natural, and they are easily able to understand the importance of accepting a spiritual master, and making tangible progress on their path.

What are the Vedas?

The *Vedas* are thought to be the earliest literary record of the Indo-Aryan civilisation, and the most sacred books of India. They are the original scriptures of Hindu teachings. They contain spiritual knowledge encompassing all aspects of our life. *Vedic* literature, with its philosophical meters, has stood the test of time and is the highest religious authority for all sections of Hindus in particular and for mankind in general.

Veda means 'wisdom', 'knowledge' or 'vision', and it manifests the language of the gods in human speech. The laws of the *Vedas* regulate the social, legal, domestic and religious customs of the Hindus to the present day. All the obligatory duties of the Hindus at birth, marriage, death etc. owe their allegiance to the *Vedic* ritual. They draw forth the thought of successive generations of thinkers, and so contain within them the different strata of thought.

* The Rigveda contains hymns to be recited by the presiding priest;
* The Yajuveda contains formulas to be recited by the officiating priest;
* The Samaveda contains formulas to be sung by the priest that chants;
* The Atharvaveda is a collection of spells and incantations, apotropaic charms and speculative hymns.

In *Vedic* educational systems, the focus is on progressive life, ultimately leading to service and surrender to the Supreme Lord. There are many gurus in one's life, beginning from the mother, then father, then teachers, and finally the spiritual master. So the system of *Gurukula* is very deep and significant in the life of a devotee, and is one of the stages in accepting the authority of the spiritual master. For this reason it is very important that there is a seamless transition between family and school and back again.

The Teachers

Our first teachers are our Parents. We all have a story, as my Mother would say, never judge a person till you hear that story. My parents met in Leicester, England in 1950. I was born in Kirkuk, Iraq in 1955 to Joan Lamb and Abdulahad Khachik.

They came from diverse backgrounds but had one common aim, and that was politics and to help people be free. In the end my father was imprisoned for his human rights work and my Mother and I fled to England with my younger siblings.

My own life has been exotic, brutal, loving, passionate and honest. This is all because my parents told me that courage was the one thing in life that would get you through.

I honour your memories and thank you
for everything you taught me.
I will pass your knowledge on
to my own children and those I teach,
with courage.

Looking at the lessons life has taught you …
…if you had to describe yourself in one word,
what would it be?

The Guru

The Sanskrit meaning of Guru in its simplest form is 'Teacher' but it has a deeper meaning:

To take one from Darkness to Light

Undoubtedly one of the greatest Yoga Masters of the 20th century, Swami Sivananda is the inspiration behind the Sivananda Yoga Vedanta Centers.
The teachings of Swami Sivananda are summarised in these six words:

Serve, Love, Give, Purify, Meditate, Realize

Swami Sivananda Saraswati

Swami Sivananda was born in 1887 in Pattamadai, Tamil Nadu in South India and was then named Kuppuswami. He was a brilliant young academic student as well as a gymnast. He was naturally inclined toward spiritual and religious practices and was eager to join his parents twice daily for worship. Kuppuswami had a natural selfless spirit that was to lead him into a career in medicine. His amazing eagerness and ability to learn and assimilate his studies earned him the respect of his professors, who invited him to attend surgeries while still in his first year of medical school.

The young Dr. Kuppuswami felt a strong urge to go to Malaysia where he felt there was great need. In a short time he was given the responsibility of running a hospital. During these years Dr. Kuppuswami was well regarded, being both an excellent doctor and a true humanitarian. Very often he waived consultation fees for patients too poor to afford his services and on many occasions provided medicine for free to his most needy patients.

Dr. Kuppuswami had the opportunity to cure a wandering *Sannyasin* (renunciate or monk) who then gave the doctor instruction on Yoga and Vedanta. From that day on his life changed, and gradually Dr. Kuppuswami became more introspective and could not stop thinking about the great questions of life. He felt the need to help people on a more profound level now, not just healing their physical body but helping them to find a cure for all Human suffering. Not unlike Siddhartha who became The Buddha, The Enlightened One.

Filled with a tremendous desire for spiritual growth and enlightenment, Kuppuswami spent time in Varanasi then travelled north to the Himalayas in search of his Guru, Vishwananda Saraswati. It was there in the holy town of Rishikesh, which means 'the abode of the sages', that Vishwananda initiated him into the Sannyasa order and gave him his monastic name. After initiation, Sivananda settled in Rishikesh, and immersed himself in intense spiritual practices (*Sadhana*).

Swami Sivananda Saraswati, as he would be known henceforth, started an extremely intense daily *Sadhana* and *Tapas* (austerities) for the next ten years. By the end of that period many other Sadhus felt drawn to Swami Sivananda for his instruction and his spiritual inspiration.

During this time he also continued to nurse the sick. With some money from his insurance policy that had matured, he started a charitable dispensary at Lakshman Jhula in 1927, serving pilgrims, holy men and the poor, using his medical expertise.

From that time Swami Sivananda became one of the most hardworking and inspiring Yoga teachers the world has known. Although he rarely left the little town of Rishikesh, having only two India tours and no visits abroad, Swami Sivananda's teachings spread quickly throughout the planet. He personally wrote, by hand (no computers at the time), more than 200 books on Yoga and Philosophy. He wrote in a style that was direct and dynamic, full of spiritual energy. Many who read his books felt their lives deeply touched and transformed. Students came from all over India and the world, to learn from him directly, to be in his presence.

It was in 1957 that Swami Sivananda sent his devoted and industrious disciple Swami Vishnu-devananda to the West where he then established the International Sivananda Yoga Vedanta Centers.

And so it was for me that I was lead to the doors of The Sivananda Yoga Vedanta Centre in trendy Notting Hill back in 1983.

Photo taken in 1984 by Anne-Marie, during her visit to Ananda Kutir with Gary Newland, at the home of the late Swami Sivananda, in Rishikesh, on the banks of the Ganges.

Swami Vishnu-devananda initiating Anne-Marie in 1983

My Guru

Swamiji's smile is the resonating aspect of who he was, what he stood for, and why he has lived within so many students' lives no matter if they walked away from the Yoga principles or not. Who forgets a smile? No one. Yogis can be so sour at times; personally I believe that if practicing Yoga makes you hard, cruel or unhappy then give it up; you are not being honest and it's that that will make you ill... not the Yoga! A happy mind and heart will radiate a happy smile, most of the time anyway!

Swamiji (an endearment given to a Swami, a celibate and renounced monk) was born in Kerala, South India, in 1927. As a small child one of his main traits was a strong will and an even greater determination. I often saw the flash of anger in his eye and the look he could cast if you were not paying attention! His mother, now known as *Mataji*, who later on became a *Sannyasin* (vow of renunciation) from Swami Sivananda, said that whenever her son wanted something, nothing or no one could stop him. An interesting anecdote tells how as a youngster he had the strong desire to go to school and learn. When told that it was not possible since the nearest school was located

Swami Vishnu-devananda

more than 5 miles away, the child decided to pack some food and go early the next morning for the long 5 mile walk through the jungle. He walked back that evening and did the same for many years to come. Interestingly I see many parallels in my own quest. I wanted to go to school but was too young but got onto the bus one day and went anyway! I did this every day for many months until my mother realized I had stopped eating until I finished my homework and that I was setting high goals for myself at four! Nothing has changed, I am still the same. I do believe in the idea that we can do anything we choose to as long as the intent and desire is for self-knowledge and human endeavour.

As a teenager, without financial resources for University, Swamiji turned to the army to receive the scientific education he longed for. During this time, as he looked for a lost paper in a waste basket, his eyes fell upon a paper entitled '20 Spiritual Instructions' by Swami Sivananda. The pamphlet began: 'An ounce of practice is better than tons of theory'. The practicality and inherent power of these simple words lead Swamiji to travel across India during a 36 hour leave to meet Swami Sivananda in far away Rishikesh in the Himalayas.

This short visit left such an impression on the boy's mind that he made his mind up to return as soon as possible.

On his second visit, the young disciple received two powerful lessons from Swami Sivananda. The first lesson came when Swami Vishnu-devananda felt too timid and a bit arrogant to bow to the Guru Swami Sivananda. So the Master Swami Sivananda prostrated fully before the young student, demonstrating the lesson of humility. The second lesson came during *Arati* (worship ceremony), to *Ganga* (Ganges River). Swamiji was perplexed and doubtful as he pondered why intelligent people would worship what scientifically is merely H2O. The Master then smiled subtly and gazed at Swamiji who instantly beheld the river as a vast, bright, cosmic light. Swami Sivananda then invited the young boy to remain at the Ashram to study and become a Yogi. Swami Vishnu-devananda spontaneously replied, "Yes".

For the next ten years Swami Vishnu lived at the Sivananda Ashram and trained in all aspects of Yoga with Swami Sivananda. Swamiji quickly became an adept in the path of Hatha Yoga and was a tireless Karma Yogi. One day Swami Sivananda gave Swamiji a 10 Rupee note, this is less than £1, and his blessings to travel to the West and spread the teachings of Yoga. "People are waiting", he told him. I heard this story many times over the years I spent with Swamiji and it seemed as if it was the first time I heard it.

Swamiji's energy and profound inspiration lead him to found and direct the International Sivananda Yoga Vedanta Centre. He created the first Yoga Teacher Training Course, which to date has trained more than 26,000 certified teachers in the field of Yoga and spirituality. My own certificate from him is number 3096!

I feel Swamiji was able to clearly place the principles of Yoga into 5 simple steps for life. These are easy to understand and to practice: Proper Breathing, Proper Exercise, Proper Relaxation, Proper Diet, Positive Thinking and Meditation.

Swami Vishnu-devananda also recommended the daily practice of the 12 basic postures. These were headstand, shoulder-stand, plough, fish, sitting forward bend, cobra, bow, spinal twist, crow, standing forward bend, triangle and locust. Traditionally, Yogis practice the Sun Salutation, before the *Asanas,* and this also aligns with the logical warming up of all the body's muscle groups.

Throughout his whole life, Swamiji was deeply concerned about the wellbeing of the world and the constant disaster of wars. This led him to learn to fly and then personally pilot a small plane over several troubled areas of the world. Not only did he create discussion and awareness in the news media, but he also 'bombarded' these war torn areas with flowers and peace pamphlets while repeating the peace Mantra: *Om Namo Narayanaya.* I know this was Swamiji's own mantra because he told me so when giving me the same one. He always said he felt that this mantra, sacred sound, and *Om Namah Sivaya* were the most powerful to use in our time.

Do nothing that is not born of Joy,
for a joyless human is a chance lost to send that Joy to others.

AMN

I found this quote many years after he died. It says much about the man he was and his utter recognition of the failings of those put in high places. I am honoured to have met him and to remember the times he lost his temper, the times he made us laugh with his funny stories, but ultimately remembering that he was a simple human man with the playfulness of a child.

He always said be child-like not childish.

I have given you all I have with all my heart and love. It is for you to give to others. Sometimes I may not know all the answers, and I know that I have a long way to go. If you didn't get anything, that's because of my lower emotional nature. If there was anything good you got, it came from my great Master Sivananda. I don't say that I'm an unemotional person. I scolded and talked endlessly. I acted like a dictator. If I were like my master, or like Jesus, I could wash the feet of my disciples. But for that one must be very high. It can only be done when the ego is gone. If I were to do it, it would be hypocrisy. I'm not that high. Once, some years ago, I prostrated myself before a man to whom I had been rude and impatient. As I was doing it, I was thinking, "How humble I am." So don't look for an easy way to overcome your ego. For years I've tried. I watch myself as my ego manifests itself. I analyse. But it clings like a leech. When we can't control ourselves, we should offer it to the Lord: "Oh Lord, I offer it to Thee!" And now, if in any way I hurt your feelings, I ask you with all my heart to pardon me.

Swami Vishnu-devananda

Indra Devi: Yoga's First Lady

Founder of Sai Yoga

Eugene Peterson was born in 1899 in Russia. Her mother was a member of the Russian nobility, while her father was of Swedish origin. She died in 2002 in Buenos Aires, Argentina, at the age of 102. 'She was like a national treasure' the *New York Times* quoted one Argentina writer in its story of her passing.

Eugene was happy travelling all over Europe as part of a theatrical company. On her travels she met an Indian philosopher who was also a Yogi, and her life changed forever. This remarkable story of the transformation of Eugene Peterson into Indra Devi, the film star, is astonishing for its time. It proves beyond any doubt that we are chosen for our Spiritual Path no matter where we are born or whom we are born to.

Eugene's transformation into 'Indra Devi' began when, with her Mother, she had to move to Germany in 1917 just as the revolution in Russia was igniting. Eugene had trained as an actor and dancer and was part of a theatrical troupe that toured all over Europe. During the course of her travels she met the renowned philosopher Yogi J. Krishnamurti and she became intrigued with Indian Theory and Philosophy.

Obsessed about visiting India, but without the funds to do so, she got her chance when a wealthy banker proposed to her. Eugene agreed on one condition and that was that he paid for her trip to India before the wedding. He agreed and they were engaged and soon she was on her way to India. Three months later, upon her return and her first meeting with her fiancée, she returned her ring. She felt she had no choice but to be honest with him as she felt that her home was in India.

Eugene sold all her possessions, including the few jewels and furs she had, and took a one-way ticket to India in 1928. Soon she became a Bollywood movie star with the stage name of 'Indra Devi', and she was married to a Czechoslovakian diplomat. She was leading the high life, meeting politicians and celebrities, but she felt that something was missing and that this was not the reason why she had come to the country. She prayed for direction.

Soon her prayers were answered. In 1937, when she suffered from some kind of cardiac illness, she was directed to take treatment from the renowned Yogi Krishnamacharya. However, when she visited him he refused to give her treatment. This was the first time a western woman had approached him and he was not sure of her level of commitment; apart from that, Yoga was always traditionally for Men. Women were the ones who kept the home flame of Spirituality alive. Indra Devi was persistent and Krishnamacharya relented. Within a few months he had cured her.

At that time in India the 'Yogi' had a bad reputation. They were seen by most as odd, even crazy men in loin-cloths, covered in ashes and often smoking cannabis. Men were beginning to embrace a modern India and the climate was right for economic growth and a yearning to meet the West at its own game, competing for businesses and new innovations.

But, seeing her dedication, Krishnamacharya offered to make her into a Yoga teacher and she accepted. She ended up staying with him for a year, feeling for the first time that her reason for being in the country was being answered. She probably was the first westerner taught by Krishnamacharya to be a Yoga teacher. Krishnamacharya taught her a gentle style of Yoga, given that she was just recovering from a heart condition.

Soon she moved to Shanghai when her husband was transferred there. In 1940 she opened a school in Shanghai at the house of Madame Chiang Kai-shek, wife of the nationalist leader and a new Yoga enthusiast. Amongst her students were many Americans and Russians and she was also giving free lessons at local orphanages.

After World War II, Indra moved back to India. Her husband died suddenly and she took this as a signal to move back to the USA, and her Yoga became a hit with celebrities.

It was at this time that she legally changed her name to Indra Devi. In 1953 she married a renowned doctor and humanitarian from Los Angeles. In the same year she published one of the first books on Yoga by a westerner called *Forever Young, Forever Healthy* that became a bestseller. In 1960 she visited Russia and was meeting Russian high officials at the invitation of the Indian embassy.

It was because of these meetings that she was instrumental in legalising Yoga in Russia. Just a note – Yoga at the time was seen formerly as a religion and was banned in the communist-atheist country.

After her second husband died she moved back to India. She was a prolific traveller and when she visited Argentina she fell in love with the country and moved there permanently. A single television appearance gave her a rock star status and many people took up Yoga. Argentina is still a centre for Yoga in South America, with a long established Sivananda Ashram there. She spoke fluent Spanish and there is still a small film of her *Satsang* (lectures) to be seen on YouTube. Amazing to think we can see her today with as much passion and love for Yoga as the first day she was discovered by it.

Indra Devi has played a prodigious role in propagating Yoga all over the world. *Mataji*'s (Mother) contribution to Yoga places her with the Saints of other faiths and she is truly 'The first lady of Yoga'.

Her first book *Forever Young, Forever Healthy* can still occasionally be found in old bookshops. On my shelves I have her second book *Yoga for You*; an original first print with such Hollywood stars as Gloria Swanson in a perfect tree pose. The book also has a wonderful six week course very like mine and it reminds me that Yoga is always relevant no matter what century you happen to be born in!

Indra's reach was universal and to this day she is recognized as a Luminary.

Swami Sivananda Radha

One other female Yoga luminary is Swami Sivananda Radha, a German Yogini who moved to live in Canada and founded the Yasodhara Ashram in British Columbia. Swami Sivananda Radha founded the Ashram nearly 50 years ago. She stands as a strong example of *Shakti* (female energy), a visionary.

What is a Visionary? A Visionary is a person with original ideas about what the future will or could be like. They are not always highly educated but have had some sort of revelation or Epiphany (a moment of sudden and great revelation or realisation) that has changed their lives in a single moment. A path shows itself clear and strong and they walk towards that Vision of another life and another way of living and being.

At age 44 she travelled to India where she met and studied with her guru Swami Sivananda. Her trip was inspired by a powerful dream vision of her teacher. She was the first western woman to become a *Sannyasin*, a person who is dedicated to self-realisation. Her guru requested she return to Canada to 'update the teachings for the western mind'.

So Swami Radha, with little money after her travels, returned to Canada. She founded the now internationally recognized Yasodhara Ashram at the remote Kootenay Bay. She wrote ten books on Yoga and began Timeless Books, a publishing company, and there are now many Radha Yoga Centres around the world.

One of Swami Radha's many legacies is the form of Hatha Yoga practiced at the Ashram. It is called The Hidden Language and is a contemplative practice that involves *Asana* (physical postures) and journaling. In lessons the teacher may ask, "What does it mean to be a visionary?", as a pointer to the Hidden Language within the theory and postures practiced at the Ashram.

Try practicing *Garudasana* (Eagle pose). The eagle is a strong symbol for clarity of vision. *Garudasana* is a balance posture that allows one to develop single-pointed awareness like that of the eagle eye. The postures are seen as gateways to deep reflection.

Ask yourself

Where am I?

What are my obstacles?

What is being revealed?

When you are deeply challenged, unbalanced or torn apart, how do you stay true to your vision?

It is not easy but it is not impossible either.

Swami Sivananda Radha

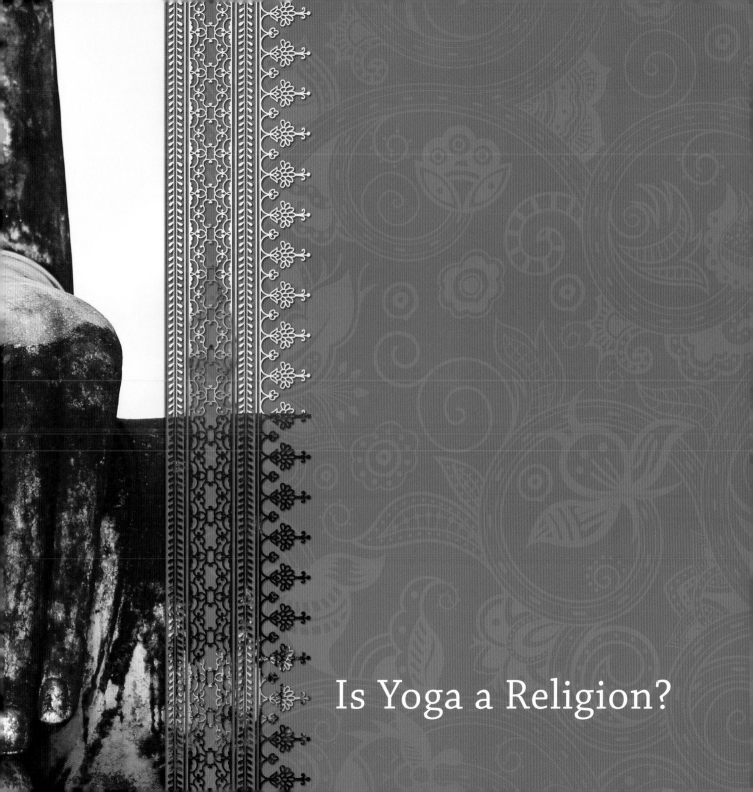

Is Yoga a Religion?

Yoga is not a Religion

Yoga's roots are closely related to the Hindu faith, but it should in no way be seen as a religion. In all Yoga scriptures you will find references to both Hindu scriptures and culture, however Yoga is more a philosophy and psychology.

Yoga is a method by which to control the mind and the body through the use of the breath.

It may be interesting to know that in Roman Latin, *Spiritos*, means 'Breath'!

All the texts relating to Yoga will have a reference to Spirituality, hence the yoking of Mind, Body and Spirit. As the West was once suspicious of the word and concept of 'Spirit' this word was dropped and replaced by the word 'Breath'.

For many, Yoga is a personal journey of self-discovery that is not associated with any particular doctrine or belief system. The path of Yoga often begins with the body which, when you consider that Hatha Yoga is one of the four paths of Yoga – that of the body (*Asanas*) – then it's a great place to start.

Yoga classes all over the world are full of many diverse beliefs such as Christian, Islam, Catholic and Jewish; you will also find agnostics and atheists. Yoga promotes unity in diversity and crosses boundaries, cultures, beliefs and abilities. My belief is that Yoga needs to be practiced with no judgement either for those around you or for yourself and certainly without 'force'.

Think compassion in your practice and you will find both your body and mind will yield and that flexibility is the reward on more than one level.

There are those who find the words, Divine, super-consciousness or spiritual focus difficult to grasp, but I do honestly believe that this does not stop Yoga having a profound affect on anyone who practices it. If one learns to do nothing but discover the health and mental benefits of breathing correctly, then all else will come in time as will tolerance and respect.

You will find your life improves and the relationships in your life too. It's a win-win situation.

Nataraj

The Nataraj is a depiction of the Hindu god Shiva as 'The Cosmic Dancer'.

He performs his divine dance to destroy the worn out universe and to prepare for the god Brahma to start the process of Creation.

It is the Universal Symbol of Yoga and most authentic Yoga centres, schools and Ashrams have one.

Prayer

Is praying religious?

I don't think prayer is either religious or philosophical; it is a natural response to love, hurt, fear, empathy and communication.

In my small life I have seen tragedy and joy. In both those moments I have prayed and seen others pray without thought, as it came from a deep human response to be heard by the Divine.

Learning to pray without a doctrine is quite frankly liberating. You don't need to believe without question, because if you do then you are wandering around with your eyes closed and still unable to 'see'. The best advice I can give you is to be still with your thoughts, ask the Question, then listen to hear the answer.

Question

QUEST-tion

You are on a personal Quest

Maya

'The Veil of Illusion'

We see the world as we perceive it,
but is it really what is there?
Allowing the Veil to drop is allowing
yourself to see the Truth.
The Truth is we are all connected
and that veil separates us from the
Collective Mind, and our
Collective responsibilities.
Are you holding it around you?
If so, why?

Yoga Philosophy made easier

I have said Yoga Philosophy made 'easier' rather than 'easy' because it just isn't easy!

Understanding that Yoga is more than one sided is the start. There are many misconceptions and misunderstandings due to the fact it is often described in rather an academic and intellectual way.

I realized very early on in life that I had some ability and insight to be able to explain complex, almost abstract concepts in a way others could grasp. When looking back now to my childhood I know I have been privy to many types of worship, politics and mind expanding ideas and it was probably this early exposure that allowed my mind to understand how big a mind is – a Universe.

As my knowledge of the Inner World grew, I also began to understand that the microcosm often thought to be the Inner World was in fact the outer world and the Inner World the macrocosm! Once I understood or rather glimpsed this world I realized that it was this realisation that led to the Sages and Mystics of this world to understand all science by simply meditating.

How often have you heard Yoga described as sitting on your bottom 'OMing'? How perfect a world if we all got to do this daily? Mahatma Gandhi said that "to change others one must change one's own Self". Sitting with one's Self is the best way to find out who you are, what you are made of and the meaning of life. 'Nothing' in itself is a concept 'Action through Non-Action'.

By not doing we sit and observe our small self that will in time reveal the True Self.

Again simple and yet deeply mysterious in its idea that there is such a Self at all!

When I work with my students I usually begin with the most difficult aspect of Yoga Philosophy, and that is The Self. The best questions are "so do you mean myself?", or "are you suggesting that The Self is not me?". Great questions; fantastic place to start!

OK, so let's start by talking about our physical body. The Mind could be housed there.

Where is your mind? Answer: "my mind is here", pointing to the skull which houses the brain. So you are saying your mind and your brain

are the same or not? Answer: "no my mind is in my brain". Really? Is it that small? What happens when the mind is full? Answer: "it stops taking in information and we forget things". But surely that is the brain, the physical part of us. Where are the emotions, the inspirations, the ideas that change the world or people's hearts and minds? Is your mind bigger than this room? Is it bigger than the city outside? Is it bigger than the country you live in? The answers are always YES! If so then the mind could be larger and more splendid than the planet? YES!

As the debate and exploration of this subject expands – and it does – it slowly dawns on us all that the mind has no skull to stop it expanding and that it is not the actions of the body or even the emotions, but possibly it is about dipping into the Greater Mind, that of the Divine or Cosmic Conscientiousness!

Well in that case, if we have now discovered the Mind is not the Brain, our next leap is to realize the Self is not the mind because the mind has been discovered by something other than the brain or the Mind........

With this realisation comes the possibility that our own mind is in fact The Collective Mind. And that we are all connected, not because we are humans, but because we were separated from the Divine Consciousness!

Therefore the Self is something even more expansive than we understood it to be and it's the motivator behind our physical body and emotions.

Reincarnation

Reincarnation is the belief that a soul is re-born into new bodies or life forms. The soul travels on an eternal path, living in one body for a time, dying, and then entering a new body to live again.

The purpose? To serve out karma from previous lives and to eventually reach a state of perfect enlightenment where additional human lives are no longer necessary. Karma is the result or consequences of actions, not just 'bad' deeds but the understanding that everything we do has a reaction.

Reincarnation is accepted in many faiths and philosophies but not by all. Some have removed this aspect, as in Christianity. I am not sure why, except that it can be challenging for us as Simple Mortals to deal with the weight of responsibility it forces us to accept, as in 'we reap what we sow'.

The message of the Bible is that God loved his human creation so he offered his 'Essence' in the form of the human Jesus Christ. He died for our sins on the cross, he took our place and paid our debt so we would not have to. As both a Yogi and Syrian Orthodox Christian I do not have a problem with this. Although Yoga is based on the Indian Hindi Teachings it is only that...**based** on them, as that was the main faith in ancient times. Why are some people so familiar and why is it that we have talents that are almost second nature? In science this is answered by understanding Ancestral Memory and the genetic make-up of the brain and the heart; it's emotional as well as physical and physiological structure. How is it that in some cases of those who have had a heart transplant, they recall feelings and memories that are not their own?

The heart is deeply connected to our psyche and is not just a pump for the blood. This was explored by Leonardo Da Vinci when he drew the function of the heart as an aural, ancestral and feeling place for the human, not a machine as the Victorians tried to make it.

The English language is so fine when describing the heart; heart-felt, broken hearted, heart rending, open-hearted, heart of stone etc. Shakespeare explored the heart of the human in so many of his plays, in the end he was illustrating human nature much like the Bible and its understanding of Jesus the Son of God, in human form.

An Epiphany is a life
changing revelation.
A moment when clarity and
messages are given for your
own salvation.
Does it come from
a past experience?
A past life?

A Door Opens
and a shaft of light reflects
across the retina of your inner eye.
You venture in without moving.
You learn without knowing
and you are travelling
without leaving a footprint,
because you have been here before.
Placing each foot in the print you left behind.
Moving forward, yet looking back.

AMN

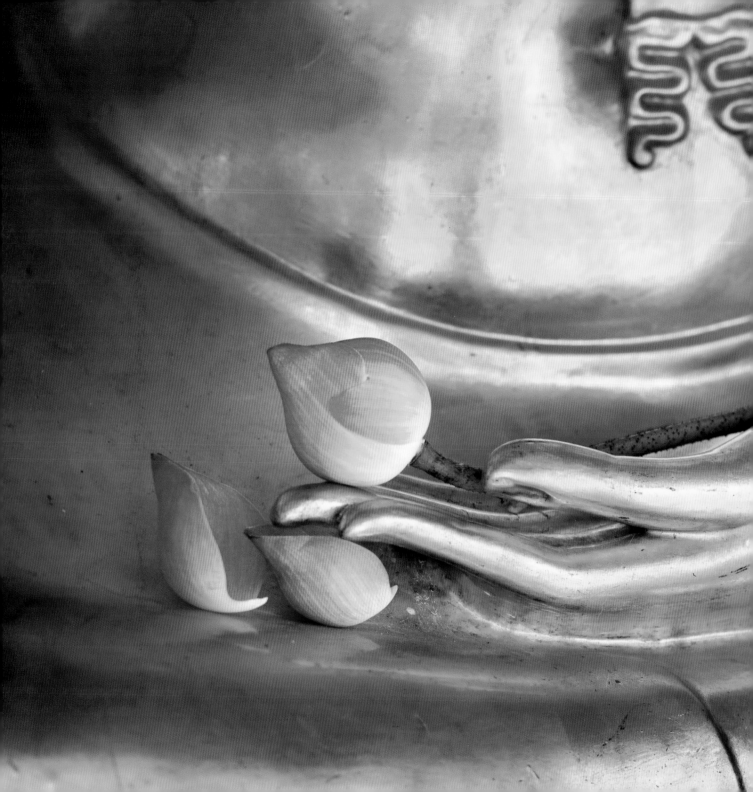

Yoga Theory

Practicing Ahimsa, on which Yoga Psychology is based

Ahimsa: Non-violence in word, thought or deed

Ahimsa is one of the five *Yamas* (see page 114) and literally means 'non–injury and non-violence'. *Ahimsa* also encompasses the physical, emotional and medical aspects of non-harming; this I find particularly interesting. Medicine and surgery have come a long way since the times of the dawn of Yoga Psychology but it is no less emotive. Medicine will always be about the need, the appropriate action and the strong or the vulnerable and we can see why this is part of the concept of non-violence.

The basis on which *Ahimsa* is built is much like the Christian ten commandments, or the five Pillars of Islam. To live with a clear mind, heart and conscience is easy to say but hard to live up to.

My four children have been brought up to 'stand alone' when needed and not to be a sheep and look on while the group maims or destroys a person, a home or a country. Courage comes from knowing what is right and acting upon it. I was thrown into this dilemma when I was as young as six, seeing a boy being bullied. First I was full of terror, then empathy for the boy and eventually rage, enough to shout and distract the perpetrators into waking up to their responsibilities. It was a pivotal moment for me. This experience opened my heart and gave me courage. To have gone home and not done anything was simply not an option for me.

The Eight Bondages or snares are: hatred, shame, fear, grief, condemnation, race prejudice, pride of family and smugness. Removal of the Eight Bondages leads to magnanimity of the Heart.

Shri Yukteswar (1855 – 1936) Hinduism and Kriya
The Holy Science by Sri Yukteswar

Ahimsa gives clear instruction as to how to think before we act; a guide to a lifestyle and way of living. The difference is that it is not a religion but a philosophy.

Our non-violence speaks only to the most extreme forms of wrongdoing. *Ahimsa*, which includes not killing, goes much deeper to prohibit the subtle abuse and simple hurt. To many of us it is obvious – we hurt a person by hitting them. Less apparently we can cause harm or hurt through our words or thoughts – cursing, backstabbing, hatred, jealousy – all are considered *Himsa*, meaning 'causing harm'.

All our actions originate first in our thoughts; *Himsa* results in bad karma and brings us deeper into the cycle of *Samsara*. *Samsara* is different to *Samskara*. What is *Samsara*? It is the cycle of life and death and *Samskara* a habit, a groove created through our present and past lives and the continual practice of either good or bad habits in the present life.

Don't fool yourself that it is anything less than your projection. What we expect out of life is what we usually get. Life is the great leveller. Be honest in your own thoughts of yourself and, if you want to love and be loved, then be the person you want to be with.

Ahimsa is all about love and the belief in the oneness of all people, animals, plants and inanimate as well as animate objects and things. Since we are one, why should we harm each other? *Ahimsa* teaches us to put up with abuses, insults, criticisms and all other physical and verbal abuse.

We could instead return the abuse with love and forgiveness; this is often the best way to deal with unpleasant situations; yet we are often blinded by

We are the architects of our own destiny.
We can reflect on our own life in the same way as seeing our own reflection in a mirror. What you see is what you give, who you are and how you have moulded your image to reflect onto others.

AMN

our intense emotions and get angry when we are being wrongly accused, and we harbour feelings of intense hatred when somebody hurts us, physically or emotionally. We tend to hold onto the past and carry this burden with us, and it is a burden because we don't have to carry it, we have chosen to do so.

So where do we hold this baggage? In our body? Perhaps we could have asked ourselves if we feel any better with hatred, anger, and jealousy inside us? Would it make us feel any better, or is a situation any better if we harbour hatred or anger? If not, why not try forgiving the person that harmed us?

Let's see if we can let it go and feel the sense of freedom and happiness we deserve when we dump those feelings because no one said, "Hold onto this please".

Tuning into our Grooves, our Samskaras

Samskaras are habits we form over a long period of time; in psychology they may be called 'learned responses'. These responses become a second nature, a way in which we deal with our own thoughts, lifestyle, other people, our families and relationships or with violence and fear that we have either seen or been involved with.

In your mind, imagine a situation that is unresolved and is still like a splinter. That splinter has bedded itself into your life; it may seem hard to imagine it not there. Your *Samskaras* are strong and involve not just this present life but also many before it. Consider a wheel within a wheel as in the Sea of *Samsara*, the wheel of Life and Death.

We can continue to go round and round, seemingly never to progress, but with a clear aim we can and do make things change if our aim is true.

All of us have some situation, or person who has hurt us bitterly, and is still possibly doing that by harbouring thoughts or feelings about us that are harmful.

Now be honest about your thoughts toward them because you would be a fool to think the damage to yourself is not greater!

A feeling of hatred or anger towards another person reflects back onto us; that is the law of the Universe. The very hardest thing for us to do is to let go of this feeling, as it has become part of our life.

These few simple words may help.

Can you try to do a little exercise?

Let your feelings out on one of your 'Note to Self' pages

afterwards, if you are able to.

As ever, try to do this without self-judgement,

without force and certainly with no expectations.

❋ What I would like you to do is close your eyes.

❋ Let yourself think for a moment.

❋ Take a deep breath, calm your mind.

❋ Slow down your breathing to slow down your thoughts.

❋ Now allow yourself to be aware of your actions.

❋ Smile even if your body resists.

❋ Smile until you believe in that smile.

❋ Smile like the Buddha; Happiness is the Way.

❋ Be free.

What has changed my friend?
You have changed.

A Map for a Successful Life

Yoga Theory can be an overwhelming subject! So I will attempt to make it 'real'. In other words, bring it into your everyday life. Theory is only that after all, until it's put into practice. Most of us had our first taste of this ancient and often strange practice in a class, performing complicated moves. You may be like me and went along to a class having no idea that Yoga was a theory, a philosophy and a way of living.

The postures were all I understood of Yoga and I think that is why theory could be introduced earlier by way of simple explanation, tiny seeds, as I like to call them. As a trainer I ask that my teachers explain the literal meaning of the word 'Yoga' in the first lesson. As we know, Yoga means to unite mind, body and breath, and without these three aspects it could not be called Yoga. You will also hear people say, "I practice Hatha Yoga", as if it was a style of Yoga.

So what is Hatha Yoga?

There is often confusion about this branch of Yoga. People think that all Yoga is Hatha. Hatha Yoga is the **physical** aspect of Yoga, not all Yoga.

Yoga is more than a Move; it's a Meaning

The greatest written work on Hatha Yoga is *The Hatha Yoga Pradipika* (see page 290), the 'Bible' on Hatha Yoga. The author, Swami Swatmarama, collated writings from other previous texts and added his own experiences. This is what makes this unique. Swami Vishnu-devananda always told us we could not describe Yoga; we had to 'know' it, that 'knowing' came from personal experience. I believe that Yoga is more about that 'experience' than technique. We feel right in poses when our body, mind and breath is aligned correctly, very much like we know when important aspects of our lives are either in correct alignment or not.

Living a Yoga Life does not mean walking around and behaving like a monk, saint, perfect person or one that is better than others because you practice Yoga; it's about finding a way to survive it. Heaven and Hell reside not in the past or the future but in this very moment. It forces you to look at the smaller self so you can recognize the Greater Self.

The words of Mahatma Gandhi, "Be the change that you wish to see in the world", expresses the true nature of life; that it is about taking responsibility for your actions and not expecting others to change to make life easier for you.

Gandhi also said, "I will not let anyone walk through my mind with their dirty feet."

You cannot let anyone defile you without your permission.
Take responsibility!

What is Astanga Vinyasa Yoga?

Astanga Vinyasa Yoga is usually referred to simply as Astanga Yoga and is a style of Yoga systemized and popularized by K. Pattabhi Jois during the 20th century. Jois began his Yoga studies in 1927 and by 1948 had established the Astanga Yoga Research Institute. Astanga Yoga is named after the Eight Limbs of Yoga mentioned in the *Yoga Sutras of Patanjali*.

The Sanskrit word *Vinyasa*, broken down into its Sanskrit roots, means *Nyasa* (to place), *Vi*, (in a special way). *Vinyasas* are used to enter and exit *Asanas*, creating a sequential flow of postures.

Yoga Sutras of Patanjali

Astanga means literally 'eight limbs', creating a 'wheel of practice' and four paths. These were devised by Patanjali. The *Yoga Sutras of Patanjali* deal with the mind and meditation and it gives practical advice on how to overcome the obstacles to meditation. These obstacles are the mind's habit of always trying to take you away from a place of 'one-pointedness' to that of self-doubt. This can be so insidious that we are unaware of these grooves, patterns we live with. Our own hands, minds and hearts forge these 'patterns of habit' daily. Any guidance we can get we should take without hesitation!

Patanjali was a spiritual father who did not author the Sutras but spoke of the need for us to have a set of rules to help us achieve a better life.

His followers began to note the things he said as beads on a string, hence Sutra, which means thread. These 'pearls of wisdom' were before the writing of Bhagavad Gita in Indian spiritual literature. My understanding of the *Yoga Sutras* is a 'Science of Union', a text that lays out a route map for achieving absolute freedom from the ego and the suffering endured in the world of cause and effect. It offers the *Sadhaka* (Spiritual aspirant) a path to Enlightenment based on an understanding of the ego and how to gain steadiness of mind, spiritual discipline to enter the 'Cloud of Virtue' (*dharma-megha*), also known as *Samadhi*.

The movements of the mind are described so the *Sadhaka* can recognise them and bring a discriminatory attention to bear on incorrect knowledge and mental behaviours, i.e., holding onto past memories, which depreciates the quality of awareness in the present moment.

Similar to the Buddha who predated him; Patanjali describes an Eightfold Path, although these paths are not parallel. Commonly known as the Eight Limbs of Yoga, Patanjali describes a holistic system of ethical, behavioural, physical and mental disciplines to purify mind, body and spirit and expand consciousness awareness into a state of *Samadhi*.

The *Yoga Sutras* are concerned with awareness of the nature of the mind, stilling the mind and denying the ego, and using Yoga as a system of spiritual practice to find the true Self. The *Sutras* are a beautiful expression of a fully enlightened mind and are accessible to anyone who desires to free life from suffering.

The Four Paths of Yoga

'There are four main paths of Yoga – Karma Yoga, Bhakti Yoga, Raja Yoga and Jnana Yoga. Each is suited to a different temperament or approach to life. All the paths lead ultimately to the same destination – to union with Brahman or God – and the lessons of each of them need to be integrated if true wisdom is to be attained.'

Swami Sivananda recognized that every Yogi, or human being for that matter, possesses and identifies with each of these elements: intellect, heart, body and mind. He therefore advocated everyone to practice certain techniques from each path. This came to be known as the 'Yoga of Synthesis'. He also taught that in accordance with individual temperament and taste a person could choose the practice of certain Yogas over others.

Karma Yoga

Karma Yoga is known as the Yoga of Action.

You will find that those with an outgoing nature often choose this path, as it insists on being able to work with others as well as alone. There is also the ethos that any work is worth its value in effort and good attitude. I like working; it cleanses my soul, focuses my mind and allows me to be in the moment. It is not surprising that many women start to frantically clean when their mind is fractured by stress, hurt or anger! Men 'go to' work to free themselves from emotions encountered at home that they couldn't deal with in an instance if confronted with them face to face.

When I teach this part of theory I explain that it is part of life, not just a formalised Spiritual practice. We all perform Karma Yoga in our own way.

Every job is a teacher; you can learn different skills by doing different jobs. Each job has different requirements in terms of time, degree of concentration, skills or experience, emotional input, physical energy or will. Try to do whatever job you are doing, well. My Mother brought me up on the old phrase, "If a job's worth doing, its worth doing well".

'Karma Yoga is the selfless devotion of all inner, as well as the outer, activities as a Sacrifice to the Lord of all works, offered to the Eternal as Master of all the soul's energies and austerities.'

Bhagavad Gita

This example of the Gita may seem harsh, disconnected and a long way from the work we do each day. I like to bring Yoga theory alive, to bring it into the context of everyday life. Such an example is, having cleared the kitchen, going back and finding it is a mess again! As a Mother of four this is a daily occurrence! I must find some strength to teach without anger, judgment or humiliation. I try to talk quietly and ask they consider the entire household when making a mess and not clearing up...very tough indeed and I fail often! But the lessons are, as ever, two-fold, for the child and myself! Attitude is the key; not what we do, but how we do it! There is no place in the home for arrogance or hierarchy; we are all part of that tiny teaching and learning community that prepares us for the world outside.

When you can't handle your anger, find a quiet space, gather your thoughts and start again.

Bhakti Yoga

Bhakti Yoga is known as the Path of Devotion.

Performing the daily rituals at the altar, temple, or home shows the act of Devotion. Candles, incense, flowers and often, small offerings of food are placed at the feet of the deity and or guru. These are signs of humility and respect. Chanting sacred mantras in the form of Kirtan, singing, is performed too, usually by the women at home and the men at the temple in traditional circumstances. Bhakti Yoga is a path often taken by those with an emotional nature and with a deep sense of empathy. They may also have a desire for beauty around them that reflects that devotion.

My own experiences in India convinced me that, as well as a Karma Yogi I was a Bhakti Yogi, as I was mesmerised and profoundly moved by my visit to Vrindavan. Vrindavan is the birthplace of Lord Krishna and, when walking past windows in this village, I heard chanting of popular mantras, accompanied by the harmonium. *Hare Krishna, Hare Krishna, Hare Hare, Krishna Krishna!*

Remembering Vrindavan in 1984, I recall colour, joy, song and the Spirit of Krishna in each child I met. I felt as though I had stepped back in time and had been transported to an ancient yet living Krishna.

There were two temples (*Mandir*) I remember in Vrindavan. One was the new Temple built largely by donations from other countries as well as India. I visited this brand new temple a few months after it opened; it was beautiful, clean but a little clinical. At the other end of the main street, after passing the sari market, there is an old Mandir. When approaching it, the first thing that hits you is the smell! It's a melange of incense, marigolds, pigeons and cows. That combination could be bottled as the 'Essence of India'!

When I entered this very busy, noisy temple I had mixed feelings. Why is it so dirty? The pigeons were roosting overhead; their droppings all over the building. Flowers were strewn across the floor, often crushed under foot, and for a moment I felt very English and could feel my nose turn up in disapproval! So, being the forthright character that I am, I asked one of the devotees why the temple was never cleaned? His answer was as direct as my question, "We are too busy praying and celebrating the Divine Krishna!" I put my hands up then and there to those who practice and do not preach! A very humbling experience.

Raja Yoga

Raja Yoga is known as the Yoga of meditation.

The Eight Limbs of Yoga: The Yoga Sutras, also known as The Eight Limbs (*Astanga*) of Raja (King) Yoga, were the first developed and recorded Yoga system. Created through lectures to students by Patanjali around 2nd century BCE (meaning Before Common Era), this system colours much of the Yoga practiced today. It is clear that most of the sutras are based around Yoga of the mind, but what is practiced here in the West seems to be more concerned about Yoga of the body – Hatha. Somewhere along the way, we've begun practicing the movement of Yoga in isolation to its philosophies. We have become obsessed with Yoga gymnastics. I put this down to such luminaries as B.K.S Iyengar, who took apart the trinity of Yoga – Mind, Body, Breath – and taught it separately. Such Gurus as Sivananda processed a system that was integrated, allowing *Pranayama*, Raja Yoga and Hatha Yoga to be practiced in equal measure. This suited me perfectly. It was the first time that I understood the cohesion and practice of Yoga as a theory, philosophy and practice in one session.

Everything we do has its roots in the mind, whether it is speech, movement, emotion or thought. In order to gain a profound change in your life, you must face up to the issues at the centre of your reason for needing to change in the first place.

I do believe that at some point in our lives we are given the opportunity to make a deliberate and long awaited transformational re-direction.

It can happen in a moment.
One second of clarity;
a window that pours light into us;
a door that swings open.
It may be a voice, but whatever it is,
the need to act, react, grasp or cling to it, means we have to engage,
and this also means we are forced to take responsibility for that change.

Right Here! Right Now!

Hoping your life is about to change by going through the motions and practicing only the physical poses is like painting over the cracks in a wall. On the surface, while it may seem to have solved the problem, the heart of the problem still exists and is travelling deeper into the foundations and structure of the building. When we ignore deep-seated issues, those cracks continue to penetrate our minds. This then affects all aspects of our lives such as thought, word and deed, which is then reflected in our speech, emotions, and actions. Patanjali's Eight Limbs of Yoga were designed to help us deal with the mind and how it will do anything to stop us dealing with our foundations, the very platform that supports us.

If you want to reap the full benefits of the Yoga experience, I strongly recommend you implement the Eight Limbs of Yoga into every part of your life. I know from personal experience that this can be quite intimidating, as much for advanced practitioner as for the beginner.

I have tried to break down the Yoga Sutras into a simple everyday manner, while also trying to keep the integrity of the original teachings.

The first and second limbs, *Yama* and *Niyama*, form our foundation. Here, awareness and realisation are established. *Yama* and *Niyama* lay the footings for everything that comes with practice. My first Yoga teacher was a builder and he would talk about erecting a strong scaffold to support a mental structure and this is the *Yama's* and *Niyama's* role.

1st Limb

Yama | Self-Restraint.

This 1st limb is different from the 2nd limb in that it helps develop your relationship with the outer material world and interaction with those you live, work and battle with. The second limb deals with your inner world, that of your Spiritual journey and of the minds control over your bigger Self. Learning to step back in conflict is an important aspect here; to think before doing what you always do and reacting from a purely emotional place. This is often called a 'learned response'.

1. *Ahimsa:* Non-violence in thought, word, and deed; not inflicting injury or harm to others and ourselves. When we reach a level where there is no longer *Ahimsa* in our thought, speech, and actions, our aggressive tendencies can be overcome, causing others to let go of any hostile feelings in our presence. If we don't force our will on others, but allow ourselves to yield, then there can be no force or fight,;it takes force to create and maintain force.

2. *Satya:* Truth, to be expressed in thought, word, and action. When you practice *Satya*, and true integrity, what you say becomes a reality.

3. *Asteya:* Non-stealing and non-covetousness. Not desiring should even be practiced to the extent that you should curb desiring something that is not yours. When you become a living example of *Asteya*, you will be trusted with the greatest of treasures. Desire destroys the very fabric of our being, eating away at it like a moth on cloth.

4 *Brahmacharya:* Sometimes translated as 'abstaining from sexual intercourse when not married'. In the case of married people, practicing monogamy and not having sexual thoughts about another person who is not your spouse, is what this sutra is all about. When *Brahmacharya* is fully realized in marriage, the sex lives of both improve because the level of trust and devotion deepens their connection. It is also said that for the celibate person, the energy and zest for life increases. This is tough for some, easier for others. Having lived with *Brahmacharya* (celibate yogis, monks, priests) in an ashram, I can say that I have met both genuine *Brahmacharya* and the charlatan. Living up to a difficult lifestyle can make a man or woman feel they must stick to it even when in truth it may not be their path. Having said that, I do believe that all of us have either been forced to try it or found that after a difficult relationship it is a great leveler for the emotions.

5 *Aparigraha:* Non-possessiveness or non-greediness . When you manage a high level of *Aparigraha*, others are automatically drawn to share with you, giving freely their time, possessions and successes.

These values are as important today as they were centuries ago. The *Yamas* are not a moral straight jacket, but are meant to help develop an honest relationship with the outside world, helping to establish a greater awareness about our individual place in the world.

It is therefore not surprising that this is the first limb and must be practiced as the first action or step to our transformation. When taking steps to transform our inner world, our outer world becomes a reflection of this. We are what we think! All action starts with thought. So mind what you think!

2nd Limb

Niyama | Personal Observances

The second limb helps refine our Spiritual path. Think of it as a 'Self-study' course that develops our relationship with our 'Self', the Greater 'I'.

1   *Saucha:* Cleanliness of thought, speech, and body. When you develop *Shaucha*, unwholesome thoughts and acts that lead to suffering are cleared.

2   *Santosha:* Contentment – to be satisfied with what one has. When you achieve *Santosha*, bonds to the material world are broken and authentic peace and happiness is established within. Being content is like being on a sofa with a hot cup of tea, or playing a round of golf on a languid afternoon. Being content is a great gift if you get it because it allows you to let go of expectations of your own achievements. Without that desire to achieve, we are free to revel in the joy of living in the moment.

3   *Tapas:* Self-discipline that is sometimes associated with austerity and being able to conquer the body and mind through mental control. When *Tapas* is attained, laziness is overcome and willpower and character are developed.

All that know me will tell you I am very self-disciplined, and it's true. I try to do something to test my self-discipline every day. How? By taking a deep breath and marking that extra paper when I just want to put my pen down and go to bed. The simple action of marking that last paper develops my self-discipline, and I celebrate my tenacity when I do. As a young child I had an inherent understanding of this aspect of my personality. I started school at four in Baghdad, Iraq, where I was born (school does not start until seven in Iraq) and it wasn't very long before my mother put a stop to it! I began to show signs of severe austerity. When I got home after a long school bus ride I would refuse to eat until I did my homework. What homework I hear you say? Trying to remember all the things my teacher had said in the day and preparing to improve on them for the next school day. I began to get headaches and couldn't sleep in case I missed the school bus. I travelled with the older girls and I was emulating them. This would be a blue print for my future as a self-motivated, driven individual!

4   *Svadhyaya:* Self-study that leads to introspection and a greater awakening of the soul and the source of creation within and around you, traditionally studied through *Vedic* scriptures. *Svadhyaya* leads to a greater awakening of your true potential, providing you with a better sense of reality and your place in the world. Each of us has a purpose. Finding that purpose is one of the mysteries of life. As a mother, my greatest duty is to assure my children that they have a purpose, but as a path seeker I also know that I can only guide, light their path and watch. Self-study is a study of the 'Self', in a word. It is of no use to you if you read a book on self-development and then never act on it during your day. A spiritual book with guidance on how to survive, change and benefit, may take me 18 months to read. I work on the page (and myself) for the following day. Work it out in the playground, work, in the shops, with your neighbours, family and friends.

5   *Ishvarapranidhana:* The 'surrender to God'. When *Ishvarapranidhana* is developed, the vision of ultimate reality helps destroy the ego, thus strengthening your practice of all the limbs leading up to *Samadhi* (the eighth limb).

Asana and *Pranayama* are the third and fourth limbs. They give us health and longevity, allowing us more time to achieve the ultimate goal of Yoga – enlightenment, not waste time chasing the material world or compound our suffering by acts of ignorance. The third and fourth limbs are important, as they prepare the body for meditation, which will be the key to stilling your mind and discovering your true potential.

3rd Limb

Asana | Seat or Posture

All poses in Yoga practice need to reach a place of steadiness (*Sthira*) and lightness (*Sukha*). Concentrating on the sound of *Ujjayi* breathing, the most commonly practiced breathing technique in Yoga, where you slightly close the epiglottis at the back of the throat, creating a sibilant sound. It can be heard and felt and encourages a complete exhalation as well as a full inhalation. This in itself can provide the steadiness. If you lose your breath, it is most possibly because you are working too hard or forcing your practice; if this is the case then back off from the pose and let the pose ease into the breath. My feeling is ...

Let the Breath lead the pose.
Each breath directs the energy
and texture of that pose.
I breathe therefore I move.
AMN

Postures help keep the body disease free. When we are happy in our bodies we are 'at ease'; when we are not we come to feel 'dis-ease'; they help prepare us for meditation, relieving tension and protecting the body from disturbances by purifying the nervous system. There is no such thing as a perfect pose; let the poses come like the steps of a dance. Just like in dance, when we focus too much on the mechanics, we let go of the ability to enjoy the music. While the mechanics of alignment are important to prevent injury, never forget the final goal. Feel the music of life flow through you as you do each pose and your body will learn the moves naturally. There are more than enough postures (around 80,000) to keep you busy for the rest of your life, so allow yourself to let go of ambition and enjoy the journey. Incorporating a combination of forward bends, backbends, twists, and inversions in your Yoga session is optimal for health.

4th Limb

Pranayama | Control of Breath

Breathing right is fundamental to our very existence and there are many types of breathing techniques (*Pranayama*) in Yoga. Your brain feeds on oxygenated blood, which is supplied with each inhalation. If you are unable to draw oxygen into your body, you will become brain dead after a few minutes. On the other hand, proper exhaling helps dispel carbon dioxide. If your body were to shut down for 24 hours, impairing your lymphatic system (which can be considered as the body's sewage system) and your ability to exhale, you would most likely die due to the toxic build-up of carbon dioxide and poison.

Stress also tends to negatively affect breathing patterns, which contribute to a chain of effects that cause wear and tear on both your body's nervous and immune systems. In fact, ninety percent of illness is stress-related and for this reason, more attention should be put on breathing properly.

5th Limb

Pratyahara | Sense Withdrawal

Our perception of reality is predominantly influenced by our sensory experience; what we see, feel, hear, touch, and taste. *Pratyahara* refers to the withdrawal of the senses from their external objects. Our minds are constantly being pulled outward to evaluate all the information the senses bring in. Evaluation means categorising what has been perceived. Often, we grasp onto what we believe is desirable, push away what we think is undesirable, then ignore what we believe to be passive. *Pratyahara* gives our minds a moment to rest. Imagine a lake. When you throw a pebble into that lake, the ripples distort your reflection. Your mind works in very much the same way, as every thought creates a ripple that distorts the ability to see your true self clearly. Continually disrupted by these ripples, you begin to believe that the distorted reflection is who you really are. Watching, being the witness to your actions and then watching again cultivates a Still Mind.

Practicing *Pratyahara* stills the mind, allowing you to see yourself clearly. Not only will your view of the surface be clear, but your view of the bottom, from which everything grows, becomes clear as well. With enough practice, your unconscious thoughts can then become conscious ones, allowing mannerisms, like addictive behaviour, to lessen and have less of a powerful hold on you.

6th Limb

Dharana | One Pointed Concentration.

Dharana helps to prepare us for meditation. Practicing one pointed concentration clears the mind of all distracting thought. This can be achieved by focusing on your breath, counting, reciting mantras, observing a candle flame, or an image. Because we are constantly entangled in reliving past memories or living in anticipation of what is to come, it is very seldom that we live in the present moment. It is even less common to be mindful of the present moment with a calm and focused mind. However, this is crucial when trying to build the ultimate future for us.

Your Power is in the Here and Now!

7th Limb

Dhyana | Meditation

There are many ways of executing Yoga poses either through technique or dynamics, and there are many ways of meditating too. Meditation is a form of inner contemplation, allowing you to access a state of mind that has both recognized and bypassed the ego. All meditation leads to a state of full awareness that does not discriminate or label things in a dualistic manner. This is the part of you called 'the Observer', a way of stepping back, not getting involved with the drama. 'Life is a stage and each one of us a player.' This is how Shakespeare described the daily dramas we often allow ourselves to take part in. A role we choose when we could just stand back and observe, remaining detached yet open-eyed and open minded.

8th Limb

Samadhi | Total Absorption

Samadhi occurs when the analysing mind becomes silent and 'oneness with the object of meditation' is experienced. Total absorption involves the feeling of oneness with all creation, dissolving all lines between the act of meditation and the object being meditated upon. The goal of all Yoga is Enlightenment or, as we say in the West, self-realisation. By consistently meditating on these philosophies, your understanding of these fundamentals will gradually deepen.

Every moment in your life gives you an opportunity to practice the Eight Limbs. Learn at your own pace, but stay focused on the steps you take and enjoy your life journey.

Forget that 5 year plan!! Live now!!

To believe in something, and not to live it, is dishonest.
Mahatma Gandhi

Jnana Yoga

Jnana Yoga is known as the Path of Knowledge.

This is the most difficult path, it insists on a tremendous amount of will and intellect. Taking the philosophy of Vedanta, the Jnana Yogi uses his mind to inquire into its own nature. We perceive the space inside and outside a glass as different, just as we see ourselves as separate from God. Jnana Yoga leads the devotee to experience his unity with God directly by breaking the glass, dissolving the veils of ignorance, *Maya: The Veil of Illusion*. This veil can be explained as thinking you see the truth only to find out that when it drops away you can see clearly. I like to explain this as falling in love. After the love has gone you see that 'beloved' as smaller, sillier and even unlikable! You wonder what you saw in them.

Shakespeare expressed this perfectly in *A Midsummer Night's Dream*, when Puck spots Nick Bottom, a stage-struck weaver. Puck transforms his head into that of a donkey. Bottom's singing wakes Titania, and she immediately falls in love with him under Pucks spell. 'Beauty is in the eye of the beholder' sums this up well!

Before practicing Jnana Yoga, the student needs to have integrated the lessons of the other yogic paths, because without selflessness and a love for truth, strength of body and mind, the search for self-realisation or actualisation, can become a notion and not an action.

Engage with the person you are.
Admit you have choice and will.
Act out the true nature of your Self
and all will be as it should be.
OM TAT SAT

AMN

Vedanta

Vedanta is the philosophy that comes from the sacred scriptures called the Upanishads.
Veda means 'knowledge' and *Anta* means 'end'.
Therefore *Vedanta* is said to be the philosophy that leads to the End of Knowledge,
the place where all is absorbed as one and there is no-'thing'-ness

The Upanishads

The Upanishads are the final part of the ancient texts known as the *Vedas* and form the core of Indian philosophy. Aptly described by Sri Aurobindo as 'the supreme work of the Indian mind'.

The Upanishads are the high thinking on mankind and the universe, designed to push human ideas to their very limit and beyond.

These give us both spiritual vision and philosophical argument, that it is by a strict effort that you can reach the truth.

Upanishad literally means, 'sitting down near' or 'sitting close to', and implies listening closely to the doctrines of a spiritual teacher, who has experienced the basic truths of the universe.

The Three Vedanta Schools

The three main schools of *Vedanta* are:

1 *Dvaita* – the dualistic approach;
2 *Advaita* – the non-dualistic approach; and
3 *Kevala Advaita* – the pure non-dualistic school.

The main exponent of *Vedanta* was the great sage Adi Sankara who was an adept of the Kevala Advaita Vedanta path.

Vedanta and Jnana Yoga

The beauty of *Vedanta* is that it transcends dry philosophy and mere intellectual concept. *Vedanta* is an actual life experience, a philosophy in practice. This practice includes the many techniques of Jnana Yoga, The Yoga of will and intellect. In the end it's not what happens to you that forges your character, but how you handle it!

The Art of Sacred Geometry

Tantra, Yantra, Sri Yantra and Mandala

'Sacred Geometry is the geometry used in the construction and design of religious structures such as churches, mosques, temples, religious monuments such as tabernacles and altars as well as sacred spaces like a holy well or village green.' Looking at the list here it is clear that all religious faiths adopt this Sacred Geometry and not just the Ancient Indian as one might expect.

What is Tantra?

'A Hindu or Buddhist mystical or magical text, dating from the 7th century or earlier.

The adherence to the doctrines or principles of the Tantra, involving mantras, meditation, Yoga, and ritual.'

Tantra itself means to weave, to expand, and to spread, and according to tantric masters, the fabric of life can provide true and ever-lasting fulfilment only when all the threads are woven according to the pattern designated by nature.

When we are born, life naturally forms itself around that pattern. But as we grow, our ignorance, desire, attachment, fear, and false images of others and ourselves tangle and tear the threads, disfiguring the fabric.

Tantra *Sadhana*, or practice, reweaves the fabric, and restores the original pattern. This path is systematic and comprehensive. The profound science and practices pertaining to Hatha Yoga, *Pranayama*, *Mudras*, rituals, Kundalini Yoga (Yoga of the latent energy dormant in the lower spine, the coiled serpent), Nada Yoga (Yoga of sound), mantra (spoken sacred words), mandala, visualization of deities, alchemy, Ayurveda, astrology, and hundreds of esoteric practices for generating worldly and spiritual prosperity, blend perfectly in the tantric disciplines.

In the same way as any religious tasks, Tantric Rituals need the same five skills.

The Tantra beliefs are that:

1. **Mantra**, a sound, word, or phrase that is repeated by someone who is praying or meditating, provides the energy for the ritual, based on what the ritual is intended for.

2. The mantras are different for every ritual.

3. **Tantra** is the knowledge of how to carry out the ritual, for example which mantra to use, which deity to pray to, the offerings to be made, the rules and regulations.

4. The intention and mind are carried by the devotee; the stronger the will and intent and the more concentrated and pure the mind, the better it is for the ritual.

5. The **Yantra** therefore, is the tool and the vessel that converts, uses and stores the energy for the purpose designated for that particular ritual.

Yantra: the Tantric Symbol of Cosmic Unity

A Yantra is a visual sound mantra; the sound of sacred words replicated into a picture. The Yantra always includes the point, a Bindu, as well as triangles and circles. Each Yantra is home, a space or a vessel for a chosen deity. The Geometric Cosmic Yantra has a sense of spirit held within its shape, asking the meditator to 'enter' into its power for 'one-pointed-ness'.

We can try to simplify the meaning of the Yantra if we think about what we do in our daily lives.

There are five skills we need if we desire to finish any job well:

1. The will – that's the motivation;
2. The mind's application;
3. The energy to complete the job;
4. The knowledge required to know how to release the energy to perform the task;
5. The tools or the vessel that contains the energy, which converts it in the way the job requires.

Sri Yantra created in an electronic vibration field, an experiment in the translation of sound into vision.
A similar experience is 'sensed' during ritual worship when the yantra pattern 'dematerialises', appearing
to dissolve into a sound-pattern or vibration field of spoken mantras. Still from a film by Ronald Nameth.

From the book *Yantra, The Tantric Symbol of Cosmic Unity* by Madhu Khanna

What is the Sri Yantra?

The Sri Yantra is the Sacred Geometric shape that encompasses all other Yantra. All Yantra are a 'key' to both unlock and lock our physical, emotional, psychological, conscious and super-conscious mind. Sri Yantra is composed from two words: *Sri* (power, light, grace, regality) and *Yantra* (the means to allow the expression of 'something').

The Sri Yantra, in the field of spirituality, is a 'Regal Tool' which keeps in itself, the keys to reading and understanding acts which allow access to higher states of consciousness that, otherwise, would be very difficult, if not impossible, to be reached through other symbols, such as for example, words.

Sri Yantra, also known as Sri Chakra, is called the Mother of all Yantra because all other Yantra derive from it.

In its three dimensional forms Sri Yantra is said to represent Mount Meru, the cosmic mountain at the centre of the universe.

The Sri Yantra is conceived as a place of spiritual pilgrimage. It is a representation of the cosmos at the macrocosmic level and of the human body at the microcosmic level and each of the circuits corresponds to a chakra of the body.

The Sri Yantra is a tool to give a vision of total existence. This allows the Spiritual aspirant to internalize its symbols for the ultimate realization of his one-ness with the cosmos.

The goal of contemplating the Sri Yantra is to rediscover our primordial sources. The circuits symbolically indicate the successive phases in the process of becoming and then becoming One.

The shape of Sri Yantra is complex in design, yet simple in concept; many Yantra laid one on top of the other. It looks like a landing pad or a mandala. It is in effect the cosmic maze, a journey to the centre.

A Yantra is a dartboard, the mind, the arrow, the Bindu at the centre is the bull's eye and the One point is the goal of Realisation.

AMN

Mandala

A Mandala is usually seen as a circle and the Sanskrit word *Mandala* can be loosely translated as such. A circle has a centre that draws the eye, the heart and the mind to it. Creating your own Mandala is a unique opportunity to draw your senses to a clear point. They are often very exotic and beautiful in design and colour making them a joy to create and to contemplate.

What are Yantra mandalas? A Yantra is a Visual Mantra, a verbal or mental repetition of a positive affirmation such as a Sacred Sound like OM or *Om Namah Shivaya*. Mother being the potency of the Yantra Mandala It is a symbol particularly of a goddess a Devi in geometric form.

A Mandala literally means a circle, and is viewed as sacred, normally allowing the observer to settle into a higher or heightened state of awareness.

Yantra mandala is considered to be a geometric embodiment of a Hindu deity enveloped in a sacred circle. This embodiment is said to arouse our awareness and point our concentration towards the qualities of whichever deity is represented in the Yantra.

When we focus on a Yantra mandala, the mind begins to resonate with the energy relevant to that particular deity. As the mind tunes in to these energies, higher awareness is gained, so a Yantra mandala is a road to higher understanding: Enlightenment. This is not gained from the Yantra mandala; this is a vehicle or tool for higher awareness.

Hindu theology is diverse and intricate. This aspect of Hindu belief is no exception, and the samples of the deities represented are brief descriptions with an emphasis on the exotic beauty that these Yantra contain.

Keep in mind the deeper philosophical and theological understanding of the vast Hindu system, which takes a lot of study so these are three examples. Each Yantra is based first on the primal triangle; the emblem of cosmic energy is Shakti, the female energy. The Yoni, the womb or vagina is the symbol of the Goddess Shakti (or Devi), the Hindu Divine Mother and is represented as that primal triangle.

Yantra Mandalas and their Power

Dhumavati Yantra

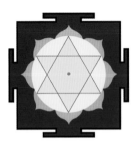

Beholder of Smoke, her persona is deceptive. To those who only see her outward appearance Dhumavati is fearsome and without beauty. To those who look deeper, and beyond the superficial, she bestows powerful blessings with her right hand and represents the Divine Mother. Focus on this Yantra will aid in dispelling false perceptions, and seeing the beauty in ugly situations.

Durga Yantra

Durga was created as a warrior goddess to fight the demon Mahisashur who could not be defeated by god or man. Allegorically, she slays the damaging misconceptions we hold, offering us clarity of mind and spirit. The Durga Yantra aids the focus on the qualities of Durga, facilitating strength, feminine energy and creative consciousness

Kali Yantra

Kali represents destruction and creation and is an aspect of the Hindu Divine Mother. The Kali Yantra invites the observer to go about the business of manifestation as play time. Kali keeps evil at bay as we focus on our creative powers, and live in the joy of creating a life that brings happiness to ourselves and to those around us. When meditated on, the Kali Yantra is said to speed spiritual transformation and allows for quick resolution to problems.

Life is a circle, ever increasing and decreasing. A Mandala, a Yantra, a Mantra and the Art of Sacred Geometry all have one purpose, to discover the meaning of life. Through the beauty of these deep and embracing shapes of colour and light we endeavor to find that purpose as we travel our own Spiritual journey to Enlightenment.

AMN

The Gunas

What are the Three Gunas and why do Yogis live by them?

Let us take a look at the Three *Gunas*, or energy complexes, found in all of Nature. They are *Sattva*, *Rajas*, and *Tamas*. These qualities are present in everything, including food. *Satvic* food is pure – ideal food for yogis. *Satvic* food promotes balance, calmness, clarity, harmony, and ease, and will support your efforts to live more peacefully and joyfully, as well as meditation practices. *Rajasic* food overly stimulates the passions, emotions, and creates a sense of drama, and restlessness. *Tamasic* food has little or no life force (*Prana*) present in it, and therefore is incompatible with the very nature of your living body! They make one inert, dull, and lazy as well as producing turbid, cloudy thought processes.

Satvic Foods are Yogi Foods

Fresh, local, seasonal, organic, prepared the same day, made with love – Milk, butter, ghee (clarified butter), cheese, yogurt, kefir; various whole grains and their flours, including rice, quinoa, oats, corn, millet, arrowroot, wheat, spelt; legumes: lentils, peas, most beans; fruits: all, including dried (preferably soaked or stewed); vegetables: almost all, including sprouts; others: whole sweeteners, such as honey, sugarcane, and molasses; almonds, peanuts (unsalted, unroasted); many seasonings and spices, such as turmeric, ginger and coriander; apple cider vinegar; lacto-fermented items (foods with beneficial flora like raw sauerkraut, miso, and yogurt).

Be mindful of your thoughts; they have power.
So think positive, hopeful, calm and compassionate thoughts at all times.

Rajasic Food is the enemy of Meditation

Overly flavoured, over-processed, refined, deep-fried, animal products: fish, eggs; vegetables: radish; stimulants: coffee, tea, chocolate and related products; others: chili's, very hot, spicy seasonings, prepared mustards; white sugar, artificial substances. Over stimulates the mind as it raises the heart rate.

Tamasic Foods dull the Mind and Body

Meat, mushrooms, vinegars other than apple cider vinegar, onions, garlic, margarine, artificial substances, fermented items, any intoxicant or drug; old leftovers or under cooked food, stale, rotten or unclean foods that sit on grocery store shelves for months without apparent changes! If it looks grey don't touch it!

Part of raising your vibrations is to hone your mental prowess and to listen to your inner teacher, your Intuition. If in doubt, don't!

Start your food journey wherever you are right now, today and simply be with your unique, dynamic process, avoiding constricting concepts of static perfection, as only the Divine is perfect!

The Three Gunas, in all areas of life

The Three *Gunas* are not only reflected in food but in personalities, actions, attitudes and environments. My children, when they were teenagers, knew what *Tamasic* meant! When they lay around when things needed doing they would hear me say "don't be so *Tamasic*!" That word is so clear, I don't think you need to know what it means, and its vibration says it all!

Take a look at the people you have around you; even your Yoga teacher can be *Tamasic* you know! Swami Sivananda said, to know where you are in the world in terms of Spiritual progress, look at your life and especially the people, the environment and how you feed yourself and how you think too. Thoughts are also divided into the Three *Gunas* and in fact this has to be the most potent and important, as we are what we think.

The Mind's Relationship with Food

Food is a very emotive subject; it creates fear, anger, pleasure, and joy. It ultimately feeds the mind as well as the body and creates an outer material world that either sharpens the mind or clouds it.

The body is our outer uniform, a protective clothing against the cold, heat, infection and injury. But this body is also an expression of our inner-most feelings. An artist has a canvas to express those feelings, a musician an instrument and a writer, words. What do most of us have to express those feelings? We use the body as an exercise machine or punch ball, as a canvas, and tattoo or harm it. But we also eat to relieve sadness, stress, to express love and contentment, so it makes sense that food is also an expression of our minds and our minds an extension of our inner world.

Swami Vishnu explained, in simple everyday ways, that complex subject 'mind', in these simple words, "If you want to know the state of your mind, look at the people you hang around with."

I would also say that the way you see yourself is often distorted by the way you think people see you. So when we feed ourselves we take control or we lose control.

Practising Yoga is an aid to positive control of food. We are what we eat, maybe, but our minds are affected by the food we eat and that is certain.

It's the chicken, egg thing; what comes first? The mind wants the food or the food we want becomes our mind? We can read our thoughts by noticing what we want to eat.

As an ex-ballerina I am also an ex-anorexic. These two paths inevitably cross for most dancers. I had always had a healthy appetite and attitude to food; I loved it and enjoyed mealtimes. At 16 I began to go through puberty, I was late, as most extreme exercise stunts the endocrine system and therefore going into puberty is often delayed. Olga Korbut, the great Russian gymnast, ballooned after retiring at 21; she became a woman almost overnight.

This happened to me, and by 17, I was told I was plump. I stopped eating that day. At no time did I get any nutritional advice or help and support. I became reclusive, demented and crazy.

I was obsessed with food, with the art of not eating. If I had performances and rehearsals I ate, if not I did not eat, so this often meant eating for 5 days out of 7. But the calorific value of my eating day was 500 calories possibly...usually less. I survived each day just about. I had no friends and I learned all about loneliness and the feeling of worthlessness. If I was plump I had no place in the rehearsal room or on the stage. Life was not worth living. The thinner I became the more I was praised so I carried on with my destructive relationship with my food. I could cry for that young me, who had no idea that food would dominate my feelings about myself for the rest of my life. I did take control though by practising Yoga with my eyes closed. Closing my eyes meant not seeing my external body, but noticing my breath and therefore my thoughts. I discovered I could watch my breath and switch off those thoughts.

It was this revelation that transformed my body image and changed my mind. My understanding that food is survival and that survival depended on my eating to live was what I needed to accept.

The wise say 'Drink your food and eat your liquid' in other words take your time and get the most out of your food. We break down our food on the tongue first with saliva and if we just swallow our food we lose the nutrition it gives us.

This is another reason why, in spiritual communities, they eat in silence. Giving the food, blessed as it is and full of *Prana*, the chance to do its work, that of nourishing the body in preparation for nourishing the mind through meditation.

The Tibetan *Book of the Dead* says this about the body, the soul and the mind.

The body, which thou hast now is called the thought-body of propensities. Since thou hast not a material body of flesh and blood, whatever may come – sounds, lights, or rays – are, all three, unable to harm thee: thou art incapable of dying. It is quite sufficient for thee to know that these apparitions are thine own thought-forms.

As a simple aid to understanding your own relationship with your food and therefore your mind I have put a small work sheet together. It may help you recognize something about your habits, whether good or not. Please do not judge yourself, nor force anything on yourself, simply recognize and witness.

Ask your-SELF this:

❋ What do I love to eat rather than cooking?

❋ What liquids do I crave and why?

❋ How can I improve my diet in a simple and effective way?

Food and Mood

Taking a look at what you feed yourself and how you give yourself energy

❉ What is the first drink of the day and when do you drink it?

❉ How often do you drink plain water?

❉ What is the first meal of your day and when do you eat it?

❉ Do you manage to eat three meals a day? If not how often do you eat?

❉ Do you snack during the day and what are those snacks?

❉ At what time of the day do you 'crash?'. How often in a day?

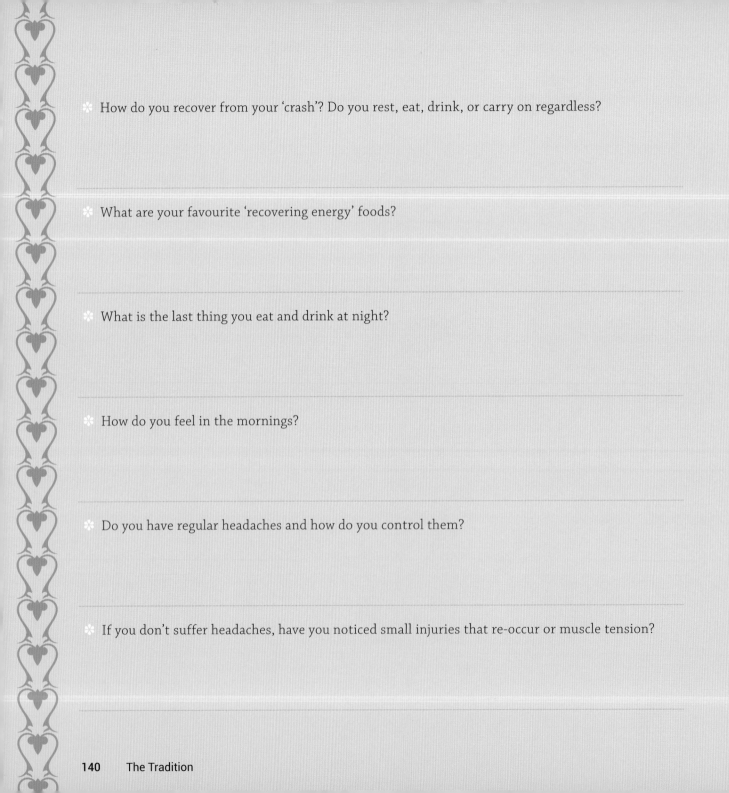

❋ How do you recover from your 'crash'? Do you rest, eat, drink, or carry on regardless?

❋ What are your favourite 'recovering energy' foods?

❋ What is the last thing you eat and drink at night?

❋ How do you feel in the mornings?

❋ Do you have regular headaches and how do you control them?

❋ If you don't suffer headaches, have you noticed small injuries that re-occur or muscle tension?

✻ Are your headaches or stresses ones you get in the morning, afternoon or evening or do they stay all day?

✻ When you are very stressed from exams, rehearsals and performances how do you manage your energy levels? What is your 'quick fix?

✻ When do you feel happy?

✻ When do you feel down or depressed?

✻ What would your ideal mood be and why?

* Had you considered that what you *feel* like has something to do with what you eat and drink?
* Uppers and Downers?
* How does this affect your mind?
* Is the food affecting your mind or is your mind affecting what you eat?
* Write down here what that statement means to you after looking at your answers.

When you practice Yoga you need to consider your food, so this is a small checklist:

* Eat something before you practice. Don't go to class hungry, be sensible.
* Increase your vitamin C intake to fight colds and infections. You cannot store it, so replenish it by squeezing fresh lemons on all your food.
* Take more iron, either by way of a supplement or food such as green kale, lentils and prunes. *but*, spinach does not contain absorbable iron so add lashings of lemon juice/vitamin C to make it usable within the body.

More exercise and more care!
However, a little of what you fancy does you good!

Moderation in all things
Sivananda

Some tips for a Loving Body and Healthy Mind

* Have a treat every day; replace one meal if you wish. My Mother advocated a small treat each day; she practised moderation in all things!

* Don't go overboard with changes to your food; try one or two changes a week and only depending on your workload that week.

* Consider not eating any carbohydrates after 5:00pm; have protein and vegetables for dinner (not pasta or bread for instance).

* Eat a Rainbow, a colourful plate. Have plenty of greens, reds, yellows and oranges.

* Use the palm of your hand for portion sizes or a bowl that is beautiful and inspires respect for yourself and what you eat.

* Eat protein in two meals and remember 8 almonds will give you your daily proteins so don't overload on dairy for instance.

* Try eating five small meals daily instead of three big ones!

* Try and have your last meal no later than 7pm; this will give your body a resting time and a fast from 7 to 7 approximately.

* Always eat breakfast even if you think you can't; its just another habit you have created. Break-Fast is just that...breaking the fast. Protein is good, fresh fruit too but stick to red fruits that are low in sugar.

* Drink at least 6 large glasses of water a day, 8 when you practice.

* Get 6-8 hours sleep and if you find it hard to sleep then practice *Savasana* (Corpse pose). Talk your way through to a relaxed demeanour by using your 'inside eyes', looking into your body using Auto-suggestion, Yogic sleep.

* Eat vegetables and fruit before protein, potato and bread.

* After your Yoga practice (within 30 minutes) eat a colourful mixed meal of salads, seeds, raw vegetables and protein such as tofu, seaweed and tahini. Tahini has 11 times more calcium than a glass of milk. Perfect for vegans.

The best advice I can give you on food is to love what you eat but don't fool yourself that junk food is 'good' for your body. Your mind will tell you that you 'need' it. When you meditate you become healthy in mind and body. You find yourself wanting to eat vibrant, alive foods.

A last thought.

Bless your food and you will be blessing your Self and your body's mind.

Best nourishment you can get!

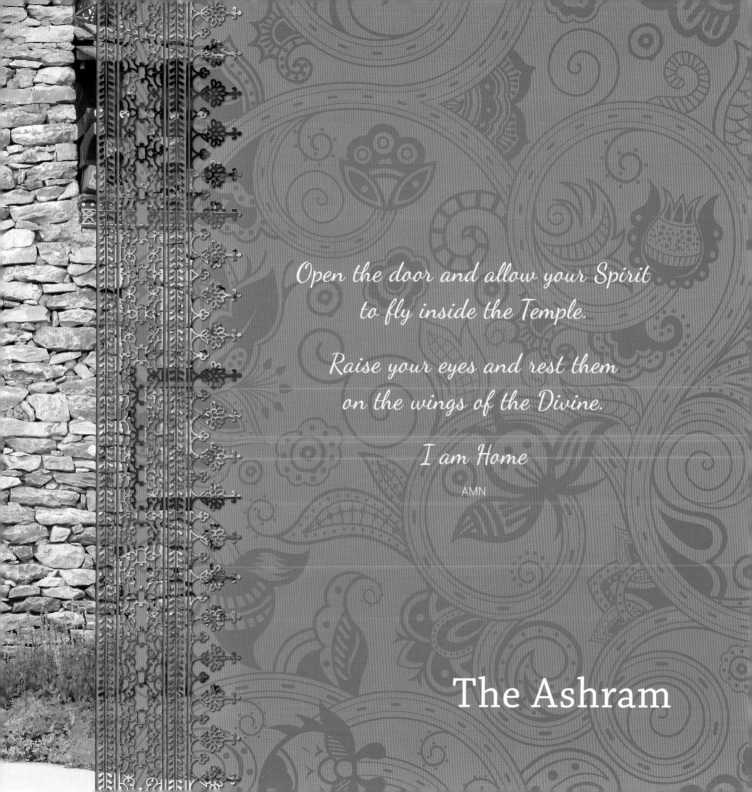

Open the door and allow your Spirit
to fly inside the Temple.

Raise your eyes and rest them
on the wings of the Divine.

I am Home

AMN

The Ashram

What is an Ashram?

An Ashram is filled with Ordinary people,
living an Extra-ordinary Life

The Sanskrit word *Ashram*, or sometimes spoken as *Ashrama* in the South of India, originates from the Sanskrit root word *srama* which literally means, 'giving the meaning of making an effort towards *Moksha* (liberation)'. In parts of India these are called *Ashram Shala*, (Ashram schools), where knowledge is given and the student enlightened.

My first visit to an Indian ashram was in 1984 when I took up my first Yoga teaching qualification. I had already been to one in Canada during 1983 in the Laurentian Mountains studying with Swami Vishnu-devananda. The Sivananda HQ in Canada was based on the Ashram in Trivandrum, South India. Both places were uniquely different but the content and delivery the same.

Personally I loved the severe discipline; it was not unlike my three years at boarding school when I was studying to be a ballet dancer. The hours were long and the regime harsh. In the first week of the teacher training 27 people left out of 120; they just could not accept the concept of acceptance, of letting go of their own routines at home and the pure rigor of hours sitting either in meditation or listening to lectures.

This is the most difficult part of ashram life, the sitting. Swami Vishnu-devananda, a direct disciple of Swami Sivananda of Rishikesh, taught me and I know that I am blessed to have been in the right place at the right time. But he was a serious man as well as a comedian! He could not tolerate laziness, the lack of commitment to a job, asking too many questions and fidgeting in meditation or worse still falling asleep!

I took him very seriously and, to be honest, he scared me, but that fear was a deep respect for a man from another era watching the West try to get their heads around an ancient Indian theory for living a successful life.

Satsang

A Gathering of Like-Minded People

The Sanskrit: *Sat* – true, *sanga* – company

Satsang is one of the pivotal points of an ashram day, usually taking place in the morning after meditation and then in the evening, also after meditation. Each ashram has a similar timetable but depending on the specific courses or activities going on they do differ slightly. Typically, *Satsang* involves listening to or reading scriptures, reflecting on, discussing and assimilating their meaning, and then meditating on the source of these words, and bringing their meaning into one's daily life. These discourses were such fun with Swamiji. He had a great sense of humor and often made complex subjects easy to understand.

One such story is this one. "So you must see, that if we find our mind difficult to control imagine how hard it is when we have a family. You meet a girl you fall in love, 'kissy kissy'; you then get married, now you have two minds. Then you have a baby, oh dear three minds, then two, three, four children; by then you have lost your mind!!"

I still chuckle at this story, especially as I have four children and yes, no mind!

I had some lessons to learn and I learned them by sitting at his feet witnessing how knowledge poured from him endlessly, and for hours and days and weeks, and how his energy never seemed to fail us. I always pass my working day to him and Sivananda, to work with me and through me. It would be pretty vain of me to imagine I do all the 'work'. I am, as was Swamiji, an instrument of the work of the Divine. What a huge responsibility it would be if we thought we did everything!

An ashram houses such luminaries, men and women who have walked a different and often difficult path. These people are all around us but their work is not on the front of newspapers or magazines, not on the 6o'clock news or passed on through the social media.

If I am the flute at Krishna's lips, then the Divine is the breath that passes through it.

AMN

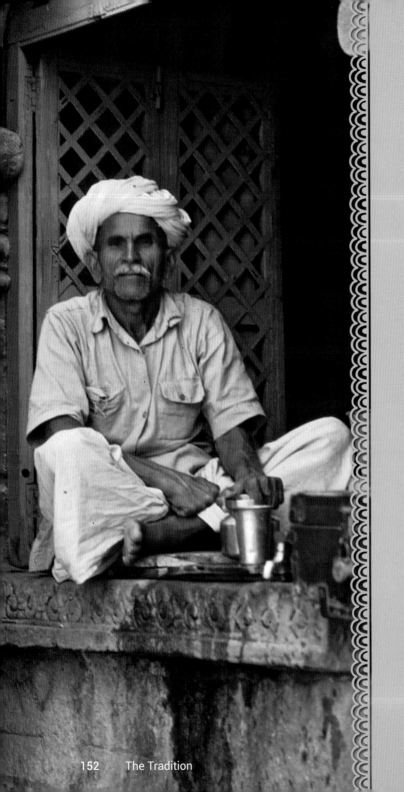

These exceptional human beings, of whom you could be one, are the silent, often invisible souls that get on with their work, day after day after day.

A humble person shows their humility by not being noticed.

My vivid recollections of this ashram life is easily recalled through one particular practice that has remained with me and will do all my days.

We woke before dawn when it is the best time to meditate without distraction. A powerful rule was strictly adhered to – no one was allowed to speak at all from waking to breakfast. The purpose was that the mind remained in the sacred place after sleep and before action. This place is the 'Still Point' and the 'Art of Non-Speaking' is called *Mauna*.

Mauna

What is Mauna?

Understanding what *Mauna* (or *Mouna*) is, does not have to be complex, it is however very thought provoking in essence. When the human learned to speak it was to communicate and to manoeuvre through a world that was full of silence and also full of sound. The silence was between humans but the sound was the universe, the cosmos, the earth, the wind and the movement of flora and fauna. The expression 'Silence is Golden' is expressed here perfectly.

Sri Ramana Maharishi explains,

Mauna is the state that transcends speech and thought.

That which is, is Mauna. How can it be explained in words?

The ancient Sages (wise souls) say that it is the state in which the ego, the word 'I' does not rise in the least when in Mauna.

The silent self is God alone, alone is self (Swarupa) in Jiva (soul).

Self, Alone is the Ancient World.

All other knowledge is only petty and trivial knowledge,

The experience of Silence is the real and perfect knowledge.

Mauna Vratham, the Vow of Silence

The Sanskrit Maun-Vrat, literally means 'a Vow to keep Silent'

For any spiritual growth to really happen it is essential that our speech is monitored. To acquire the control of our speech the practice of silence is important. Hindu religious texts give this practice of *Maun-Vrat* for the purpose of disciplining how we talk, as in the end it's our thoughts that we let out of our mouths!

In *Bhadon*, which is the sixth month of the Hindu calendar, 16 days of *Maun Vrat* are suggested. It is believed that through silence we are able to achieve the desired quality of mind for a better life with others and ourselves.

Along with the practice of *Maun Vrat*, it is essential that some time is spent in offering prayers, and this is very important to your personal faith and beliefs in my opinion; I feel that dogma has no place in any Spiritual practice. I must, you must, they must; for me it needs to reflect that I am willing and ready in all aspects of my life and that includes prayer.

One of my favourite spiritual books on the subject of *Mauna* is *Silence Speaks*. This gem of a book is full of surprises. Baba Hari Das is a monk who does not speak. His path as a Yogi is the practice of keeping silent.

'Its aim is less about silencing the voice and more about silencing the mind which, as we know, tends to be filled with worries, desires, and clinging. This book offers the privilege of being touched with the advice and teachings of a spiritual master who, out of that silence, gives form to the unexplainable and sheds light on our daily life predicaments'. Taken from the cover notes of my own copy, purchased in 1983. It is worn out with being constantly used as a reference book on most of the daily issues of life.

Babaji writes, 'There is an inner silence. It cannot be heard by the ears, only by the heart.'

Living a life as Babaji does, in profound silence, he can still communicate wisdom and guidance when asked. As he cannot speak Babaji uses a blackboard and he asks that we 'listen' to his help and advice. He gives guidance with questions on many varied topics such as Spiritual Practice,

relationships, healing, death, parenting, drugs, and rebirth. When I was pregnant with my first child and living by the Yogic moral code of a vegetarian, I craved fish. I looked up the subject in this amazing little book. The answer was there! It is the baby needing the fish therefore it would be harmful to not fulfil that craving! Thank you Babaji! I needed one portion to feel I did not need more.

Don't think that you are carrying the whole world. Make it easy. Make it play. Make it a prayer.

Baba Hari Das

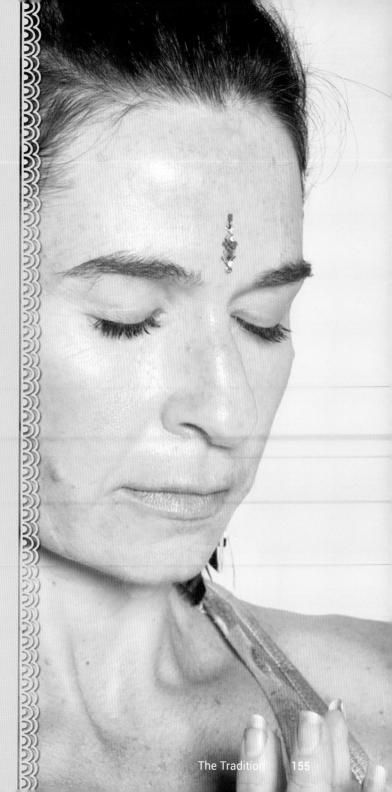

Mahabharata

In Sanskrit the *Mahabharata* means 'Great Epic of the Bharata Dynasty', one of the two epic Sanskrit poems of ancient India, the other being the *Ramayana*. The *Mahabharata* is an important source of information on the development of the Hindu faith and is regarded by many as both a text about *Dharma*, Hindu moral law, and a history of 'what happened' so far, up to the point when it was written, said to be between 400 BCE and 200 CE.

Although it is unlikely that any single person wrote the poem, its authorship is traditionally given to the sage Vyasa. The Bhagavad Gita is part of the *Mahabharata* and is probably one of the Epic's greatest pieces on the dilemma of a human and the battle between right action and the reality of a materialist incarnation.

Often, the aim of a pilgrimage to an ashram was not tranquillity, but to ask for instruction in some art, often that of warfare.

A battle raged within, and the art of war was as much about the skills of Conscious practice and discipline as about using a sword.

Ramayana

The *Ramayana* depicts the duty of relationships, portraying ideal characters like the ideal father, the ideal servant, the ideal brother, the ideal wife, and the ideal king. The name *Ramayana* is a compound Sanskrit name of *Rama* and *ayana* (going, advancing), translating to 'Rama's Journey'. It is probably the first soap opera ever written, as all the elements mentioned here make up a best seller, nothing changes much when it comes to the human personality! Always a goody and always a baddy – the duality of life!

The *Ramayana* is made up of 24,000 verses, in seven books. I do believe the English word 'yarn', the word for a long story, originally came from the Sanskrit.

In the Hindu Epic *Ramayana*, the Princes Rama and Lakshmana go to see Rishi Vishmamitra at his ashram to help protect his teachings from being defiled by the emissary-demons of *Ravana*. The literal translation of *Ravana* is from the Sanskrit 'crying' or 'causing to cry'. I find this a very interesting translation, bringing the scriptures to life, by using human emotions.

After Rama and Lakshmana prove themselves worthy, the princes receive martial instruction from the Sage (the wise one) in the use of Divine weapons, called *Divyastras*. The Sanskrit meaning of *Divya* is 'Divine' and *Astra* 'a missile weapon', like an arrow, as opposed to *shastra*, which means 'a hand-to-hand weapon', like a mace.

In the other great Epic the Mahabharata, the young Lord Krishna goes to the ashram of Sage Sandipani to gain the knowledge of both intellectual and spiritual matters.

The Bhagavad Gita

The Bhagavad Gita, literally meaning 'The Song of the *Bhagavan*',
often called simply, The Gita. It is a 700 verse Hindu scripture
that is part of the Hindu Epic *Mahabharata*.

What was the purpose of the Bhagavad Gita?

The Bhagavad Gita is a poem, a song, and its purpose was to deliver mankind from the darkness of a material existence. Every one of us is in difficulty in so many ways, just as Arjuna was in difficulty because of having to fight the battle of Kuruksetra. Here he saw both sides of his direct family preparing to fight one another. He could not bring himself to align with any side. As human beings we know that there have been times in our lives when whatever we did there would be consequences. We create Karma the moment we are born; its what being human is about. Our actions create a ripple throughout the Universe, our Souls journey and this is forever recorded in the *Akashic* records, the Library of the Divine, where all that we have experienced in life is recorded.

So the conversation Arjuna (us) has with Krishna (God Consciousness) is about duty. How can he choose? Krishna explains that in effect he has no choice; it is his duty to fight for the good of the whole. It still means creating ripples and waves that will come back to us, as we are the centre of the lake, but this is inevitable. What comes around goes around.

In your Note to Self, recollect a situation in your own life when whatever you decided there was a consequence for someone. Being cruel to be kind is a metaphor for this situation I think.

Arjuna surrendered to Krishna and consequently the Bhagavad Gita was spoken.

It was not only Arjuna that was full of anxieties because of this material existence ... every one of us is too. We are trying to exist here in the material world but the atmosphere of the material world is nonexistence; we are not meant to be threatened by nonexistence because our existence is eternal.

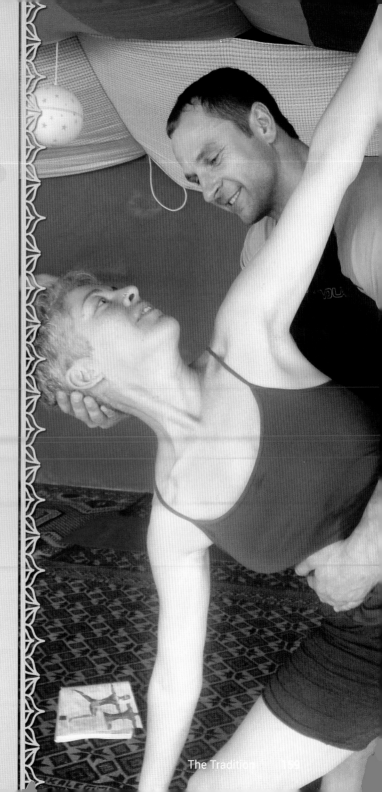

And so what we say has as much impact on our lives and on others as our actions do. Speak sweetly, with consideration for all. That makes us human and therefore compassionate.

AMN

But somehow or other we have been put into this temporary material world and because of this we are threatened with nonexistence.

Out of so many human beings who are suffering, there are only a few who are actually enquiring about their position, questioning what they are, why they are put into this difficult position, and so on. Unless we can come to the point of questioning our own suffering, unless we realize that we don't not want to suffer, but rather we want to find a solution to the suffering, then we cannot be considered a human being. Human life begins when we begin to question our actions, motives and responses. We are suddenly awake after having been asleep! Living a mind-full life as opposed to a mind-less one!

From the Bhagavad Gita on *Mauna*:

Contentment of the mind, amiable temperament, silence, religious meditation and good thoughts reflect austerity of the mind.

Silence is placed mid-way between other qualities. It begins with control of the mind. Once the mind is controlled, one becomes friendly. One begins to look kindly toward others. One cuts down on useless speech and thinks more of God within. One begins to generate good thoughts.

From Chanakya Niti: c. 370 – c. 283 BC An Indian teacher, philosopher, and royal advisor. He said:

Whoever can remain silent everyday for a full year becomes worthy of thousands of years of praise in heaven.

Silence can change the personality of an individual. Through silence a person controls anger and speech. One grows stronger through greater determination and self-confidence. One is more at peace and free of tension. There is conservation of energy and a person experiences greater inner strength.

The Purpose of Mauna

1   *Maun Vrat* sees you with heightened Spiritual Awareness.

2   It gives you a lot of tranquillity and spiritual satisfaction.

3   It protects you from the detrimental effects of chattering and gossip.

4   It will conserve your energy levels.

5   It will dampen your anger.

6   Your creative potential will increase by many times.

7   You will realize the importance of speech.

8   Your personality stands totally refined.

9   You will grow above mundane thoughts.

10   You will have attained contentment.

The ashrams were as close to nature as possible, as this was an aid to silent practice or a life-style based on the principles of Meditation, which for any Yogi or spiritual seeker was the ultimate goal. Communing with and in Nature highlights our supreme and privileged position on this earth and that we are caretakers of what we have around us in the plants, trees and animals.

India is very noisy and busy and it made sense to me, after travelling the breadth of India, that they developed the art of meditation to such a Royal Road, Raja Yoga. Raja Yoga being the ultimate aim of all Yoga practices. But *Mauna* means you don't fall into chitter chatter, brainless talk. Talking like a monkey leads to acting like a monkey as it were! Those who constantly talk, ask questions without waiting for an answer, cannot bear silence and self-examination of the mind, need *Mauna* the most.

An ashram timetable is a deep groove, a positive groove to aid you in a way of life that will lift you and change you. I still feel so deeply affected by that timetable and find it's always there as a faint thread connected to most of what I do and who I am. I use it in my training intensives and after a short time people find it uplifting though very challenging.

Ashrams demand a commitment from you; you become a *Sadhaka*, a spiritual aspirant.

Sadhana (Spiritual Practice) means getting up at 5am, meditating for a couple of hours, then intense Hatha Yoga practice for three or four more, followed by the first of two meals a day. Work, Karma Yoga, is given to all students regardless of their physical or mental capacity, or their position in the world. On my course, the Indian men and women who had always had servants or Mothers who would not let them do anything, had to clean the toilets! Speaking to some during my course, they said they loved it but knew they would not be allowed to clean them when they got home, what a shame! I reminded them that there was still a lot they could do, like work for their community and the less fortunate than them.

What would be the point of training with someone like me (of the old school and a task master) at such a deep level if you left the same as you arrived? That could only happen if you had not been stretched or challenged and had not found some aspects painful, physically as well as mentally!

No point at all!
Reach out of your comfort zone!

Change takes Courage!

Anne-Marie teaching at the Sivananda Yoga Ashram, India in 1984.

An ashram would traditionally be located away from humans, either in a forest or in the mountains. There are now ashrams in the West that align themselves with a Spiritual leader and are also located in such remote places as Holy Island and Snowdonia in Wales. There are Christian monasteries in India that are called ashrams, run by the Nasrani Orthodox churches. The Saint Thomas Christians, also called Syrian Christians or Nasrani, are an ancient community of Christians from Kerala in South India, who trace their origins to the evangelist Thomas the Apostle, often known as the Doubting Thomas in the 1st century. So an ashram, though an ancient Indian concept, has been adopted by many faiths. In the West they may be known as Silent Orders, Convents or Monasteries.

Interestingly you will find many Catholics in Goa on the West coast of India. Portuguese sailors, traders and families settled there when exporting the spices of India to Europe. As a Syrian Orthodox Christian, born in the Middle East, I can clearly see my own affinity with India as I study faiths across the globe. There is also some evidence that Jesus travelled India and practiced Yoga, though for many obvious reasons the Church has suppressed this. If you are interested, I can suggest you look up *The Lost Years of Jesus: The Life of Saint Issa*, A Translation by Notovitch. *The Gospel of the Essenes* is also fascinating reading. Between the age of 12 and 33 there is nothing written about Jesus in the Bible, so it's good reading and mind expanding, if nothing else.

Maybe that is why Yoga should never be misinterpreted as a religion, because it crosses so many faiths, countries, ideas and minds.

When you live in an ashram, or visit one for a short time, you will regularly perform Karma Yoga; work in the ashram, deep intense meditation and physical exercises, such as Hatha Yoga. You will also practice other sacrifices and penances, such as *Yajnas*. *Yajnas* are rituals performed at the fire, where chanting Mantras and the throwing in of sacred herbs is also performed. Fire represents cleansing and clearing of the past, of old habits and of an old life. Cleansing the spirit and clearing the way for those new positive habits, mental grooves and the path to a new life is made possible by performing *Yajnas*, rituals for both the body and the mind.

Many ashrams also served as a *Gurukula*, residential schools for children under *Guru-Shishya Parampara* tradition. This meant that the Guru and disciple lived together and learned by example, as well as the instruction and practice of the scriptures. This practice still exists, though with the (supposed) banishment of the caste system it is not so popular, as it was the higher castes that were sent like a gift or offering to the Divine. The West also practiced this in the Catholic faith.

The caste system of India was a harsh existence for those born into low castes, as it meant they could only perform menial tasks and had no access to education. In reality it is still practiced, as these old traditions have never been truly eliminated. Mahatma (Great Soul) Gandhi tried without success to make people see how against Spiritual growth and compassion it was to view another human being as lower than oneself.

Ashrams have been a powerful symbol throughout Hindu history and theology. Most Hindu kings, until the Middle Ages, are known to have had a sage who would advise the royal family in spiritual matters, or in times of crisis. He was called the *Rajguru* (royal teacher) and literally translates as the King's dispeller of Darkness, of ignorance. A world-weary emperor going to his Guru's ashram, to find some solace and tranquility, is an on-going theme in many folk stories and legends of ancient India.

Even in the West, ancient epic myths and legends include a wise man or woman, magician or sorcerer that advises and assists in either noble matters or matters of the dark arts, the most popular being King Arthur's Merlin, Macbeth's Witches, The Hobbit's Gandalf and Harry Potter's Dumbledore!

So the Ashram is the world and
its entire peoples; its issues,
its troubles, its challenges,
its triumphs, all under one roof.

Welcome home traveller and rest
your weary head. Still your mind
as your breath steadies your
thoughts and stills your actions.

Accept there is a Silence beyond
all understanding.

Note to Self

the purpose

Rituals for
Faith and Hope

In Yoga Practice, why do we do ...?

When I first travelled through India in 1984, I was struck by what I now call 'Living Spirituality'. In other words, it was everywhere. Riding on the bus and looking at its psychedelic artwork of Krishna, Om symbols and lotus flower murals left you with a feeling of immersion in a culture so linked to its faith that it was easy to just absorb it.

Of course it is easy to romanticise India, but its poverty is anything but romantic. One can appreciate why Faith keeps people going in a land where the elements, lack of social care and political corruption affect the most vulnerable on every level; Ritual and Faith keep the mind from considering the futility of life and instils Hope.

I returned from Mother India as one more child of Faith and Humility.
I learned to accept crowds – even on an empty bus, people sat next to you –
to stop complaining and to be a witness to the joy in a child's face
though they had nothing.
It changed my life forever.

Why do we perform certain Rituals?

All over the world Indian Spirituality is respected as both beautiful and deep in its reverence for knowledge and ultimate experience.

Each ritual and custom performed in the temples, ashrams or homes of India has a scientific, historical, philosophical, logical, or spiritual purpose and significance.

I explain to my students that the *Mudras* (Yoga of the hands), are not simply there to look pretty but have a profound affect on our mind and body. At the tip of each finger are a network of nerves relating to certain parts of the inner and outer body. Everything we do in our Yoga class and practice has a true meaning and purpose, not simply there for decoration.

We perform Rituals without thinking about their meaning

The most powerful effects of Yoga are the control of the mind and attempting to still the thoughts that crowd it. Associating smells and sounds will take the mind to a place, a person, or situation.

Memories create emotions, and this creates waves in the mind as we relive those memories; whether good or bad, the mind is moved. As the mind is moved so too is the heart.

When we light an incense stick our senses react to the fragrance and we think, its time to practice meditation or practice our *Asanas*. If we smell perfume that belonged to a loved one, we think of them. If we smell coffee we may also have associated thoughts, like it's time for a break or a meeting with friends. The point is that simple rituals create deep and powerful grooves in the mind and a way of changing our habits. If we used to smoke we try to avoid places, people and situations that may make it hard to stick to being a non-smoker. The smell of the gentle smoke of sandalwood will soon replace the smell of tobacco, I know because I did it!

Places we visit have smells, objects and actions that fix the mind on the atmosphere of the building and the reason for its existence. A church has ether that exudes silence, prayer, deep thought and a feeling of communion with both people and the Divine. If we walk into a club we hear popular music, loud voices, laughing and the smell of alcohol and bodies! Both of these spaces have the atmospheres that have been created by thoughts.

What is Pradakshina?

Why is it practised?

On visiting a temple or sacred place, and after offering our prayers, Yogic tradition dictates we walk in a clockwise circle around the central covered sanctum or altar. This walking around the sanctum is called *Pradakshina*. We walk in a clockwise circle because it is generally accepted that The Divine is on our right and is seen as auspicious.

The traditional chant recited while performing *Pradakshina* is:

'Yaani kaani cha paapaani
Janmaantara krtaani cha
Taani taani vinashyanti
Pradakshina pade pade.'

'All the sins committed by an individual from innumerable past lives, are destroyed by each step taken, whilst doing the *Pradakshina*.'

What is its meaning and purpose?

We cannot draw a circle without a centre point. The Divine is the centre, the source and the essence of our lives as Yogis and seekers. When we recognize the Divine as the focal point in our lives, then we also embrace that essence in all the daily chores and duties we perform. When we walk around that sanctum we are reminded to live a good and auspicious life. Symbolism is part of everyday life and the small rituals we perform form the threads of our experiences with our families, friends and selves.

Yoga is a Rich Tapestry
created with many Hands and Hearts

Lighting a candle or oil lamp

Knowledge is an everlasting inner wealth, never to be lost, and it's this kind of accumulation of wealth that will enhance not just your own life but also others. Knowledge supports all our actions, good and bad, and it's for this reason that we keep a light shining during auspicious times as a witness to our thoughts and actions.

Why don't we use artificial light? This would also remove darkness. The traditional use of a lamp or candle has other significances. The oil or wax represents our *Vaasanas* (negative tendencies), and the wick our ego – the small self, me.

When the flame is lit with spiritual knowledge the *Vaasanas* become exhausted and eventually the ego perishes. Everything performed in Yoga ashrams, prayer meetings, and classes or at home has a meaning and an aim. These rituals help fix our mind on higher thoughts and actions.

Light represents knowledge
and darkness ignorance.
Therefore knowledge removes
ignorance just as
light removes darkness.

The flame of a lamp or candle always reaches upwards, and it is to this aim that we aspire, as well as that of raising our consciousness. A single flame can light hundreds of others and we can do the same as teachers, religious and political leaders and parents, when we pass on truth and knowledge. This passing on benefits both the giver and the receiver.

A single flame can light
a darkened room
and the Guru light the
mind of the Student.

AMN

What is the Purpose of an Altar or Sacred Space?

Most Indian families have a prayer room or altar. A light is lit, incense burned and flowers or food is offered to the Divine as a reminder that the Lord of Creation is in all we do, think or become and the home is also the Divine's home.

Each room in our homes is dedicated to a specific purpose and the Prayer room has its function as the centre or heart of the home. The reality is that our behaviour should be mindful in whatever room we use but having the luxury of a payer room is also a privilege. I believe that the western altar has become the television and it is for this reason that adopting an ancient spiritual tradition is so worthwhile in aiding that balance between tradition and modern life.

Most of us can understand that space is a luxury, so if we are able to dedicate a corner, a shelf or area to the reminder that the Divine works in us and around us, then it is a tool to aid our understanding that we can and do need small symbols or Rituals to help us stay on track. In the end it is about helping us to change our daily routines into meaningful actions.

The Yoga Shala, The Sacred Space, is where we pray, meditate, practice Japa meditation (repetition of the Divine name) and chant. With regular practice we are creating a sound vibration in the ether, so when we enter that Sacred Space we 'feel' it. Spiritual thoughts and vibrations accumulate through daily practice and these pervade the space like the fragrant scent from the jasmine flower. When we are tired or agitated, by just sitting there for a while we can feel calm, revitalised and certainly Spiritually uplifted!

Why do we do Namaste?

Many Asian cultures greet one another with 'Namaste'. The two palms are placed together at the heart centre and the head is bowed as the Sanskrit word *Namaste* is spoken. It means, 'I bow to you, my greetings or prostrations to you'. *Namah* is literally translated as *Na aham*, 'not I'. It has a Spiritual resonance, that of reducing the ego in the presence of others.

The real meeting between people is the meeting of their minds, so when we greet each other we do this with a gesture that is gracious and extends both friendship and respect.

The Spiritual meaning is much deeper. *Prana*, Life Force, the Divine, the Self or the Lord in me is the same in all, a reflection of that greater power. I was attracted to that concept, immediately recognising that unlike other greetings it was deep, respectful and meaningful, yet not religious.

Once we understand the deeper meaning of this gesture and word, it can never remain superficial. We find ourselves communing with others with respect and Divine love, rather than simply being polite.

Namaste

I honour the place in you
in which the entire universe dwells.

I honour the place in you which is of love,
of truth, of light and of peace.

When you are in that place in you
and I am in that place in me,
we are one.

AMN

Terry Williams, founder of
The Bluefields Project, Jamaica.
Dear friend who passed over, 2013.

When we prostrate with
humility and respect,
we invoke the perfect ground
for those blessings to expand
and to grow in nature,
in our cells and in our lives.

AMN

Why do we Prostrate?

Prostrating before Parents, Elders, Teachers and Noble Souls is an ancient Indian tradition. Man stands on his feet, so by touching the feet you accept that these feet have walked many miles in terms of experience and knowledge. In turn these elders touch our head or brow as a simple blessing.

Prostrations are performed daily in some Indian schools and homes and specifically on birthdays, auspicious religious days, ceremonies, or festivals, as well as at the start of a new task.

Prostration symbolises our recognition of others' selfless love for us and the sacrifices they make on our behalf. We are accepting greatness in another and the strong family ties, which is one of India's long lasting strengths.

These good wishes (*Sankalpa*) and blessings (*Aashirvaada*) of the elders are valued highly in India. We prostrate to seek the good wishes and blessings.

Good thoughts, wherever they come from, create positive vibrations. Good wishes that spring from the heart are full of power. When we prostrate with humility and respect we invoke the perfect ground for those blessings to expand and to grow in nature, in our cells and in our lives. This is why, if we prostrate either standing or kneeling, it allows the whole body to receive the energy given through those blessings from our elders, teachers or parents.

The different ways of showing respect

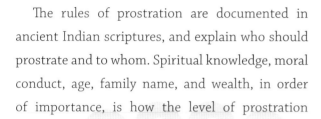

* *Pratuthana* – Rising to welcome a person;
* *Namaskaara* – Paying homage in the way of Namaste;
* *Upasangrahan* – Touching the feet of Elders, Teachers or Parents;
* *Shaashtaanga* – The whole body touching the ground;
* *Pratyabivaadana* – Returning a greeting.

The rules of prostration are documented in ancient Indian scriptures, and explain who should prostrate and to whom. Spiritual knowledge, moral conduct, age, family name, and wealth, in order of importance, is how the level of prostration is judged. A full prostration would be for the Guru, or Spiritual teacher. This is why a King of the land would prostrate to a Spiritual leader. Epic writings like the *Ramayana*, and the *Mahabharata* have many stories highlighting this aspect.

This ancient tradition of Prostration creates an environment of mutual love and respect among people striving for harmony in the family and the greater society.

AMN

Why we never touch people, books or papers with the feet.

I can remember, when I studied with Swami Vishnu and other revered Teachers, that there was a very strong emphasis on tradition and the respect of knowledge no matter through what medium it was expressed.

In Indian homes children are taught that if their feet touch papers, books, people, musical instruments or any educational equipment, by accident or not, that they must touch that item with their hands and then touch their eyes as a way of an apology.

Knowledge is Sacred and Divine and needs to be given respect at all times. The sign of our times is that we separate that which is sacred from that which is useful, but in reality we should surround ourselves with beautiful and meaningful things that are useful and Sacred for the way we use them, with awareness and mindfulness.

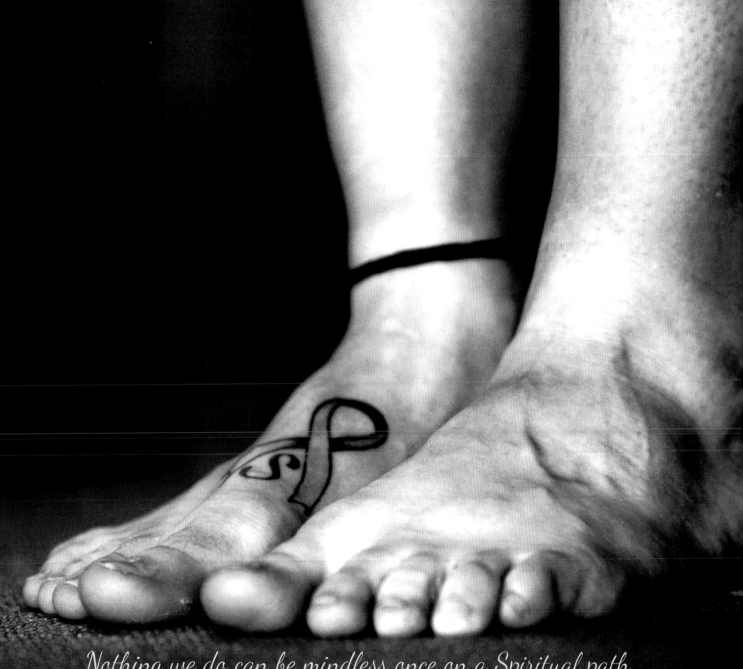

Nothing we do can be mindless once on a Spiritual path
Be in the moment, step-by-step and breath-by-breath.

AMN

Why do we consider the Lotus Flower as Auspicious?

The Lotus is India's national flower. Not long ago the lakes and ponds of India were full of lotuses of many colours. The Lotus is the symbol of *Satya* (truth), *Shivam* (auspiciousness) and *Sundaram* (beauty).

The Divine-God too is of that nature and is compared to a lotus such as Lotus-eyes, Lotus feet, Lotus hands and the Lotus of the Heart.

Indian scriptures and ancient literature extol the beauty of the lotus. Both art and architecture portray the lotus in various decorative motifs and paintings. Many are named after the lotus flower such as *Padma*, *Kamala* or *Kamalakshi*. The Goddess of Wealth, Lakshmi, sits on the lotus and carries one in Her hand.

The lotus flower opens in the dawn light and closes at night. Our minds expand and open up with the light of knowledge. The lotus will grow in wet marshy areas remaining beautiful and untainted, reminding us that we too can strive to remain pure and beautiful no matter what the circumstances.

The lotus leaf never gets wet though it is always in water, it symbolises the *Gyaani* (man of wisdom), who is ever untainted by the world of sorrow and change.

Our bodies have energy centres described in the Yoga Shaastras as Chakras.

The crown chakra is known as the *Sahasrara*, The Thousand Petalled Lotus.

A lotus emerged from the navel of Lord Vishnu the Preserver (one of the faces of God). Lord Brahma the Creator originated from the lotus to create the world. So the lotus symbolises the bridge between the creator and the Supreme Cause, the purpose of life itself.

The lotus flower conjures a depth of feeling from inside of us.

It is serene, it is still and it is without judgement.

It exudes spiritual growth within us.

The lotus stem is the ladder to Enlightenment

and the petals the opening to Spirit.

AMN

Why fast?

Fasting in Sanskrit is called *Upavaasa*. *Upa* means 'near' and *Vaasa* means to 'stay'. *Upavaasa* therefore means staying near (the Lord) meaning the attainment of a close mental proximity with the Divine. So what has *Upavaasa* got to do with food?

Anna Yoga

A lot of time and energy is spent finding food, cooking it and then eating it. If we practice Anna Yoga, the Yoga of food, then we know that everything we do, including the food we eat and prepare, needs to be shown respect and honour.

We are what we eat after all, and that includes the attitude, input, mood and way in which we prepare and eat our food.

Our very tissues are made up of whatever we choose to ingest. Yes, food affects how our bodies look and feel, but also the quality of our minds. Experiencing the difference dietary changes make in us, and consciously noting them, is one great way to become an Anna or food yogi. Our inner intelligence is always present and can serve us well if we choose to tap into it. This way, although we may benefit from learning through experts and books too, we awaken our own inner teacher, a faculty deeper but complimentary to our intellect. We can then truly incorporate knowledge in a personally meaningful way. Keeping a food experience journal is one clear way to keep track of your dietary evolution. Even a few quick notes can highlight insights and keep your intention clear. Note how you feel after eating specific foods and see if that creates relative balance or imbalance.

Most Yogis and religious Hindus fast on a regular basis especially for special occasions and festivals. On these days maybe no food is taken or only fruit or a special simple diet is eaten. The purpose of fasting is to deepen spiritual practice in its truest form.

Drink your Solids and
Eat your Fluids.

Fasting and Mental Clarity

My own experiences of fasting have been many. The first time was at the Sivananda Yoga Vedanta Centre in Notting Hill back in 1983. The centre had monthly weekends of fasting and deep meditation to open the mind's locked potential and to heighten awareness. We began with an enema with coffee and then an inversion, either the headstand or shoulder stand. This would make certain that the enema used was giving the best benefits to clearing the bowels of residue.

This was certainly old school and, in my opinion, the most effective as it included *Asana* practice. As a Yogi I practice what I preach, and use Yoga in all areas of my life. That includes fasting with the right action and intension.

Part of the focus of fasting at the Centre was to enter into deep meditation, elevate consciousness and raise mental vibrations.

As we are human, and our aim is to survive, we are preoccupied with food. So when we fast we take away that very physical stimuli. The mind will fight the desire to find food and with intense meditation and gentle *Asana* practice we can control that overpowering feeling of hunger. Rest on fasting days is a must; those who work too hard lose the point of mindfulness and end up consumed with trying not to notice how the stomach feels! While this is happening the mind is in effect allowed to run riot. The purpose of fasting is to watch the mind, to observe it from a place of equanimity and detachment.

After three days the mind is under control and the aim and goal of heightening awareness and raising vibration is achieved. Not only does the mind feel light but so too the body which in turn is filled with an awakened, Divine and uplifted heart.

After three days I realized I wanted to do this everyday and in fact decided I would try fasting by making sure I never ate till I felt full and that I would consider what food was for. Eat to live don't live to eat.

The Bhagavad Gita urges us to eat appropriately, neither too little nor too much, (*Yukta-aahaara*) and to eat simple, pure and healthy food, a Satvic diet, even when not fasting.

Why do we chant OM?

OM is the most chanted sound symbol in the Eastern world and over the last 30 years it has been chanted here in the West with as much intent. The true practice of Yoga must include the spiritual practice of the potency of chanting OM.

You can ask a child what is Yoga and they will sit on their bottom in a crossed legged position and chant OM! Oh the wisdom of babes.

The Yoga of Sound is called Nada Yoga, as the sounds work on the *Nadis*, the energy points in the subtle body, like meridian points. It is said there are thousands of these points and the Yoga of Sound can reach these points through the vibrations produced by chanting OM.

The sound OM has a profound effect on the Mind and the body and the surroundings too. Most Mantras (repetition of God's name) start with OM. All auspicious actions begin with OM. It is even used as a greeting. While in Vrindavan, the birthplace of Krishna, you would hear "Hari OM" from all around and especially the children. Hari is another name for Krishna.

In the Bible it begins with, 'There was the word and the word was God', in Hindu philosophy it is, 'There was a sound and that sound was OM'.

OM is the universal sound of God. It is what the Cosmos is based on – vibrations.

I have a recording of the sound of the orbit of the Earth, and it is very clear that the sound is OM. It makes sense that it is sound that shapes the very Earth we exist on and the Universe we exist in. Sound moves rocks, mountains, the deep core of the Earth, and its results are earthquakes, volcanic eruptions and tsunamis.

The sound coming from the vocal chords start at the base of the throat as a hard 'A'. With the coming together of the lips, 'U' as in 'put' is formed and when the lips are closed all sound ends in 'M' as in Mum.

The three letters represent the states of consciousness, waking, dream and deep sleep. They also represent the three deities: Brahma, Vishnu and Shiva, also the three *Vedas*: Rig, Yajur and Sama and finally the three worlds: Bhuh, Bhwah and Suvah. The Divine is all these aspects and beyond.

The chant OM should have the resounding sound of
a bell, 'AaaUuuMmm'. It fills the mind with peace,
makes it focused and absorbed with subtle sound.
People can meditate on its meaning and attain
Realisation, Nirvana, absorption into the One Source,
it is all consuming and ever changing in its purpose.

OM symbolises everything.
It is the Goal and means of life, the world and truth behind
both the material and the Sacred.

All Forms and yet all Formless

OM Shanti Shanti Shanti OM
OM Peace Peace Peace OM

ॐ IS the symbol of OM, PRONOUNCED A-U-M. It REPRESENTS ALL THE STATES of CONSCIOUSNESS AND IS THE highest AND MOST POWERFUL of ALL SOUNDS OR MANTRAS. REPEATING OM, SILENTLY OR ALOUD, BESTOWS LIBERATION, INNER PEACE AND BRINGS FEELINGS of love AND TEARS of DEVOTION AND Joy.
OM IS INFINITE, ALL PERVADING, PURE, PERFECT, ALL KNOWING AND ETERNALLY FREE. REALIZE OM. OM ELEVATES THE MIND, BRINGS INSPIRATION AND INTUITION, HEALS THE BODY, MIND AND SOUL.
LIVE IN OM. MEDITATE ON OM.
BREATHE OM. TAKE REFUGE IN OM.
DRAW STRENGTH FROM OM. BECOME OM
OM IS BLISS. OM IS ANANDA.

Symbols of
Protection

Symbols of Protection

It is always interesting to me to hear people negate the power of symbols. If you practice Yoga or any other type of psychological, philosophical theory or practice then you know the power of the mind.

The Body does what the Mind believes!

So whatever your religion, faith or personal belief, you will surely have a symbol that aids you to fix your thoughts and actions to that belief system. It may be a seed that symbolises potential or it may be a religious symbol that you keep close to you. Whatever that symbol is, it's the mind you are working on and working with.

Personally, I think it goes deeper than that, these symbols, deities and or/images also attach themselves to the heart. Without heart there is no passion; without passion there is no point.

However, let's not fool ourselves, because we know that not all symbols are seen as positive; many have been stolen from one faith and made to represent something 'evil'. One such example is the Hindi swastika (from the Sanskrit *svástika*) that Hitler used as his logo for the Nazi party. Hitler was well versed in the Hindu scriptures and was very well read, but as in all things, we choose our path. We choose either to be at peace with all or to be in pursuit of power over all.

In Hinduism, the two symbols represent two forms of the creator god Brahma. Facing right it represents the evolution of the universe; facing left it represents the in-volution of the universe, meaning the inner and outer worlds of the 'Self'. It is also seen as pointing in all four directions, north, east, south and west and signifies a grounded stability.

There are so many symbols across the world that I could not choose them all so here are six that mean something to me and may be of interest to you.

Ganesha, the Elephant God

There is something very comforting about this Elephant god that inspires both trust and safety. Ganesha is a symbol/statue used in many Hindu homes and Temples, usually placed by the front door or entrance. Ganesha should be the first deity you see as you enter. Often described as 'the remover of obstacles' because of his strong trunk that moves felled trees with ease. Those obstacles can be anything from trying to find a new home, a partner or starting a new business and the need for a 'clear path through the forest'.

As with so many symbols, Ganesha has many qualities and meanings. Ganesha also represents the destruction of pride , vanity, and selfishness and is the god of failure as well as success. I think this is very interesting, the idea of having a god of failure. There is a saying that 'we learn more from our failures than we do from our successes' and I personally believe this to be true. We often accept our successes blindly and move on but with a failure we are challenged and therefore forced to be introspective and search for reasons and solutions.

Why Ganesha has an Elephant Head

Here are two stories that are based on Hindu myth and legend. People in the ancient past could neither read nor write as education was only for the higher castes, the privileged, and therefore these complex texts needed to be delivered to the masses in a way that they could be understood.

Concepts such as God were explained in simple stories and images such as God high up in the clouds, tales of humble animals, and celestial angels. The same can be said of the Bible in my opinion, and this is why God is shown as a Father figure sitting on a cloud. How do you explain something greater than us in words alone? But the Yoga concept of God is that which is within our selves, not a human but the spark that gives us consciousness, and is the greater Self. It is for that reason that Yoga is not a religion but a philosophy, a psychology and crosses all faiths too.

The story of the birth of this 'zoomorphic' deity goes like this:

The goddess Parvati was desperate for a son, as she was often alone while Shiva, her husband, was away. One day, while bathing, she created a boy out of the dirt of her body and assigned him the task of guarding the entrance to her bathroom. When Shiva returned, he was surprised to find a stranger denying him access, and struck off the boy's head in rage. Parvati broke down in utter grief and, to soothe her, Shiva sent out his troops to fetch the head of any sleeping being who was facing the north, the auspicious direction for positivity and courage. The company found a sleeping elephant and brought back its severed head, which was then attached to the body of the boy. Shiva restored its life and made him the leader (*pati*) of his troops. Which is why Ganesha is often called 'Ganapati'. Shiva also placed on Ganesha a gift, that people would worship him and call his name before undertaking any venture in travel, business or personal endeavour.

However, there's another less popular story of his origin, found in the Brahma Vaivarta Purana, one of the major eighteen *Puranas*, a Hindu religious text of the 10th century AD. It is divided into four parts. The first part describes the creation of the universe and all beings, the second part relates to the description and histories of different goddesses. The third part is mostly devoted to the life and deeds of Ganesha and the fourth part details the life and deeds of Krishna.

Shiva asked Parvati to observe the *punyaka vrata*, one of the ancient holy books of the time, for a year, to appease Vishnu, in order to have a son. When a son was born to her all the gods and goddesses assembled to celebrate the birth. Lord Shani, the son of Surya (Sun-God), was also present but he refused to look at the infant. Perturbed at this behavior, Parvati asked him the reason, and *Shani* replied that his looking at the baby would harm the newborn. On Parvati's insistence Shani eyed the baby and the child's head was severed instantly. All the gods started to bemoan this tragic outcome, so Vishnu, the Preserver, hurried to the bank of the river Pushpabhadra and brought back the head of a young elephant, and joined it to the baby's body giving it life.

Lord Ganesha Mantra for Success in Sanskrit:

Vakratunda Mahakaya
Surya Koti Samaprabha
Nirvighnam Kurumedeva
Shubha Karyeshu Sarvada

Lord Ganesha Mantra in English:

O Lord, with large body, curved trunk and the radiance of a million suns. Please make all my good work free of obstacles, always.

Hand of Fatima

Oh Hand of the Protector, guide my words, my actions and my life.
Reach out your Hand in times of confusion that I may hold it.
Stop me when I am lost and show me the way.
Hand of Love, rest on my worried brow and smooth out my stresses.
My hand in your Hand I walk with the strength of the Lion
and the Peace of the Dove.

AMN

The Hand of Fatima is a symbol I love. It instils in me home, safety and family as well as protection. As an Arab, the eye often seen in the palm of the hand is part of my childhood. As babies and up to two years old we are given the 'Evil Eye'. This is so, should the 'Evil Eye' try to catch us and take our spirit into evil, it will see we are already cursed. So simple and so logical!

'The symbol of an eye embedded in the palm of an open hand has had several names throughout the ages, including the Hamsa, the Eye of Fatima, the Hand of Fatima, and the Hand of Miriam'.

The symbol is sometimes shown as a natural hand and at other times symmetrically with a second thumb replacing the little finger.

The *Hamsa* has often been interpreted as a Jewish, Christian, or Islamic amulet – a talisman, as well as a pagan fertility symbol. This magical form remains shrouded in mystery and academics debate every aspect of its emergence but it is widely recognized today as a Kabbalistic amulet and as an important symbol in Jewish art.

Historical Origins

As the references to Fatima, Mohammed's daughter, and to Miriam, Moses' sister suggest, the amulet carries significance to both Jews and Moslems. One of the most prominent early appearances of the Hamsa is the image of a large open hand which appears on the Puerto Judiciaria, the Gate of Judgment of the Alhambra, a 14th century Islamic fortress in Granada, Southern Spain.

The Alhambra Hand of Fatima seems to draw upon the Arabic word *khamsa*, which means 'five', a number which itself is identified with fighting the Evil Eye. The Alhambra motif, as well as other Spanish and Moorish hand images, hints at the five pillars of Islam; faith, fasting, pilgrimage, prayer, and tax, in the five fingers of the hand.

I think this story is both moving and almost simplistic in its message, certainly very human. According to Islamic folklore, Fatima's hand became a symbol of faith after her husband Ali came home with a new wife one day. Fatima, who at the time had been cooking, dropped the soup ladle she had been using. Yet she was so preoccupied by the new arrival that she continued stirring using her bare hand, hardly noticing that she was burning herself.

It would not be unusual for an Islamic symbol to find its way into Sephardic Jewish culture; Jews from Spain flourished alongside Islam. However, amulets are somewhat problematic in Judaism. One law allows the carrying of an approved amulet on the Sabbath, which suggests that amulets were common amongst Jews at some points in history. Having travelled this part of Spain, what struck me the most was the past integration of Christian, Jewish and Moslem societies who lived side by side with both respect and integrity.

The art historian Walter Leo Hildburgh suggests the possibility that the Hamsa has Christian roots, and might be influenced by the Christian artistic form where Mary often carries her hands in a 'fig' pose, a *mudra*, or a configuration where the thumb is tucked under the index finger beside the middle finger. In Yoga this *mudra* is very similar to the Chin mudra!

Interestingly, according to Professor Ahmed Achrati of the University of Chicago, the Hamsa did not necessarily arise in a religious context. The form of the open hand appears in Paleolithic cave art, at the time when stone tools were being used, in France, Spain, Argentina, and Australia, including one site in Algeria that earned the name 'The Cave of the Hands.'

The Evil Eye

The Evil Eye is first recorded by the Mesopotamians about 5,000 years ago, on clay tablets. The Evil Eye may actually have originated as early as the Upper Paleolithic age that we mentioned in the Hand of Fatima.

Again this symbol is found in Jewish, Christian and Moslem cultures, as well as Buddhist and Hindu societies. This common tradition finds a new identity in the 3,000 year old glass craftsmanship of Anatolia, Turkey. A glass master Nazar Boncuk combines the power of the eye figure with the power of fire and creates a new talisman, the Evil Eye Bead, which is seen all over the Mediterranean and Middle East.

It is thought that there are three types of evil eyes. The first are unconscious evil eyes and these harm people and things without intending to. The second type means 'to harm'. The third one however is an unseen, hidden evil that is the most powerful and harmful one. It was also believed that this eye saw all the wickedness in the world and removed poverty and ignorance.

When Horus, the Egyptian god, opened his eyes, the world was enlightened, when he closed them, it became dark. From Egypt, the eye talisman had spread to the Mediterranean, Middle East and Europe. The bead reflects the evil intent back to the onlooker. It somewhat resembles an eye and it is said the typical blue colour is a factor in protecting the user.

The Nazar Boncuk charm, the Evil Eye Bead, is an 'eye', often set on a blue background. It stares back at the world to ward off the evil spirits and keep you safe from harm. Since then the people have been attaching this evil eye bead to everything they wished to protect from the evil eyes, from newborn babies to their horses and to the doors of their homes.

No visit to this part of the world can be experienced without this constant symbol. It is either in paintings or objects and the Evil Eye, with its radiant blue colour and mandala-like centre is there as both protection and reflection!

Oh Dream Gatherer, spend some time with me through the night and before the day.

Let your light and the coloured feathers filter the dreams coming to me and for me.

I am the child of the day whose eyes reflect the Sun and you the open window of the stars and Moon.

I will sleep at peace knowing you drift above me and the earth stone protects me as the One Divine Mother and Father hold me safe.

AMN

Dream Catcher

The Dream Catcher is a small hoop containing a horsehair mesh decorated with feathers and beads, believed by American Indians to give its owner good dreams.

Dream catchers are arts and crafts of the Native American people. The original web dream catcher of the Ojibwa people was intended to teach natural wisdom; nature is a profound teacher. Dream catchers made of twigs, sinew and feathers; have been woven by the Ojibwa since ancient times.

They were woven by the grandfathers and grandmothers for newborn children and hung above the cradleboard to give the infants peaceful, beautiful dreams. The night air is filled with dreams. Good dreams are clear and know the way to the dreamer, descending through the feathers. The slightest movement of the feathers indicated the passage of yet another beautiful dream. Bad dreams, however, are confused and confusing. They cannot find their way through the web and are trapped there until the Sun rises and evaporates them, like the morning dew.

Originally the Native American dream catcher was woven on twigs of the red willow using thread from the stalk of the stinging nettle. The red willow and twigs from other trees of the willow family, as well as red twig dogwood can be found in many parts of the United States. These twigs are gathered fresh and dried in a circle or pulled into a spiral shape depending upon their intended use. They used natural feathers and semi-precious gemstones, one gemstone to each web because there is only one creator in the web of life.

The Cross

Question What is the meaning of the cross?

Answer Simply put, the meaning of the cross is death. In ancient times from about the 6th century BC until the 4th century AD, the cross was an instrument of death by the most torturous and painful of ways.

Crucifixion was an ancient form of execution in which a person was either tied or nailed to a wooden cross and left to hang until dead.

Death would be slow and excruciatingly painful; in fact, the word excruciating literally means, 'out of crucifying'. However, because of Christ and His death on the cross, the meaning of the cross today is completely different.

When researching the Cross, I was taken aback with the findings but also it all made sense. The Romans used the cross to crucify the Spartan rebels who defied the Roman Empire and it was not a Christ symbol until after His death.

It is not unusual therefore to use this most powerful tool of power as a tool for peace. This was the way of Jesus, 'Forgive those who trespass against us', 'Forgive them for they know not what they do', 'Turn the other cheek'. These words are the epitome of the Christian faith and it is hard to recognize that all Christians may not live by those words, but still hold the Cross as the symbol of their faith. But in essence Christianity is founded on Forgiveness and therefore Hope.

The cross is an amazing symbol and no more beautiful than when carved from simple wood.

AMN

Isis – Angel Wings and Heart

Oh winged Angel of Mothers and Children and of the slave and ruler, give me your wings to free my soul. Put my sorrowed heart in its place and put my body back together. The heart the symbol of Love is the arrow by which you travel the world searching for the one you love. Let me fly with you.

AMN

Isis was first worshiped in Ancient Egypt, and later her worship spread throughout the Roman Empire and the greater Greco-Roman Empire. Isis is still widely worshiped by many today in diverse religious contexts, including a number of distinct pagan faiths and the modern Goddess Movement.

Isis was worshipped as the ideal mother and wife, as well as the patroness of nature and magic. She was the friend of the slaves, the sinners and the downtrodden, but she also listened to the prayers of the wealthy, maidens, aristocrats and rulers. Isis is often depicted as the mother of Horus, the falcon-headed deity associated with king and kingship, although in some traditions Horus' mother was Hathor, the Ancient Egyptian goddess, who personified the principles of joy, feminine love, and motherhood. Isis is also known as protector of the dead and goddess of children.

The name Isis means 'throne'. Her headdress is a throne. As the personification of the throne, she was an important representation of the pharaoh's power. The pharaoh was depicted as her child, who sat on the throne she provided.

In the typical form of her myth, Isis was the first daughter of Geb, god of the Earth, and Nut, goddess of the Sky. She married her brother Osiris and she conceived Horus with him.

Isis was instrumental in the resurrection of Osiris when he was murdered by Set the god of storms and chaos, much like Rudra the Hindu god of the same. Using her magical skills, she restored his body to life after having gathered the body parts that had been strewn about the earth by Set.

It was believed that the Nile River flooded every year because of the tears of sorrow which Isis wept for Osiris. Osiris' death and rebirth was relived each year through rituals. The popular motif of Isis suckling her son Horus, however, lived on in a Christianised context, from the fifth century onwards, as the popular image of Mary feeding her infant son Jesus.

When I visited Egypt, and the Valley of the Kings, I saw a modest carving of an arrow, the modern symbol of the heart, a dagger, wings and parts of a body. This was the story of Isis and Osiris and how she travelled the world putting his body back together. She managed this through love and devotion. I was so stunned to see the heart symbol there on a wall thousands of years old.

The Heart is the most powerful of symbols no matter who we are and what we believe; it is the human part of us that is not simply a pump but that which measures that which makes man:

Conscience

Medicine Stones

Rangoli Sand Symbols

Ganesha

Dalai Lama

Zen Circle

Dream Catcher

Angel wings

Isis

Eye of Horus

Buddha's Eye

Chakra Stones

Love Hearts

Yin and Yang

Swastika

Hand of Fatima

Ankh

Om Mane Padme Om
Tibetan Mantra

Note to Self

the practice

Yoga Nidra

The Yoga of Conscious sleep in Savasana

A good yoga class or session should always begin with relaxation. If you learn nothing but how to relax then you will have everything that makes a good life great!

The Sanskrit word *Savasana* means 'corpse'. This name derives from the deep stillness in both mind and body that comes from relaxing every part of the body one step at a time. Yoga Nidra, what we call 'autosuggestion', is a conscious releasing of muscle tension by placing the thoughts into a muscle group or specific part of the body. As the mind focuses on each area and we consider our breath, our thoughts slow down and so does the breath.

'Relaxation does not mean sleep. Relaxation means to be blissfully happy; it has no end. I call bliss absolute relaxation; sleep is a different matter. Sleep gives only mind and sense relaxation. Bliss relaxes the *Atman* (Soul), the inner Self; that is why Yoga Nidra is the doorway to *Samadhi* (Enlightenment).'

Swami Satyananda Saraswati, a disciple of Swami Sivananda, from *Yoga Nidra*.

Proper relaxation is an essential aspect of life and yoga. This pose is commonly translated as 'Corpse' pose, indicating the apparent absence of the breath during deep relaxation. This observation highlights the intricate interconnection between the breath and the body: when the mind is agitated so the breath is affected...short, shallow, and rapid. When the mind is still, so the breath is still and attention, presence and awareness are all called into the present moment. Thus it follows that gaining control of the breath also has an influence on the physical systems of the body.

Breath is the bridge between the mind and body.

AMN

Savasana is an excellent way to develop and achieve deep relaxation and is considered one of the most important yoga *Asanas*. Learning how to relax properly is a key benefit of life and helps to counteract the negative effects of excess stress.

Stress is a natural and necessary response of the body and mind that motivates us to take action. Only when we have too much stress does it become a problem.

Try and hear the sound of you clicking your fingers very lightly. Notice what happens to the breath? It stops briefly. Why? Because you were concentrating.

Achieving Savasana

* Lie down on the floor with legs mat width apart and arms 25 cm away from your body, fingers naturally curled in.
* Let your feet fall open from the hips. Relax your ankles.
* Pull your shoulder blades down to reach ears way from shoulders.
* Make sure your body feels like it is lying straight; lift your head to check.
* Stretch the back of your neck and ensure your chin points towards your sternum.
* Conduct a full body scan, being aware of any tension you are holding.
* Establish abdominal breathing, place hands on lower abdomen, imagine a balloon filling and rising as you breathe in, lowering to breathe out.
* Inhale for 3 counts, hold for 1 count and exhale for 4 counts. Try this a few times mentally till you get a rhythmic flow of breath.
* Only then create *Ujjayi* breathing.
* Systematically bring your attention to each part of your body and relax it.
* Always begin body scan head to feet to combat mental busyness but at the end start with feet and ending at the head because of physical fatigue.
* Stay in *Savasana* for at least 10 minutes to gain proper benefits of the relaxation

Note: Low blood pressure? Roll onto left side to come out of *Savasana*. This helps to massage the heart after a period of inactivity.

Breathing for Life and Peace of Mind

As long as there is breath in the body, there is life
Therefore, regulate the breath

Hatha Yoga Pradipika Ch 2:5

Pranayama

Prana – Life force, *Qui*, *Chi*, or vital energy
Ayama – expansion, extension, control

Prana is the vital, subtle energy that permeates and sustains the whole of creation. On the level of form, the human body can connect with *Prana* through the breath. Yogis have always considered the control and flow of *Prana* to be of great importance.

We attempt to increase our lung capacity to absorb not only oxygen but also *Prana*, which will charge our spirit, the battery of our Soul! Expansion of *Prana* is the reward for your practice.

The science of *Pranayama* starts with how to learn to use the full capacity of the lungs and the proper control of the diaphragm as well as the respiratory muscles.

Stress causes us to tense our intercostal muscles. These muscles move, relax or contract the ribs. If they are tense, the lungs are unable to reach their full capacity and breathing is constricted.

We think we are breathing deeply but actually as soon as we relax those ribs we breathe so softly and wholly that it's a pleasant surprise.

Don't just believe me! Try it!

So what is 'normal' breathing as opposed to 'Yogic' breathing? Physiological breathing is in the thoracic area, including the ribs and the back, from between the shoulder blades. Yogic breathing is known as 'full' breathing. This starts from the pubic bone all the way up to the collar bones, where the lungs end. On the exhalation we also start from the pubic bone up to the collar bones. (see page 228)

Regular practice of the following 3 simple stages of 're-learning' to breathe, will enhance your life by helping you to enjoy feeling good both in mind and body, as well as preparing for advanced *Pranayama*, such as *Kapalabhati* and *Anuloma Viloma*.

Be the flute of Krishna and
let God's breath move through you.

Be still and listen.

Notice the in and out
of Breath and Prana
as they flow gracefully,
travelling as one.

With each breath
your world turns outside in
and there before you lays the
landscape of your Soul's journey.

Light and dark have merged and
created the colours of the spectrum.

To each a path and
to each a purpose.

AMN

1. Breath-Awareness.
Taking notice of the action of breathing.

Breathing is part of the Autonomic Nervous System, also known as the involuntary nervous system. The body breathes without needing to make it happen but it needs to be noticed so we can also read our mental state. The breath and the mind are inter-dependent. One illustrates the other.

If we are angry, upset or in emotional or physical pain, the first thing we notice is the change in the breath. It may become difficult, laboured, irregular or stop for long periods. This breathing pattern is telling us the mind is feeling danger and fear or even terror. The breathing can be the same in a panic attack because that person truly feels like they are dying. Panic attacks are very real and should never be ignored.

So where do we start? With the mind or the breath? Breath must come first because it is the physical aspect we are able to control and in the end the mind can then be controlled by the breath. When we are calm and in balance, the breath will be calm and in balance too. We need to actively engage with *Prana* in all our breathing, as it will triple the benefits not only physically but emotionally too.

Breath? What Breath?

Learning how to breathe may seem simple but it is a known fact that we take our breathing for granted until we have a problem with it and it's then that we take it seriously! As we become older, from childhood to adulthood, we become stressed with work, family and even friends. Our breathing becomes shallow; this means we breathe in the upper part of the chest and don't engage our belly in the process. It is easy to begin this awareness by implementing five simple steps.

Sit on a chair or lie down, either on the floor or bed. Make sure your hands are resting on your knees if sitting, or by your side if lying, with your palms up. Whichever position you adopt, separate your feet hip width apart. Close your eyes. Now just observe your breath. Notice if you breathe in and don't breathe out or breathe out and don't breathe in. Notice if you have an even rhythm or if it is erratic. Spend a few minutes becoming aware of the breath. What you are doing is focusing the mind on one job, allowing the mind to let go of a lot of thought and becoming more mentally and physically still.

2. Yogic Breathing – Abdominal Breathing

Re-learning to breathe as you did as a baby. Look at a young child and you will notice they naturally breathe into the belly. After all that is how we took in oxygen when in our Mother's womb – through the umbilical cord, not through the mouth and lungs.

The 5 Simple steps:

1. Gently place your hands onto your lower belly.
2. Connect to your breathing by closing your eyes and visualizing the breath coming in through the nose down into the belly. And then watch the breath as it leaves your body again through the nose.

3. The belly should fill up like a balloon. Imagine it has a colour, this helps make it real. Imagine you are filling it with your breath. Then as you breathe out visualize it getting smaller and emptying. Draw the belly towards the spine.

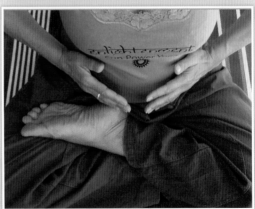

4. Begin to scan your body with your inside eyes and register any areas that feel tense, like your shoulder, neck and the ribs. The ribs can be so tense they restrict your lungs from breathing deeply.

5. If your thoughts begin to wander off and get involved in a drama then pull them back to the breath. The mind is like a muscle – it needs strengthening!

USEFUL TIP! The slower you breathe in, the more oxygen you take in, the slower you breathe out the more stale air you expel.

Practice this for at least five minutes. If you did this each day you would notice stress levels dropping, sleep improve and your ability to focus improve, as well as feeling a lot calmer!

When the ground is moving...be steady!
When the sky has no rainbow...believe!
When all around you are blinded...hold your vision!
When all else fails Breathe!

AMN

3. Ujjayi – Victorious Breath

Ud – upwards/expanding
Jaya – Victory/conquest/success

The three main benefits are:

You can hear it, feel it and it helps the mind fix on the breath because of those two reasons.

Ujjayi is also a *Kriya* as it cleanses the throat of mucus and stimulates the blue throat Chakra, Vishudda.

Begin this in *Savasana* after abdominal breathing is established, then sitting, re-enforce it.

INHALE through the nose softly then **EXHALE** out through the nostrils as you slightly close off the epiglottis, the valve at the back of the throat. This is like whispering 'ahhh' with your mouth closed. One student said it sounded like a Darth Vader growl! It also sounds like the waves coming up on a pebble beach or the wind through the trees. Use any image to help imagine and feel the sibilant sound created as you practice it. Beginners do this on the out breath only. More advance can try on the in as well.

Ujjayi breath encourages the mind to focus on a tangible aspect of the breathing process, which is helpful in calming mental noise in readiness for, and during, *Asana* practice. *Ujjayi* also promotes complete inhalation and exhalation because the breath can be followed audibly. It also generates heat, with air molecules being warmed due to the constriction in the back of the throat as the breath is drawn in through the nostrils. *Ujjayi* has been called the 'mantra of Astanga' as it is used consistently throughout an Astanga yoga practice and I prefer to use this in any yoga class as the 'music' of yoga practice.

Ujjayi breathing calms and soothes the mind and internalises the senses as *Pratyahara* (withdrawal of the senses). This is the 5th limb of the Eight Limbs of Patanjali's Astanga Yoga, mentioned in his classical work, *Yoga Sutras of Patanjali* (see page 108).

Oxygen is the biggest detoxifier in the body.

Kapalabhati
Dynamic Diaphragmatic Breathing

This strong fiery breathing technique is not for beginners, but for those who have mastered the Yogic abdominal breathing. Usually after 3 weeks of abdominal breathing and *Ujjayi,* this can be introduced into your practice.

The benefits of *Kapalabhati* (Shining Skull), named so for the light-headed feeling it induces, are many.

Regular practice increases lung capacity, exercises and strengthens the respiratory system, tones and massages the internal organs, builds a strong abdominal cavity, as well as flooding the body and brain with oxygenated blood.

Those wanting to give up smoking will find they are more aware that the lungs are for breathing to keep alive and that sensibility can take them into thinking about their health. I always encourage smokers into Yoga classes, I don't ask them to give up first!

The dangers are that those with unmedicated high blood pressure should omit doing this, as it will raise the blood pressure further.

This breathing technique should not be practised if you are pregnant, have glaucoma (pressure behind the eyes), an untreated hiatus hernia, a migraine, toothache or epilepsy. The increased blood flow to the heart and brain means these issues will be exacerbated and can, in the case of epilepsy, bring on an episode.

The action of this breathing is vigorous and can often make people feel light-headed. I always tell my students, don't worry it's only oxygen making you feel this way! We think we breath well but it's not until we energise our breathing that we discover we don't breathe in deep enough to increase our oxygen levels.

As you breathe in, your body, lungs, brain and consciousness should be receptive rather than active. Breath is received as a Divine gift and should not be drawn in forcefully.

BKS Iyengar *Light on Pranayama* p.137

The practice of this breathing exercise is something to do slowly, step by step.

❋ Sit up comfortably with a straight spine, on the floor, a chair or at the end of the bed.

❋ You could also sit up against a wall or another person, this will aid you with having something firm behind you to pull your navel back towards the spine on the exhale. Practice by putting your hands on the navel area.

❋ Try to practice blowing air out of your nostrils into your cupped hand, as if blowing something out of your nose, forcibly. You can also pant like a puppy with tongue out then close the mouth if that feels easier. Try both ways. **Blow your nose first into a tissue!**

❋ Try this a few times until you notice your diaphragm, the domed shaped muscle under your ribs, is working hard and contracting as well as releasing.

❋ Now put your hand down in chin mudra the same as your other hand and practice without the aid of the cupped hand. Do this as long as you can until you 'get the action'. This action is called a pumping action.

For beginners, try this:

* Inhale from the pubic bone to collar bones, exhale again from pubic bone to collar bones. Do this 2 times.

* To begin, inhale deeply and then pump in and out about 10 times.

* Exhale completely trying to empty your lungs of stale air by pulling the navel back towards the spine. Don't crunch your middle, keep uplifted.

* Keep exhaling until your abdominal cavity is firm.

* Breathe in deeply, exhale again, inhale half a breath and retain the breath for 10 seconds.

* Repeat this process and increase pumps to 20, hold the breath for 15.

* Repeat for the last time, 30 pumps and hold the breath for 20 seconds.

You may increase the ratio as you become more advanced. The idea is to increase your lung capacity and this is measured by how long you can retain your breath.

Practice this each day and it wont be long before you breathe better, walk better, run better, swim better and live better!

Balance the Breath

The next step is to balance your breath. This ancient breathing exercise allows you to breathe deeply, cleanse the sinuses, and balance the left and right side of the brain as well as the *Nadis*, those myriad energy points in the subtle body.

Nadi Centres

In Yoga tradition, the body's energy system is described as a network of interconnecting energy channels called *Nadis*, of which it is believed there are 72,000. The most important of these is the *Sushumna Nadi* running through the spinal cord. Extending from the perineum, below the groin, where *Kundalini* energy is seated, often referred to as 'The Coiled Serpent'. This extends up to the crown of the head, the last and highest Chakra centre Sahasrara. *Nadis* are astral tubes made up of astral matter that carry *Pranic* currents. Only the Astral Eyes can see them. They are not the nerves and should not be confused with them; they belong to the physical body. *Ida*, *Pingala* and *Sushumna* are the important ones but *Sushumna* is the most important of all.

When I teach this theory in class I explain it as a visual image. The roots of the Lotus, the *Kundalini*, the stem *Sushumna* and *Ida* and *Pingala* the Caduceus, all culminating in the fully open Lotus flower, the Chakra Sahasrara: The Thousand Petalled Lotus. This also looks like the Caduceus. The Caduceus is often used by medical practitioners and health organisations, due to a confusion with the traditional medical symbol, the rod of Asclepius, which has only one snake and is never depicted with wings.

NOTE: *Ida* and *Pingala* crisscross the *Sushumna* and connect to the left and right nostrils respectively.

Ida and Pingala

There are two *Pranic* currents, one on either side of the spinal column, often described and illustrated as entwined serpents. The left one is called *Ida* and the right is known as *Pingala*. These are *Nadis*. Tentatively, some take these as the right and the left sympathetic cords, but they are subtle tubes that carry *Prana*.

The Moon moves in the *Ida* and the Sun in the *Pingala*. *Ida* is cooling. *Pingala* is heating. *Ida* flows through the left nostril and the *Pingala* through the right nostril. The breath flows through the right nostril for one hour and then through the left nostril for one hour. As humans we are busily engaged in worldly activities while the breath flows through *Ida* and *Pingala*. You may experience a blocked nostril in the morning that changes later on in the day to the other. This is normal and this is why we do *Pranayama* nostril breathing to clear them and allow *Prana* to flow freely.

When *Sushumna* operates, 'he becomes dead to the world, and enters into *Samadhi*. A Yogi tries his level best to make the *Prana* run in the *Sushumna Nadi*, which is known as the central *Brahman Nadi* also. On the left of *Sushumna* is situated *Ida* and on the right is *Pingala*. The Moon is of the nature of *Tamas* (inertia, death, decay, end), and the Sun is that of *Rajas* (The Royal Road of Meditation). The poison share is of the Sun and the nectar is of the Moon. *Ida* and *Pingala* indicate time. *Sushumna* is the consumer of time.'

Swami Sivananda

Connected with the *Sushumna Nadi* there are seven important energy centres called 'Chakras' (there are said to be many more) and their positions correspond to the various nerve centres. Chakras can be envisaged as spinning spheres of light. (Read in more detail: 'The Chakras, what are they anyway?' from page 246.)

Practicing *Pranayama* under the strict guidance of a qualified teacher is one of the ways of activating *Kundalini* energy but you need to be cautious. This is not a game, as the energy is real. In orgasm *Kundalini* rises, you may have experienced a rush from the base of the spine, that's the serpent rising; an image used to describe *Kundalini*. Anyone with a weak disposition, a history of depression and/or drug abuse should not practice intense *Pranayama* such as Kundalini Yoga, or any intense *Pranayama*. B. K. S. Iyengar in his 'Light on Pranayama' is very clear about this subject and its dangers.

Anuloma Viloma
Alternate Nostril Breathing

Anuloma Viloma in Sanskrit means 'with hair and against hair', your nostril hair that is! Breathing in is against hair and breathing out with hair. These being filters for dust particles and other pollutants that can enter and affect your lungs.

Using this technique on a regular basis will help prevent mucus building up in the nose, throat and sinuses and allows for easier breathing. It is also mentally soothing.

* You will need to start by sitting up straight, on the floor, in a chair or on the edge of your bed.
* If using a block or cushion to sit on, sit at the front third so your pelvis tilts forward to release your hips and lengthen the spine.
* Those sitting on a chair or bed, place feet and knees hip width apart.
* Try not to drop your shoulders or your spine as this will press down on your lungs.
* Keep your chest lifted and open and your chin in line with the floor.

a. Bring the first 2 fingers into your palm creating the Vishnu Mudra. Vishnu is the Lord of Preservation and here we are preserving *Prana*.

b. When retaining the breath, create a pincer with the right thumb and 3rd and 4th fingers.

❋ Take your right thumb and block off your right nostril just below the cartilage of the nose.

❋ **Exhale** out through your left nostril.

❋ **Inhale** deeply for 2 counts through the left nostril.

❋ Then pinch both nostrils closed with your free fingers and **hold the breath** for 8 counts.

❋ **Exhale** out through the right nostril for 4 counts.

❋ **Inhale** through the right nostril for 2 counts.

❋ **Hold the breath** for 8 counts.

❋ **Exhale** out through the left for 4 counts.

❋ Repeat 3 times.

NOTE: Always start by inhaling on the left and finishing on the left; that is one round. You can increase the ration to inhale 4, hold 16, and exhale 8 as your lung capacity increases.

Mudras: Yoga for the Hands

What is a Mudra?

A *Mudra* is a Seal; it is Yoga for the hands, to activate, stimulate and access latent energy. This energy, *Prana* is in all cells and nerve systems of the Subtle or Astral body, as it is also known.

Hand gestures are part of every aspect of Human culture and civilisation, such as Mayan, Ancient Egyptian, Roman, Greek, Ancient Indian and Chinese as well as African, Inuit and Native American nations. They all use the language of the hands and you probably do as well. Watch a primate, a small animal, a baby and notice the use of the hands to communicate.

Hand gestures originated from The Mudras of Ancient India and used as an art form in Egypt and Greece. They became part of religious and festive occasions to mark the advent of rain, the full Moon as well as predicting the nature, personality and destiny of a person. Hand astrology is as ancient as the human race. It was from here that hand gesture dancing travelled to Rome.

During the reign of Roman Emperor Augustus, puppet plays had hand gestures down as an art and there were many competitions to find the best artist for this discipline, known as Hand Gesture dancers. The most highly honoured was known as The Dancing Philosopher.

By 190 AD there were 6,000 performers in Rome devoted to the art of hand gestures and they continued in favour until the 6th Century AD.

During the reign of Emperor Nero, an Armenian King visited Rome and, asked what he would like to take from his visit, he replied, "The hand dancer because he speaks better with hands than his people with words!"

We are all familiar with hand gestures, so much so that we may not be conscious of them. Consider the Christian church and the many paintings depicting Christ, the Disciples and Angels; we see many gestures depicting grace, blessings, protection, knowledge and for receiving guidance from the Divine. The hands in prayer must be the most powerful and accepted of seals, *Anjali* the Heart seal.

Native American Indians is another culture that is not unfamiliar to us. Being born in the 50's I remember the films we watched as children. If we played cowboys and Indians we would salute the cowboy with 'How' meaning 'hello'. For a long time the White settlers thought the Native American nation had no language, as their hand gestures were so refined!

It would be more unnatural not to use our hands to communicate, as they are after all the extension of our mind and heart.

If it is not unusual to use our hands, what is it that makes these specific Mudras a science? It is the intent behind the Mudra that makes it a science and the specific nerves activated that relate to areas of the body and mind. They are both powerful and profound. When practising, use sincerity, and honesty, don't 'play a part' but be the Mudra you are using.

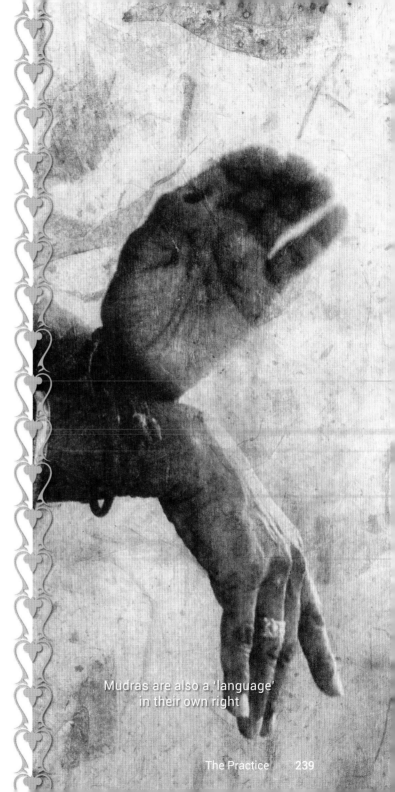

Mudras are also a 'language' in their own right

Chin Mudra – Conscious Breath Gesture

Chin Mudra is the most common gesture used in Yoga classes and for meditation. Chin Mudra is also practised with the palm down on the knee. The palm up is sometimes called Jnana Mudra, that of Knowledge.

In Yoga Philosophy and theory this Mudra has a specific representation. The thumb as God, the index finger as man and the three extended fingers as the Three *Gunas*, *Sattva*, *Rajas* and *Tamas*.

Placing the first finger and thumb together and the other three fingers open encourages a sense of discipline, preparation and, on a physical level, encourages good flowing abdominal breath. Sit with a straight back and follow the breath in through the nose, inflating the belly, and then follow it out again through the nose, deflating the belly. Do this at least seven times.

Abdominal breath relaxes the whole body as it allows for deep breathing. Use anytime especially if you feel rushed and seem to be breathing in a shallow manner.

Tse Mudra – The Secret Gesture

For fighting sadness, fatigue, depression and loss of mental focus

Fold the thumb of both hands into the palm. Fold the four fingers over the thumb. This will look like a fist.

Sitting comfortably, with a straight spine, either on the floor, against the wall or on a chair, place both hands onto your thighs.

Close the eyes and bring your awareness to your breathing.

As you breathe in, acknowledge your state of mind, hold for 2 counts and, as you let the breath go out again through the nostrils, imagine your worries, tiredness, sadness leave the body by drawing in the belly toward the spine.

Do this 7 times in each session.

Notice how quickly you feel drawn into a space that is very still and centred. It's so fast acting that it can be used when you feel like you need to focus, want to relax the mind or in an emergency.

You may have noticed you have used this before as an adult or as a child. It is very commonly used when feeling a strong lack of confidence or alone-ness.

It works!

Original artwork by Sylvia Reitzema

Shankh Mudra – Indian term for Conch

The Shankh Mudra is for relieving the throat and healing speech ailments. It resonates with Vishudda the Blue throat Chakra.

Shankh Mudra resembles a conch shell which is traditionally used in Hindu temples for worship and is blown to create pure sound vibrations. These vibrations attract the mind and attach it to a place from where we can worship – stillness. The bells of a church do much the same thing, drawing both the senses and people to gather for prayers or communion.

Similarly, Shankh Mudra helps those with speech and throat ailments. Shankh Mudra helps by clearing the throat. It relieves stammering. It gives a quality to your speech by restoring the pitch and resonance.

It also balances the thyroxin secretion from the thyroid gland. However, the use of Shankh Mudra should be limited to 10 to 15 minutes as needed. Never do this mudra after taking your meals.

Encircle your left thumb with the four fingers of your right hand. Touch the right thumb to the extended middle finger of your left hand. The two hands should look like a conch shell.

Practice Japa of OM while doing Shankh Mudra with an affirmation in your mind.

My voice is sweet like honey.
I sing like a morning bird.
I am calm, I speak sense.

AMN

Prana Mudra – Invocation of the Life-force energy

Prana Mudra is a way of activating the essence of *Prana* (Life force, *Qui* or *Chi*) by using the thumb (God) and the ring and little finger creating a force between Vishnu the Preserver and Shiva the Destroyer. As soon as you activate this you will instantly feel the breath, carrying *Prana* up to the Heart Chakra.

Try this right now.

Original artwork by Sylvia Reitzema

Rude-ras!

We often use our hands to express our feelings; these negative mudras make us feel better somehow and are a quick abbreviation of a possibly aggressive altercation and diatribe!

I love calling these very human responses to anger, stress, rage, disrespect and lack of verbal eloquence as Rude-ras; we have all tried them and though we may feel less than polite or controlled, they get used none the less. This may be either out rightly to the intended recipient's face, hidden in the stock room or behind the intended person's back.

Wherever and however, they have the result of making us feel a little smug or downright nasty! My own children will admit they learned a lot of these on the school run, my negative karma, I accept it!

News Flash!

I have been studying Yoga since 1976, starting with Iyengar. But this just proves to me again, that no matter what you think you know; you know less!

I thought I had been rather funny, even clever to use the word Rude-ra, but as I continue to study, only today I fell upon the real Rudra!

Interestingly, the Lord Rudra is about the use of power, rage and fury. He is depicted as a Deity who creates 'thunder and lightening, ever so frightening!' This is a quote from one of my children's favourite books when they were young, and chaos is Rudra's way as was theirs!

Lord Rudra is not unlike the Hindu god Shiva who is known as the Destroyer, as without chaos there can be no rebirth or harmony. Lord Rudra is depicted in the Rigveda, an ancient *Vedic* Sanskrit script that is a hymn of both praise and knowledge. The names Shiva and Rudra are often seen as aspects of the same and can be interchangeable in these hymns.

Rudra is illustrated as the wind, or a storm as well as 'the hunt'. He is seen as a mighty figure instilling terror in many. Interesting that in all these years I had not come across him! More enlightening is that I had named the antithesis of Mudras as Rude-ras. This proves to me yet again that Yoga philosophy and psychology comes only from understanding the truth about human nature.

The next time you use any hand language remind yourself of both Shiva and Rudra before you consider they mean nothing. The Intent is as powerful as the action.

Original artwork by Sylvia Reitzema

The Chakras: What are they anyway?

An introduction to the function, the purpose and the history

The journey into the workings and power of the Chakras is an amalgam of both knowledge and experience, as you could not have one with out the other. I have been transforming people's lives since 1974 and teaching Yoga since 1984 and I would be fooling myself if I did not accept that those transformations were as much about me as my students! It is therefore my understanding that the meaning of the Chakras and why we access them has much to do with our own self-discovery than that of the subject itself. It is so important to know them if we are to engage with both our physical and subtle (Astral) body. Yoga is a journey from the outer world to the inner world, and without the deeper understanding of these vibrational energy centres we are missing the point of Yoga altogether. We *cannot* have one without the other.

Respond to every call that excites your spirit.
Rumi

The First Chakra

Mooladhara – Red Resonance – Perineum – The Root

Moola – root, source

adhara – support, vital part

This first Chakra is known as the seat of the *Kundalini*, in Sanskrit meaning the coiled one, and is often described as latent energy, like a sleeping serpent. During sexual intercourse and orgasm this energy is deeply experienced, and during the use of Tantra it can be harnessed to empower, rather then deplete, both physical and spiritual energy.

This powerful energy rises from this point at the base of the spine, and it affects the person who experiences it profoundly. Super-Consciousness is often the first effect. It may feel like you have been asleep for all time and are beginning to wake up.

The only way to know this is to experience it. You can't learn how to perfect ballet or to drive a car without doing it or at least imagining it, for we are learning how powerful the mind can be as a tool!

The Root Chakra deals with your physical and material consciousness, how you express yourself in the safety of your own environment; the 'feeling of being safe' and how you protect yourself with survival skills within the physical body. A strong Root Chakra is often related to leaders and people with magnetic personalities however if it is overactive and not conscious of Self, this can manifest as arrogance. If it is balanced, one will be a powerful healer, courageous, with a strong sense of 'life intention and purpose'. When the centre is blocked or underactive a person can become low in Spirit or feel depressed.

You gain strength, courage, and confidence by every experience in which you really stop to look fear in the face.

Eleanor Roosevelt

This is the realm of life about survival, self-confidence, social order, personal security and family. This is our basic or cosmic Chakra. All life is emotions, and all basic emotions rise from this Chakra into our consciousness. If you think of your body as having a negative and positive pole (the spinal column) from your skull to the lowest spot in your spine, you can get a better image of this. It's sort of like an electrical charging system.

Practicing Yoga is like charging your poles with a battery, which ignites your inner fire and raises your power to see yourself as a physical body carrying 'You' around. Most of us don't think of ourselves as **only** our body. That's a first step in beginning to understand that there is more to the body than just the skin and bone.

Anatomical Description

The perineum, above and between the anus and the genitals, is the centre of the 'Sushumna pole'. Just above that is the coccyx, at the base of the spine. The coccyx is in the lower back and is described as a triangular bone formed usually by fusion of the last four (sometimes three or five) (coccygeal) vertebrae. It is connected to and just below the sacrum, which is where the second Chakra is located.

The coccygeal plexus is a nerve plexus formed by the ventral branches of the coccygeal and 5th sacral nerve and by a communication from the 4th sacral nerve, giving off the annoccygeal nerves. According to Iyengar, 'Kundalini is symbolized as a coiled and sleeping serpent lying dormant in the lowest nerve centre at the base of the spinal column, the Mooladhara Chakra. This latent energy has to be aroused and made to go up the spinal column, piercing the Chakras up to the Sahasrara (7th Chakra) just above the head.'

Anatomical Areas Affected

To understand this Chakra anatomically, look at what can impair the nervous system and interfere with the nerve function of this area of your body. In fact, the first and second Chakras are often brought together as one Chakra because they are so close to one another and share many functions, but I am going to follow tradition and keep them separate. Mooladhara, one of the five spinal centres, the coccygeal, is the feeder for the brain to collect and distribute nerve impulses from the whole of the central nervous system.

The Mooladhara Chakra affects the adrenals, kidneys, lower section of the spinal column, colon, legs and bones, including the marrow, and travels down to the feet. Iyengar includes the 'pelvic plexus' as belonging to this Chakra (the triangular point between the male sexual organs and anus and the cervix for women).

The coccyx anchors the spinal cord at its core depth, so when it is out of alignment it can put stress on your entire nervous system. To help your coccyx stay aligned – which also helps this Chakra to not be blocked – choose exercises that lengthen your lower pelvic muscles. The lower muscles will then free your coccyx from unnecessary tension.

The whole spinal cord rests upon this Chakra, and the spinal cord is the inner passage to higher planes of understanding.

The spinal cord has been given many names throughout history: Jacob's Ladder, the I AM channel, the Golden Stairs, The Stronghold of Man, the Tree of Life, and many more. They all mean the same thing. Everything from this Chakra up to the cross of the solar plexus is involved with the natural functions and actions of physical life.

Being aligned physically is important to help you release your Chakra system. This is why Yoga exercises are such a great way to keep your body healthy, both the outer and inner one that is!

It is especially important for this Chakra to be healthy and comfortable in its deep location, because this is the area that rules your sense of survival, your self-preservation instincts. This is 'gut' stuff that you have a hard time to control when it is not functioning properly. The more out of sync this Chakra is with your body, the less grounded you become.

This and the second Chakra receive energy from the earth's physical force and also from the vitality of the Sun. The *Kundalini* – lying dormant in this Chakra – is referred to as *Shabdabrahman* in human bodies. *Shabda* means 'sound'. As the Goddess of sound, she 'maintains all breathing creatures'. Breath is the Goddess in Kundalini.

When this Chakra is balanced you feel great, with a lot of energy at your disposal. You feel comfortable inside your own skin and in the world. When it is out of balance, there is a feeling of being alienated from the rest of the world. You perceive yourself as not belonging anywhere.

With red the main colour here, it can be helpful to use everything that is red to awaken this Chakra. This means in the clothes you wear below your waist, in the foods you eat and drink, and on it goes. Use your imagination.

The *Kundalini* has become a symbol in religion, and even medicine. Quite misunderstood, of course. Think about the ancient mystics who worshipped the snake, the serpent power slithering up the tree in the Garden of Eden, the Ophite snake (which is shown as the serpent power concealed in the base of the human spine), and it is even symbolized by the caduceus (an insignia modelled on Hermes's staff and used as the symbol of the medical profession). I find that a bit humorous, since the majority of medical doctors know nothing about the Chakra system, let alone even believe in it! It is also thought of as the flood of milk-white light that creates a bio-energetic surge of ecstasy for many people up their spine.

Wake-up and smell the Lotus!
AMN

The Body is a Sacred Garment.

Martha Graham (Founder of Contemporary Dance)

The Second Chakra

Swadisthana – Orange Resonance – Sexual organs, lumbar four and five

swa – vital force, soul

adhisthana – seat or abode

The Swadisthana Chakra defines how we connect with others, how we choose relationships and what they mean to us, and is situated at the base of our sexual organs. People refer to this Chakra as the place where we receive and give, how we respond to others and what motivates us in our lives. It is also about reproduction and self-indulgence.

This is the realm of life that hovers around issues regarding blame, guilt, money, sex, power, control, creativity, and morality.

This Chakra also receives energy from the earth's physical force and the vitality of the Sun. A person's sexual energy can be experienced here, and its strength, or weakness. A strong Sacral Chakra can be assumed with people who attract others to them, knowingly or unknowingly, in a sensual way. If you seek a partner, honour your Swadisthana and show respect for yourself first.

If this centre is overactive then sex will become an attitude about life, a way of thinking and being. Everything will revolve around sex. If it is balanced, a person will have a very healthy sex life and usually have a good feeling about their sexual energy. Perhaps you know someone who walks as if they are holding their groin in as far as they can, hiding it with a shadow? This is certainly a blocked area. But with this comes so much emotional baggage and should be handled with great sensitivity.

Anatomical Description

The sacral plexus, where the Swadisthana is situated, aligns with the sacrum. The sacrum, the flat bone at the base of the spine, is a triangular wedge-shaped bone formed usually by fusion of five embryonic spinal segments below the lumbar vertebrae, constituting the posterior wall of the pelvis (wedged in between the hips and forms the base of the spine). It is situated below the navel, in the genital area behind the pubis, in the spinal cord. The opposite side of the second Chakra relates to the seat of the subconscious and is linked to the adrenals and the release of adrenaline into the body.

The sacral plexus are the last nerves to exit the spine at the bottom. They exit from the 4th and 5th lumbar and 1st through 3rd sacral nerves. They exit the pelvis as the sciatic nerve. They control the large and small muscles of the buttocks as well as the muscles of the back of the thighs and everything below the knees. The sciatic nerve is the largest nerve in the body and the muscles in the back of the thighs are very powerful. This nerve is involved with locomotion, standing, and therefore greatly affects your body in diverse ways. It doesn't take much to imagine what it means when this Chakra is blocked.

The sacroiliac joints are held together by powerful ligaments, which allow for enough movement to enable you to walk with a natural rhythmic gait. If the sacrum becomes fixated (stuck), normal walking and movement of the lower extremities is not possible. This is how important it is to make sure the sacrum gets proper exercise and attention. Normal motion of the sacrum is dependent upon this three-dimensional balance of the lower back area, the pelvic area, as well as the integrity of the numerous ligaments that connect the sacrum to the bottom vertebra of the spine, and the hip bones (iliac), hence the name sacroiliac joints.

Because the sacrum is at the centre of the mass of the body, pressure applied at or near to it has a much bigger effect on the entire body. The meninges (the covering of the spinal cord) attach to the sacrum and put it into reciprocal motion with the cranial bones as the cerebral spinal fluid is produced and liberated into the spinal canal.

The sacral plexus affects the pelvic organs, including the lower part of the digestive tract, and together with the coccygeal plexus controls the rectum, ankles, feet, arches, toes, lower legs, sciatic nerve, and prostate gland. It also contains gray matter of the parasympathetic nervous system where there are cell bodies connecting the nerves that come from the spine to the nerves that go to the actual organs themselves. The parasympathetic nerves control organ function and are not usually under conscious control when they stimulate function. Their counterpart, the sympathetic nerves, balance their function.

Anatomical Areas Affected

Adrenal glands, kidneys, bladder, body fluids, appendix, gallbladder, genitals, hips, large intestine, Leydig or lyden gland (where the testes/ovaries relate to the lymphatic system), lower abdomen to navel, lower back, lower vertebrae, liver, mammary glands, middle spine, pancreas, pelvis, prostate, sexual organs (both inner and outer) and the skin, spleen and stomach.

To get a visual of where this is, go just above your pubic hairline, about two inches below your navel, this is the sexual centre for women. This is also the area that in Qigong is called The Dantien for women and is often used as visualization in medical Qigong self-healing. It is here that a balanced yin-yang/male-female connection is maintained.

If this Chakra is balanced, there will be enormous capacity for creativity and partnerships with others, not only relatives. If this Chakra is out of balance, there will be emotional problems that have to do with sex. There will be addiction to feelings of guilt. The ability to be nurturing and giving to others will be hampered by self-denial and the inability to receive without a feeling of being obligated. Giving will be more out of duty, not from the heart.

When out of balance, a person is unable to let their creative juices flow. Instead, they are stuck in routine and sameness.

If this Chakra is underactive, the person just doesn't feel good about who he or she is. There is uncertainty, indecisiveness, constantly questioning what to do.

In the same way, if this Chakra is overactive, there will be self-love and more masturbation than love with a partner. The person will be stubborn. Eating disorders are common (eating too much or not at all).

A perfect example of this Chakra being out of balance is someone who needs to sleep too much to feel good and then doesn't feel rested anyway. This then becomes a 'chronic' lack of energy.

With orange being the main colour here, it can be helpful to use everything that is orange to awaken this Chakra when you are working with it. This means in the clothes you wear below your waist, in the foods that you eat and drink (mango, orange peppers, cantaloupe, and such). Use your imagination to get a sense of the energy that comes from the colour orange.

I eat to nourish my Body,
I drink to cleanse my Mind, and I create to nourish my Soul.
AMN

The Third Chakra

Manipura – Yellow resonance – Diaphragm

Manipura – navel

(Iyengar calls this the *Manipuraka* Chakra)

The *Manas* (mind) and *Surya* (the Sun) Chakras, are situated in the region between the navel and the heart. I am including them here as part of the Manipura, and mention the solar plexus here, although usually that is included in the Heart Chakra (4th). If we follow Iyengar's definition, there would be nine Chakras. He says the adrenals may stand for these two Chakras. However, since this is not what you will find when you continue your research, I'm going to stick to the seven Chakras for this series.

The Manipura, the 3rd (Navel) Chakra, is connected to everything to do with higher vitality. People with a strong 3rd Chakra have such characteristics as inner strength, a purpose in life, a career, and self-confidence as a result.

The navel and spleen (people differ on these placements), are also considered to belong to the lower fires. I place the navel with the 3rd Chakra, but the lower fires are still connected here. The Navel Chakra is known as the fire of material consciousness. It is here that we are connected to the material world at birth via the umbilical cord being ligatured or clamped and cut, so this makes sense.

This Chakra is the last of the lower three, the initiation of Thephareth, the fire of body formation. As we leave this to enter the 4th Chakra, we bid farewell to the lower trinity here. This realm hovers around issues relating to fear. There can be a lack of self-esteem, fear of rejection, defensiveness around even constructive criticism, and being secretive and indecisive.

... so all the kingdoms of earthy nature are included within our physical bodies.

Anatomical Description

This Chakra is located in the area of the lumbar and lumbar plexus. Words like 'behind the navel' and 'umbilical' are also used to describe the area. The lumbar pertains to the loins, the part of the back between the thorax and the pelvis. The origin is the five pairs of nerves that arise from the lumbar segments of the spinal cord, each pair leaving the vertebral column below correspondingly numbered vertebrae. The lumbar plexus is the one formed by the ventral branches of the 2nd to 5th lumbar nerves in the psoas major muscle (the branches of the first lumbar nerve are often included). The ventral branches of these nerves participate in the formation of the lumbosacral plexus, and this is why many people include the 1st and 2nd Chakras as one when describing physical problems.

Some people call this the solar plexus Chakra, the Seat of the Self, however the solar plexus is called the 'belly brain' in ancient books. It is written that the solar plexus is like the counterpart of the brain, and that there is, literally, a gray mass of matter that looks like the brain in this area of the body (right beneath the diaphragm at the mid-line of the torso). In my opinion, because the solar plexus is considered the celiac plexus or coeliac plexus due to its radiating nerve fibres and complex network of nerves (a plexus), located in the abdomen, it is all part of this Chakra.

Anatomical Areas Affected

Below the breast, breath, digestive system and organs, diaphragm muscle, duodenum, gall bladder, kidneys, lower back, metabolism, nervous system, respiratory system, skin, small intestine, sympathetic nervous system, stomach, spleen (in many books, the spleen is given as the exact location of this chakra, and I tend to believe this), liver, pancreas, solar plexus, and adrenals.

Physical Problems Here

When the lumbar plexus and the entire area covered above is not working properly, the following physical symptoms can appear: gas pains, chronic tiredness, irritable bowel, constipation, diarrhea, hernias, sterility, bladder problems, menstrual problems, cramps, bed-wetting, knee pains, sciatica, lower back pain, difficult or painful urination, numbness, poor circulation in legs, shin splints, swollen ankles, weak arches, leg cramps and cold feet.

In the end the Manipura or Solar Plexus is about TRUST.
I Trust in My own Inner Self,
I am the child that grows
with the Rays of the Sun into adulthood.
When I reach toward that Child, it takes my Breath away
.....and throws it out into the Universe.

AMN

The Fourth Chakra

Anahata – Green Resonance – Heart Centre

Anahata – heart (compassion)

Certain things catch your eye,
but pursue only those that capture the heart.

Native American Proverb

The Heart Chakra shows conscience and compassion when it is balanced. It's all about how you manifest love, forgive others, and how you project and inject your feelings. This is a powerful Chakra and is the one that is the most subtle in so far as it can be the most difficult to acknowledge in real, rather then abstract terms. Here we have arrived at the 'Centre of the Seven'; three above and three below. Matter and spirit are united. This is a very powerful location in the body. It is directly connected to the Third Eye and the Crown Chakra.

When this Chakra is overactive, the ego will take over and there will be a lack of love in the heart of the person. People with a Heart Chakra out of control will not want to go out of their way for others. Inconsiderate is a good description. This is the person you tell to get in touch with their feelings, or else! It can be quite frustrating. There is no good will toward others. Everything is for the Self. However, if it's underactive, the person will appear to have no sense of Self, they will seem numb.

Here we enter a higher realm that hovers around love and compassion, self-confidence, inspiration and hope. But if this is blocked, all of this greatness can turn into despair, jealousy, hate, unrealistic fear, and rage.

Again…this gives you an idea why you need to unblock Chakras. The more balanced the Chakras are, the more balanced you will be in all walks of life, regardless of what they *do*.

We have now left the Divine Trinity of the first three Chakras, the Garden of Eden with its fiery beauty. Here we enter the path of the soul upward into the higher regions of this magical system as we face the 4th Chakra, the Heart.

Anatomy of this Chakra

The thoracic area of the body includes the heart, cardiac plexus, chest, heart centre, and thymus gland, part of the Endocrine system.

The heart is the strongest organ in your body. It is the propulsive pump of the blood, about the size of a grapefruit. The better you *feel*, the stronger your heart will be. The bottom line is circulation. How does everything flow in your body? If your circulation is off, your Heart Chakra is not flowing with ease.

Sri Ramana Maharishi calls this the 'mystic centre, the Hridian centre or seat of God, the centre of the Universe, the circle with a circumference everywhere and a centre nowhere'.

The Heart Chakra also rules the lungs and lymphatic system. If you have a physical problem in any of these areas, concentrate on this Chakra.

Next to the brain, the heart is the only place where intelligence can be found. The heart has a set of nerves, which are able to function along the lines of thought, or understanding, or intelligence. These are not found anywhere else but in the brain cells. When ones reads the ancient texts on Yoga, the authors often refer to the gray matter (brain) in the centre of the body. This is probably what they were referring to, although they said it was in the solar plexus.

Others say it is the centre of the 72,000 nadis in the heart centre.

Sri Aurobindo taught 'all of these centres are in the middle of the body. They are supposed to be attached to the spinal cord, but in fact all of these things are in the subtle body (*Suksma Deha*), though one has the feeling of their activities as if in the physical body when the consciousness is awake'.

Areas Affected

This affects the entire thoracic region of the body, which affects a large part of your body. The chest-breast, gallbladder, liver, diaphragm, skin, lungs, circulatory system, blood, rib cage, oesophagus, shoulders, arms, hands, immune system, lymph glands, appendix, are all affected. There are several chambers to this Chakra that extend up beyond the chest above the main heart Chakra, and as they develop, they open. In Tibetan Buddhism, it is the navel centre that constitutes the fire centre. According to Yukteswar, it is the thoracic region.

To get a visual of where this area is, think about where the heart is. It is just to the left of the centre of the chest. If you put your finger on the centre of your breastbone, this is a good spot to visualize in your mind's eye. But then think about when you are pointing to yourself – where do you point? Just to the right of the centre of your chest. Almost everyone does this without thinking. According to Maharishi, this is the point.

Maharshi's answer to, 'What part of the body is the abode of the Self?' "The heart on the right side of the chest is generally indicated. This is because we usually point to the right side of the chest when we refer to ourselves. Some say that the *Sahasrara* (the Thousand-Petalled lotus) is the abode of the Self. But if that were true the head should not fall forward when we go to sleep or faint." 'What is the nature of the heart?' He responds, "The sacred texts describing it say, 'Between the two nipples, below the chest and above the abdomen, there are six organs of different colours (these are not the same as the Chakras). One of them, resembling the bud of a water lily, is situated two digits to the right of the heart. It is inverted and within it is a tiny orifice, which is the seat of dense darkness (ignorance) full of desires. All the psychic nerves (*nadis*) depend upon it. It is the abode of the vital forces, the mind and the light (of consciousness).'"

The Heart Chakra has to do with Love, equilibrium and joy. It is related to the thymus, the gland in the heart centre that boosts the immune system and is part of the Endocrine system. It is located in the chest. It processes lymphocytes responsible for cell-mediated immunity (which fights off disease), which means that constant unrelenting stress is damaging.

*I am free to live, I am free to be, and I am free to breathe.
I choose life over death and I choose to live with Joy!*

AMN

The Fifth Chakra

Vishudda – Blue Resonance – Throat

Vishudda – pure (wisdom)

The throat centre governs the expressive and externalizing mind,
as well as movements and mental forces
and is the transformation centre.

Sri Aurobindo

The Throat Chakra in front of the cervical region, the larynx, is a gateway to the sound of the Chakras. Iyengar points to the pharyngeal region for this Chakra centre.

'The Blue Chakra is the gateway to the spiritual aspect of man. It is the centre of the religious instinct, the devotional and mystical nature. When working in harmony with the yellow and red Chakras there is peace and balance in body and mind. It is the home of the causal body – the root cause of your present condition of life.'

S.G.J. Ouseley from *The Power of the Rays, The Science of Colour-Healing*

Obviously, being in the throat region, this Chakra is all about expression and how we use our inner voice and sound in this world to communicate with others. Anyone with a spectacular singing voice has a strong throat Chakra. How we listen and hear sound also pertains to music and how we interpret it. Our ears are the organs of hearing and how we use that sense often comes through our voice.

As we reach even higher, this 5th Chakra hovers around issues that have to do with our personal expression, how others see us, our personality and how it shines out into the world, how creative we can be, or lazy. When this Chakra is blocked, it is not uncommon to see addiction and highly critical people. There is a lack of authority, intention and focus.

Anatomy of this Chakra

This Chakra is connected to the cervical region of the body. This includes the brachial, cervical and pharyngeal plexuses, the throat medulla centre, larynx, thyroid gland, and behind the throat. This means that hearing, sound, and voice are all connected to this centre.

The brachial plexus is a nerve plexus originating from the ventral branches of the last four cervical and the first thoracic spinal nerves, giving off many of the principal nerves of the shoulder, chest, and arms. It could also be included with the 4th Chakra, but I'm placing it here.

The cervical plexus is a nerve plexus formed by the ventral branches of the first four cervical nerves, supplying structures in the neck region. This Chakra is situated precisely where that little indentation is in the throat – the organ of the voice; the air passage between the lower pharynx and the trachea, formed by nine cartilages: thyroid, cricoid, epiglottis and the three paired cartilages arytenoids, corniculate and cuneiform. Even a simple practice of cleaning the tongue daily can make a difference to the health of the larynx and this entire area in the throat (you can purchase tongue cleaners at most chemists).

The thyroid is the controller here. Anyone who has a problem with their thyroid will do well to meditate on this area.

The thyroid controls the metabolic rate of every cell in the body. It also produces thyroxin, which regulates our metabolism. This is major work we are dealing with here, and the health of this area is vital. It also regulates the body's temperature and mood.

Physical Issues

When this area of the body is not functioning properly, the following symptoms can appear: headaches and migraine, dizziness, fatigue, head colds, vision problems, hearing loss, sinus problems, allergies, runny nose, sore throat, tonsillitis, hoarseness, laryngitis, stiff neck, cough, croup, pain in upper arm, tennis elbow, wrist, hand and finger numbness or pain, shortness of breath, difficulty in breathing, asthma, heart conditions, chest pains, heartburn, and chronic tiredness.

So obviously this is another very important area of the body to keep healthy for these reasons.

'The 5th Chakra particularly has to do with communication and opens the more we recognize our free will and that of others. It is wisdom, and it's a key point that before wisdom and understanding comes love and compassion – first the unknowing leap, *Karuna* (compassion) before *Prajna* (wisdom and understanding)'

Jody Boyne

Areas Affected

The brachial plexus works with the neck muscles, shoulders, elbows, arms and forearms, wrists, hands and fingers, oesophagus, heart and coronary arteries, bronchial tubes and lungs, and the diaphragm. The cervical plexus works with the scalp, base of the skull (occiput), neck muscles, diaphragm, and all of the areas of the throat.

You are the Conductor of your own life. Communicate with those you love and travel this Road with; they need clarity, instruction and direction, as do you.

AMN

The Sixth Chakra

Ajna – Purple resonance – The Third Eye

Ajna – command

I See!

Our journey is now travelling in the direction of the higher areas of the physical body. It is here that we begin to experience formless consciousness, ESP, intuitive senses, feeling and touching and seeing beyond the five senses. This is the hard drive of the physical body, the spiritual eye. It is often called The Third Eye. Today it is easy for anyone to imagine a computer's hard drive and its secret code for storing and distributing everything in what seems no time at all. This Chakra is the same. It works to restore our soul, constantly.

Now we are reaching higher to soon rise to the crown and come out through the top of the head. This Chakra is in the realm of issues that surround everything from discipline, emotional maturity, wisdom and judgment or lack of judging others! When this is blocked, there is fear of truth, distraction from one's own power, confusion and sometimes a total misunderstanding of life as a whole.

Anatomy of this Chakra

This Chakra is located in the middle of the brain behind the brow, between the eyebrows. It expands itself all around the head. It is located along the Sushumna Nadi that extends from the Perineal (the lower or yin polarity) to the Crown (the upper or yang polarity), pituitary gland, and forehead at the root of the nose. It nourishes thyroid, lower brain, left eye, ears, nose, nervous system, head and brain.

Imagine a cobra with its large head and long body. This is precisely what our brain looks like on top of what appears to be a long snake (the spinal cord). The medulla is the lowest part of the brain. It resembles the spinal cord, which is actually a continuation of it, but it is larger in diameter and more complex. It contains many important reflex centres, controlling such vital processes as breathing, heartbeat, and blood pressure. It is a relay centre for fibres connecting the higher and lower centres. Nearly all the fibres passing through the medulla en route to or from the brain cross from one side to the other in the medulla. I find this very interesting when one stops to think about how the Ida and Pingala cross within the body. This crossing becomes evident when there is an injury to the right side of the brain and it shows up as paralysis on the left side of the body.

Areas Affected

You can see how important this Chakra is when you see what areas it can control!

This Chakra affects the pineal gland, brain, neurological system, nervous system, eyes, ears, nose, centre of the forehead, blood supply to the head, scalp, bones of the face, base of the skull, vocal chords, tonsils, neck muscles, shoulders, oesophagus, heart and coronary arteries, bronchial tubes and lungs, liver, diaphragm, stomach, pancreas, spleen, small intestines and colon.

The pineal gland is a small conical structure attached by a stalk to the posterior wall of the third ventricle in the brain. There are six smaller Chakras that are associated with this and are located in a line straight up from The Third Eye, up the middle of the forehead. This eye opens as it develops, and each has its own specific purpose.

It has been discovered that the pineal is made up of some ocular cells like those found in the retina of the external eye! So in affect the name given by the Yogis thousands of years ago was appropriate...it really is the third eye that opens into our inner world. Often called the window of inner vision, the third eye allows us access to another world and our journey into inner space!

The pineal gland is shaped like a pinecone. Secret: It's larger in women and is considered the centre of the 6th sense, a Woman's Intuition!

If you meditate on a regular basis then you can begin to open the pineal gland to get more acquainted with your Self. You will discover that you have more compassion and tolerance as you study the inner workings of the world within. The Buddha sat in deep meditation with his eyes lifted toward the third eye, lids closed but intently focused. Interestingly, we only need to look at the Buddha to feel the internal workings of the mind here and the all encompassing peace that surpasses all understanding.

According to Sri Yogananda, 'the pituitary gland secretes a yellowish fluid, and the pineal gland secretes a white fluid. When the two meet, there is a flash of light so bright this Chakra is opened. Here then, the two fluids, known in the Bible as 'the land of Milk and Honey' begin to flow down the pancreatic nerve (The river Jordan) to the third centre, which is known as the manger (where Christ consciousness is born within you).'

This fluid can be described as phosphorescence with a luminous appearance. Many people see this light when they are deep in meditation through the Third eye. It's a powerful vision to have and as Swami Vishnu-devananda used to say, "Once you are on the Spiritual path there are always illuminating experiences to keep you there!"

I breathe and I breathe with you,
I swim deep and I still breathe with you.
I dive down into the depth of my compassion,
of my love and my humanity
and see all that is within me and within you.
All loving ocean, bathe me in your light and your wisdom
that I may truly see you.

AMN

272   The Practice

Experience is all you need to connect here

When my Mother was dying of cancer I found out that she had little faith in death and a lot more faith in life. I saw her struggle with the reality of her situation and, thinking she was protecting me, never talked to me about the reality that was facing her. I felt helpless and unable to talk to her about the next step in her Divine journey. Many years before her demise she had told me that rather than be a vegetable, demented or terminally ill, she would, while she could still hold a pill, take her own life rather then suffer the degradation and humiliation of a long drawn out death. I promised her I would not stop her and had prepared mentally for that outcome.

Never imagining that my Mother would be struck down with gallbladder cancer I just shelved that talk with her, but when it came to the moment of death she hung on so savagely that I was amazed how strong her will to live was, even though her pain was never resolved and she died in agony.

During that terrible time I knew that it was me that was being challenged as much as she was! My faith was truly tested. It was the first time I understood that all things pass away no matter who we are and that the only thing we have in common on this Earth is both Birth and Death.

I dug deep into my resources and found a strength that I am proud of. I nursed my darling Mother to the end until I could not carry her. She died in our local hospice and was cared for like the Divine Mother she was and I decided to take on the role of 'Journey Master', taking her from 'here to there' through my work, my practice and my meditation. I used my Third Eye to 'see' her through and when she called me Mummy I responded with the same love her Mother would have bestowed on her child. Connecting an experience with a loved one or someone you wish to protect is what you do when working with this Chakra.

Think intimacy
INTO ... ME ... SEE

The Inner 'I' is the way to 'Seeing'

as well as the way to Compassion and Love.

Deep and Sincere Affection is a healing power

beyond all understanding.

Take the hand of the one who needs you,

close your eyes and open them again

with the wisdom and knowledge of the Divine

in all things whether great or small'

AMN

The Seventh Chakra

Sahasrara – Violet Resonance – Crown opening

Sahasrara – thousand is the 'Lotus of the Thousand Petals' located
four finger breadths above the crown of the head.

And the Sun shone out to all the Earth
and the Light to all the Heavens,
in one breath the Canopy of Stars lifted the dome of darkness
and let the Sun shine in.
Hallelujah!

AMN

'Between two thoughts there is an interval of no thought. That interval is the Self, the *Atman*. It is pure Awareness only.'

Jnana Vashistha

And now we have ARRIVED. The Sahasrara Chakra epitomizes your total energy state. Colours in this area remain the same, regardless of how other colours might change in other Chakra rays.

There are some people who say it can take on the most prominent colour of another Chakra and make it even more intense. My experience has remained the same throughout the years. A person with a strong and balanced 7th Chakra always appears to me with a sense of a large white light surrounding their body. They seem to glow, like the white light that radiates from a very powerful sun.

Anyone who has ever unblocked the 7th Chakra will attest to the fact that they are changed forever. It's like rebirthing, like being born anew. One's sense of love is magnified to the degree that everyone feels it. Perfect examples would be Swami Sivananda, Yogi Bhajan or Yogananda. These Divine Souls have opened every Chakra written about here, as well as all the others that are not even covered, for there are many more subsidiary ones. There are thousands and one needs to remember this. Self-realized men and women are transcendental in the way they communicate with others and all are drawn to them. They illuminate and radiate Love; it is visible and tangible, because we feel it when in their presence.

The Sahasrara Chakra is the Crown of them all, the Jewel in the Lotus. It is just as important to open the 1st Chakra and then move up through each one, gradually and consciously, as it is to recognize the goal. If you can visualize a tunnel without any obstacles, you can visualize the *Sushumna*, the subtle spine, the road to enlightenment, where the physical spine is located. I think of it as the Stem of the Thousand Petalled Lotus. With all of the Chakras open, whether vertical or horizontal, it will make no difference because it is the opening of the lotus flower right through the top of your head that is the crucial point to aspire to.

What is the purpose of a bud if it is never to blossom?

Once at the pinnacle you become one with 'Every-thing'. Call it cosmic consciousness, an enlightening experience, a surrendering to the spirit within, there are many ways to describe this. No matter what beliefs, theories or methods people have to reach 'at-one-ment', it is not important. What is important is to know what you are doing to prevent your body from being overwhelmed. Chakra work is profound and powerful, so show the deepest respect for it and ultimately be authentic and sincere.

Here we are at the pinnacle of the seven Chakras. We have entered a realm of spirit. Here we discover the Divine inspiration and intuition as we begin to see the broader canvas of life as it was meant to be seen as well as experienced, in true technicolour!

Be aware that if the Crown Chakra is blocked, the same wonderful attributes become their polar opposites and a lack of mission or purpose in life suddenly rears its ugly head. We are at a loss regarding what we are supposed to be doing. We are out of touch with our own spirit, our own intention here on earth. Practicing headstands can really bring the Heaven back to Earth and align your Chakras again using opposing magnetic fields of *Prana* (upward flow of Life force, *Qi* or *Chi*) and that of *Apana* (downward flow).

Anatomy of this Chakra

'The Thousand-Petalled Lotus commands the higher-thinking mind, houses the still higher-illumined mind, and at the highest opens to the intuition through which an over flowing directness – the over mind – can have with the rest of communication or an immediate contact. The 7th is sometimes identified with the brain, but that is an error – the brain is only a channel of communication situated between the Thousand-Petalled Lotus and the forehead centres. The former is sometimes called the void centre (*Sunya*) either because it is not in the body, but in the apparent void above, or because rising above the head one enters first into the silence of the Self or Spiritual Being.'

Sri Aurobindo, *Letters on Yoga*

The physical description is usually the pituitary. Often called the 'Lotus of one thousand Petals', this Chakra is actually located just above the crown of the head, above the skull according to most experts. According to Iyengar, 'The Ajna and Sahasrara and Lalata Chakras may be the brain matter, and the pituitary and pineal glands are the network of nerves in the brain.' It's definitely either the top of the cranium, or just above it.

Specifically: cerebral cortex, top centre of the head, pituitary gland, crown of the head, midline above the ears, top of head, nervous system, brain, right eye. Think of this Chakra as the abode of Shiva – located four finger-breadths above the crown of the head.

Areas Affected

All of the areas of the cranial nerves, brain stem and cranial plexus are connected to this Chakra in some way. What applies to the 6th Chakra will usually apply to this one, too.

'Yogis speak of a subtle nerve going to the crown of the head known as *Sushumna* which is located in the centre of the spinal column. When the life energy of a Yogi, it is believed, passes through the *Sushumna* and goes through the aperture in the crown of the head, known as *brahmarandhra* or 'the opening leading to Brahma', he will not be reborn in the world, but will steadily reach *brahmaloka*, the world of the cosmic Mind... The path thus traversed is known as 'the northern path' or 'the path of light'...',

Swami Ranganathananda,
The Message of The Upanishads.

The Violet Chakra at the crown of the head is the sanctuary of the spirit, the gateway to the highest spiritual influences in man. Its material counterpart is the pituitary body.
Ouseley

Double Helix and The Nadis

The Double Helix – DNA – looks exactly like the inner workings of the Chakra system. Seeing this image rotated might help you to visualize the *Sushumna* together with the *Ida* and *Pingala*.

The *Ida* and *Pingala* are known as *Nadis*, energy points, much like meridians, known in Chinese acupuncture for instance.

Ida in Sanskrit means 'comfort' and is the left side of the body and works with the right side of the brain. *Ida* is introverted in nature and is represented by the Moon (*Chandra*), female, cooling aspects of this energy potency. *Ying* is its quality and Blue the colour focus.

Pingala in Sanskrit means 'tawny' and is in the right side of the body and the left side of the brain. It is extrovert in nature and is represented by the Sun (*Surya*), heat and is Male. *Yang* is its quality and Red its colour focus.

This is the foundation of the Chakras. Just imagine a spine (a hollow tube) going straight through these spirals. And imagine that the horizontal lines are like musical notes to play upon. Yes, there is a rhythm to everything, and even Chakras have their own rhythm of energy waves. Each Chakra has its own colour, vibration, rhythm, sound, and much more. Consider here the Soul, Spirit and Life.

'Matter is the vehicle for the manifestation of the Soul.

The Soul is the vehicle for the manifestation of the Spirit.

And Life synthesizes and pervades the Trinity formed by the three.'

Truman Caylor Wadlington,

Yogi Ramsuratkumar

The earliest known mention of Chakras is found in the later *Upanishads*, specifically the Brahma Upanishad and the Yogatattva Upanishad. These *Vedic* models were adapted in Tibetan Buddhism as Vajrayana theory, and in the Tantric Shakta theory of Chakras, so we can deduce that it is ancient indeed!

Chakras are included in the ancient Sanskrit texts because the point of practicing Yoga is to begin to move the Chakras up through the body, in order to become whole, to experience the unity of the body, mind and soul. The first time I began to learn and to work with the Chakras was with Swami Vishnu-devananda and Sivananda Yoga. After performing the warm up *Surya Namaskar* (Sun Salutations), Sivananda Yoga class begins with the headstand. This is to stimulate the crown chakra and then to work and balance the rest, ending with the Mooladhara Chakra. It makes sense to me now after studying many different Yoga methods, though I personally begin with the Mooladhara as I have found students respond slowly and surely in the right direction! Onward and Upward!

The Yogatattva Upanishad (verse 83–101) lists five Chakras and describes them as being interrelated with the five elements: earth, water, fire, air, and space. The seven chakras that are written about stand for the development of humankind. I find this corresponds to the development of the child and its first seven years.

Give me a child till seven and I will give you the man.

Jesuit proverb

Our Chakras are part of a bio-energy channel system that is composed of a vertical energy axis that follows the spinal cord from the perineum, the area between the genitals and rectum, up to the top and above the head, our central bio-energy system, similar to our central nervous system. Again, it is called the *Sushumna Nadi* in Sanskrit, and it is here where the seven energy centres, the Chakras, exist. Our Chakras represent our connection to Reality and to the Universe.

'One should practice *Pranayama* (special breathing techniques) for the purification of *Nadis*. Ida flows through the left nostril and Pingala through the right nostril. Ida is also called *Chandra Nadi* (Moon) and Pingala is *Surya Nadi* (Sun). Ida is cooling and Pingala is heating. Pingala digests the food. Ida is the great nourisher of the world. Pingala is fiery red. Ida and Pingala indicate *Kala* (time), and *Sushumna* swallows time.'

Swami Sivananda

The Seven Sacred Chakras:
I am the colour of the Rainbow; I am the colour of the Universe.
In my mind and in my body my colours manifest through my breath.
Be Me, See Me, Hear Me, Feel Me, I Am Me,
I am the Creation and I am the Root.

AMN

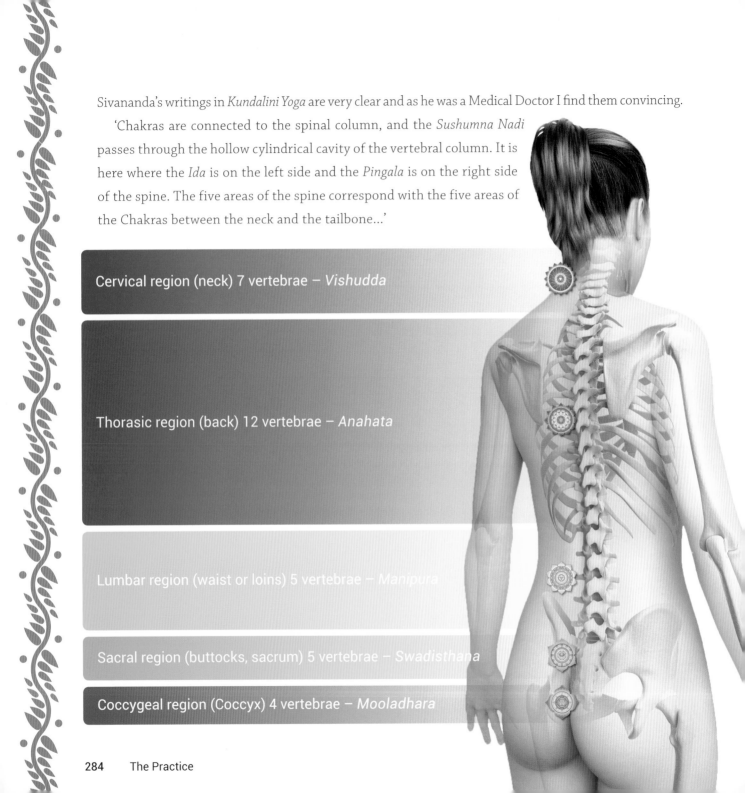

Sivananda's writings in *Kundalini Yoga* are very clear and as he was a Medical Doctor I find them convincing.

'Chakras are connected to the spinal column, and the *Sushumna Nadi* passes through the hollow cylindrical cavity of the vertebral column. It is here where the *Ida* is on the left side and the *Pingala* is on the right side of the spine. The five areas of the spine correspond with the five areas of the Chakras between the neck and the tailbone...'

Cervical region (neck) 7 vertebrae – *Vishudda*

Thorasic region (back) 12 vertebrae – *Anahata*

Lumbar region (waist or loins) 5 vertebrae – *Manipura*

Sacral region (buttocks, sacrum) 5 vertebrae – *Swadisthana*

Coccygeal region (Coccyx) 4 vertebrae – *Mooladhara*

A wonderful analogy of the Chakra system is from Sri Bhagavan Ramana Maharshi's *Cinema*:

The Cinema Show

Lamp inside apparatus	❁	Self
Lens in front of lamp	❁	Pure mind close to Self
Film (a long series of separate photos)	❁	Stream of latent tendencies consisting of subtle thoughts
Lens, light passing through it and lamp, which together form focused light	❁	The Mind, illumination of it and the Self, which together form seer or the *Jiva* (soul)
The light passing through the lens and falling on the screen	❁	Light of Self emerging from mind through senses, and falling on the world
Various kinds of pictures appearing in the light of the screen	❁	Various forms and names appearing as objects perceived in the light of the world
Mechanism which sets film in motion	❁	Divine law manifesting latent tendencies of mind

The Body Prayer

From a very young age I equated dance and movement with an intense feeling of reverence. Born in the north of Iraq, I was surrounded by a landscape both vast and liberating, with small communities of mud huts and the lush borders of Iran.

When I was old enough to stay still and respectful, my Armenian grandmother took me to our church. As a Syrian Orthodox Christian church, it was large, ornate, full of incense and candles, and it is for that reason, I believe, that Yoga and its rituals were so familiar and comforting.

As a dancer in body, mind and spirit I could not distinguish between my Spiritual life and that of my body's will to dance. I read about Anna Pavlova, the prima ballerina, whose deep religious fervour gave her performances something other than the excitement of seeing her achieve amazing grace, balance and strength, it also touched us deep inside, to our core.

It all made so much sense to dance for something more than the adulation of an audience; in fact, as a professional ballet dancer I would often get into trouble for leaving the stage before the curtain call. I was never interested in the adulation, only the feeling of giving my commitment to the dance itself.

'I am the Lord of the Dance said He', is a sentence that would keep me thinking as a young adult. Who was the Lord of the Dance? It was the first time I had considered that my love of dance might have an intricate relationship with my faith and spiritual sense of being an instrument of God. My Mother had been an actress and she always said that on stage she felt she was her true self. I know that in the 50s a woman gave up dreams of a career to marry and have children, and I know my Mother grieved for that lost life.

When my Father died, she took it up with a renewed passion and travelled the world working and acting in such festivals as the Berthold Brecht in Berlin. It was there that she became seriously ill with cancer and somehow kept going through rehearsals and performances, not telling anyone the pain she was in. A real trouper...she was 80 by then!

My feelings about performing were not the same. I did not love the applause or the praise; I danced because I felt deeply connected to the physical trigger that took me into another world. My mind became clear and one-minded and I felt free.

I had a troubled childhood and, like many other children, ballet was a sublime escape into a world of tutus and sequins. Watching Billy Elliot, the film and musical, when he dances from frustration, muted anger and rage, I knew what he was feeling, and it's the dance that can sublimate the desire to self-combust!

My Yoga practice works in the same way, as it allows me the mental space to raise my consciousness in such a way that I can step back and give myself time to make a decision...Rage or Release? Swami Vishnu called it sublimation.

Sublimation is a mechanism for defense. It allows us to act out unacceptable impulses by changing these behaviours into a more acceptable translation. So for an example, if a person is experiencing intense anger they might take up kick boxing to help them vent their frustration. The Japanese have used large models of the boss to punch and kick in the workplace to sublimate their frustrations for some time!

Freud believed that sublimation was a sign of maturity that allowed people to function normally in socially acceptable ways, giving them the opportunity to change habitual unsociable behaviour.

In Yoga Philosophy, sublimation is about redirecting thought and action. Celibacy is an important part of Yoga restraint (*Yama*) and is very difficult to attain, as sexual potency is very strong in humans, as our urge to procreate demands. But when sublimated, this energy is a powerful creative motivator, harnessing heart and soul.

Swami Krishnananda says that:

'Here, we feel that the withdrawal of consciousness from its object (of desire) would be something like tearing off our own skin from our body. How can we tear off our own skin? It would be terrible, but this is what is happening when we practice self-control. We are tearing off our flesh, and it is so painful. But the pain is lessened if the consciousness is properly educated and made to reasonably accept the background of its attitudes and the incorrectness of its perceptions, for reasons that are superior to the one that it is adopting at the present moment.'

Being the observer of the Self, or witness, is what Yoga Philosophy, and therefore a Yoga Life, is all about. Being comfortable is not progress. To reach a higher level of conscious thought and conscious action means having to be very uncomfortable indeed! No knowledge is ever attained from simple comfort; challenging ourselves to grow is painful.

When training my teachers, I will tell them on their first day that they need to expect the unexpected. Anything that could go wrong during their months with me will be thrown into the air and how they deal with it is the real Yoga they are learning about.

A posture is the first step to being uncomfortable, and as we are carrying our soul within the body as a vehicle we need to begin there. But effort is needed for that growth, and hard work, or we stay in the same place creating deep *Samskaras*, grooves of habitual malpractice, instead of true practice, where we accept the Spiritual role that Yoga plays on the mind as well as the body.

Once on the Spiritual Path, you will be tested. It's how you deal with life that matters, not what happens. Challenging, traumatic, shocking things happen all the time, and using the tools and skills Yoga develops is how we save our 'Self'.

Jesus was tempted when in the wilderness, the Devil suggesting he give up trying to save anyone, "Relax, you can't do it". How many times have we been there? In the wilderness, no hope, no way out? Many times. But if you stay steady, then keep walking one day after another, somehow we find ourselves back in a place of equanimity.

Hatha Yoga

Many people think that Hatha Yoga is only about the *Asanas* and *Pranayama* and the practice of them. The goal of Yoga is God realisation or the discovery of the 'Self'. Yoga is not a religion, but a philosophy on how to be successful at life by learning how to deal with the mind.

The greatest written work on Hatha Yoga is *The Hatha Yoga Pradipika*, a classical text describing Hatha Yoga. It is said to be the oldest surviving text on the subject.

The Hatha Yoga Pradipika

Dedicated to Lord Shiva, *The Hatha Yoga Pradipika* begins,

> 'Salutations to the glorious primal guru, Sri Adinath, who instructed the knowledge of Hatha Yoga which shines forth as a stairway for those who wish to ascend to the highest state of Yoga, Raja Yoga.'

The text explains how Hatha Yoga is a means of uniting the forces of mind and *Prana* with the mental energy of *Chitta* (consciousness). Practice of Hatha Yoga enables these two energies, which are intrinsic to everything, to become harmonious and unified into one force, *Kundalini*.

The system describes methods to prepare and purify the body through cleansing practices (*Kriya*), physical postures (*Asanas*), Pranic manipulation through breathing techniques (*Pranayama*), leading towards mental discipline through meditation, all complemented by proper yogic diet. Each technique is, ultimately, designed to cultivate the right conditions in the mind for deep meditation:

> 'An undisciplined mind is like a boisterous child, telling stories, continually distracting you from your *Sadhana*.'

Chapter 1 of the *Pradipika* outlines the five abstentions and five observances found in Patanjali's *Eight Limbs of Yoga*. Much of this part of the text is given to the description of *Asanas*, citing them as the initial phase,

> 'Prior to everything, *Asanas* is spoken of as the first part of Hatha Yoga. Having done

Asana one gets steadiness of body and mind, diseaselessness and lightness of the limbs.'

The *Pradipika* commentary mentions that …

'…the free flowing of *Prana* is essential to a supple body. Stiffness of the body is due to blockages and accumulation of toxins. Free flowing *Prana*, enabling the practitioner to bend and stretch in a relaxed manner, removes these. When the store of *Prana* is increased to a greater degree, the body will move itself and may spontaneously perform postures never done before. This is due to the relaxed state and to a greater vibrational rate of the *Prana*.'

This emphasis on *Asana* as the first 'Limb' is the main distinction between the Hatha Yoga system and Raja Yoga, which places the moral disciplines first. The principle of Hatha Yoga is that it leads to Raja Yoga (meditation) and practising *Asana* and *Pranayama* to first steady the mind and purify the *N adis* before progressing to the moral disciplines.

Swami Swatmarama, a disciple of Swami Goraknath, wrote the text in the 15th century AD, drawing on previous texts and his own experiences.

This text, as well as the other Yoga scriptures, can seem very high in its delivery and often overwhelming in context. We need to remember that in those past centuries the scholar or *Brahmin*, the highest caste people, were the ones to read and expound on these teachings. The layperson often could not read or write so images were used to explain the theory. The Bible did much the same. Priests made drawings to illustrate that God was in the heavens, on a cloud, unreachable. We, the small people, were down below looking up and made to feel that God looked down on us, we the judged as it were.

This is why Yoga has to be seen as a philosophy, because, although based on ancient Hindu scriptures, it has a life of its own that grew from those teachings. It is all embracing! All are welcome in my Yoga Shala; Hindu, Moslem, Jew, Christian, Catholic, Atheist and Angel card reader! In the ancient past it was only the male scholar allowed to practice Hatha Yoga, no women! How things have changed, more women than men now practice Hatha Yoga!

Everything taught in a Yoga class can and should be used in the world outside. Your Real class, in practice, begins as you leave your mat.

Yoga Teaching is based on *Guru Parampara*, knowledge passed on from a living teacher to a student, in an unbroken line.

In the end *Asanas* and *Pranayama* are the tools for gaining control of the mind, and *Prana* to help you towards that goal. Personally Yoga is my first-aid box full of skills on how to help me deal with life's emergencies, whether physical or emotional.

For this reason, we do not say that being a Yoga Teacher is a profession, but a *Sadhana*, a Spiritual Practice. And in the same way a student isn't just a student within the classroom but a student of Life outside.

A good teacher is also a good student. You never stop learning and, to be honest, I have found the more I learn, the less I know.

A good teacher will carry on learning from other teachers, understand that knowledge, give it, practice it and pass it on from personal experience, never from second hand!

To have knowledge and not to pass it on is also seen as a sin.

A Yoga Teacher is a Yoga Practitioner, not a Preacher.
Swami Sivananda

The Art of True Practice

Thought before Practice

Yoga can be seen as a primary form of Self-Respect, or Self-Love in the sense of an ongoing personal commitment and a caring process by which and through which we order, balance and enhance the existence of our 'being'. This harnesses Life-Energy, *Prana*, and by extension this impacts on the greater world of both Man and Society.

It is useful to remind our 'Self' of this impact when practising, and finding that suddenly we are unaware that our practice has fallen into the nature of a normal and neutralised 'routine'.

Reflect on the thought that there are millions of people, young, old, sick, well, inspired, depressed, lost and found that are practising with you somewhere on the planet Earth. They practice silently and stoically, taking courage as well as energy from this thought. Connect truly from the heart with this amazing body of humankind who walk the path you are now walking. Some may stumble, some may run, but it is a known truth that to practice as a group empowers growth and the intent of our practice.

Alone-ness and One-ness is an all-togetherness.

Take heart that through right thought and right action your practice can be a creative and ever-deepening exploration into dimensions yet to be revealed, carrying you beyond the limitations of the body and predictable life-patterns.

Remind yourself that the quality of your approach to the movements, your mindfulness, is crucial to your transformation. Mindless practice creates grooves of repetition, meaning you are a machine running though moves that are programmed. This can never replace conscious, sensitive practice and therefore deepening awareness.

Approach your practice with care, humility and a natural reverence, like walking through an ancient forest, a Mayan temple or watching the rising Sun. This will make sure you approach your prayer, practice and path with awareness and authenticity.

Consider these 5 points as Satya (Truth) before your Practice

1. **True commitment:**

To practice deeply, no matter what experience and feelings arise through that practice. Be fearless through softness in pain, grief, discomfort or tiredness.

2. **Wholeheartedness:**

Devotion to your practice and focus on it absorbs your mind and body. Stay concentrated on your Yoga, clearing away distractions and dangers that may try to stop that practice.

3. **Purity of purpose:**

Be sincere, honest and open minded, fully embracing Yoga. This then cultivates your in-tuition, that Inner Teacher.

4. **Strong inner faith:**

Trust, release, soften and strengthen that Sacred Personal Space, the Altar for your intent.

5. **Compassion:**

Practice without judgement, force or self-criticism. Place your 'Self' first and send out Love to your cells, nerves and out to the world around you.

Where there is hurt there is a chance to practice forgiveness.

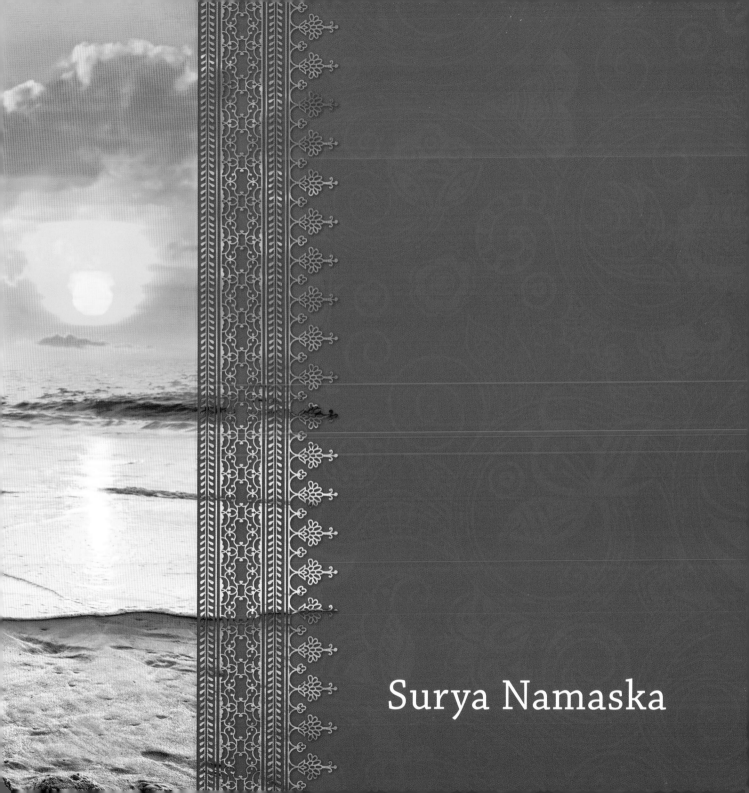

Surya Namaska

Surya Namaska – Classical

Your Body is the first place to begin your Prayer

The Sun Salutation (*Surya Namaskar*) is an intelligent and inspiring series of body moves devised many hundreds of years ago and is as relevant today as it was then. Personally I think its more relevant now. Adopting this flowing series as a regular practice is easy to sustain on a daily basis. Six rounds of the Sun Salutes can take about ten minutes. For me the traditional right and left side as one series means that you are performing 12 sides. Too little or too many rounds can produce either no benefits or too much strain. As you become more accomplished you will find that this cardiovascular exercise stimulates the heart and warms up all the body's muscle groups. No need to be jumping up and down to get these positive affects!

Traditionally practiced with the rising and setting of the Sun, *Surya Namaskar* is a flowing series that is synchronised with the in and out breath. Each move follows another and at the end of each breath the pose is ready to move into the next with the breath as the motivator. When teaching this series it is so important to point out that the flow is motivated by the breath, is lead by the breath and to avoid the breath chasing the series and creating stress and confusion. Consider any part of the series that opens up and back as the in-flow of breath, and any folding forward or closing as the out-flow of breath.

Prana cannot be ignored here and should be focused on as the deeper aspect of energy created by the Sun Salutes. Conscious thought on *Prana* means the benefits are increased. *Prana* is the life of the subtle body, just as oxygen is for the physical body. The difference with *Prana* is, it is constant in its form, never changing, unlike oxygen that exchanges within the lungs into carbon dioxide.

When we say 'our batteries are flat', that feeling of utter exhaustion that we know is deep down, we are acknowledging an energy source that cannot be increased by sleep alone. We are reminded that the mind is part of the process of self-healing.

The body does what the mind believes is a constant truth! So it's by way of autosuggestion (asking the body to act by way of instruction from the mind) that we connect to *Prana*.

Imagine you are connected to the Divine, the energy centre that feeds and nourishes the subtle body, and consciously attach your mind to the process; suddenly you are working with all the senses. The mind and thought are the most powerful tools we have. All of creation comes from thought.

*Thoughts create our destiny;
we are what we think!*

AMN

What is the Sun Salutation about?

No matter when or where we were born, or in what century, the Sun will always be the symbol of life. Without it all things die. However, without the darkness we would have no benefits from the Sun, as its endless light and heat would also kill us.

Therefore, balance is the key to harmony. Saluting the Sun as Life-Giver makes sense, and using the body, not just the mind, to praise it makes even more sense to me, as a preparation for motion, action and work in our daily lives.

There is some discrepancy about when *Surya Namaskar* originated. Traditionalists argue that the Salutation is near on 2,500 years old, probably older. Its origins were expounded during *Vedic* times as a ritual bowing down to the dawn, or sunset, practiced with mantras, the gifts of flowers, food, and water.

'The ancient yogis taught that each of us replicates the world at large, embodying "rivers, seas, mountains, fields...stars and planets... the Sun and Moon" *Shiva Samhita*, II.1–3. The outer Sun, they asserted, is in reality a token of our own "inner sun", which corresponds to our subtle, or spiritual, heart. Here is the seat of consciousness and higher wisdom (*Jnana*)

and, in some traditions, the domicile of the embodied Self (*Jivatman*).

It might seem strange to us that the yogis place the seat of wisdom in the heart, which we typically associate with our emotions, and not the brain. But in Yoga, the brain is actually symbolised by the Moon, which reflects the Sun's light but generates none of its own. This kind of knowledge is worthwhile for dealing with mundane affairs, and is even necessary to a certain extent for the lower stages of spiritual practice. But in the end, the brain is inherently limited in what it can know and is prone to what Patanjali calls misconception (*Viparyaya*) or false knowledge of the "Self".'

Richard Rosen

I don't see that 'when' it originated is an issue; the human being has always been tuned into the Universe and the subtle energies around the body as well as its connection to heart and mind. If we connect to the magnetic field around us then we also tune into the past, which means that the ether is thick with memories, inspirations and knowledge. We pick up on it. The Body has its own dance, as do the animals, birds, trees and flora on our planet, after all, they start each day with a stretch!

On the following Sun Salutations, note that I have placed Chakra symbols next to each posture so that you are aware of which Charkas are resonating in each pose. You can therefore actively engage with the property of that Chakra throughout your practice.

 Breath

 Focus

 Internal dialogue

 Sincere practice

 Moving from the Self

 Creative movement

 Grounding

EXHALE
Prayer position
NAMASTE

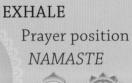

INHALE
Arch back extended
TADASANA

Prepare
INHALE
Mountain pose
TADASANA

EXHALE
Forward fold
UTTANASANA

EXHALE
8 point pose
ASTANGA NAMASKAR

6

RETAIN BREATH
Plank pose
KUMBAKHASANA

5

INHALE
Right leg back into lunge,
head back, chest lifted

4

Classical Surya Namaskar

INHALE
Cobra
BHUJANGHASANA

7

3 Rounds

EXHALE
Down Dog
ADHO MUKHA SVANASANA

8

INHALE
Right leg forward into lunge

9

EXHALE
Prayer position
NAMASTE

12

INHALE
Arch back extended
TADASANA

11

EXHALE
Forward fold
UTTANASANA

10

Right and left side is one round

Sun Power Series

A Journey from Earth to the Sun

I am often asked to explain why I used the term Sun Power Yoga. This is easy to answer, as it's exactly that, the use, the vision, the understanding of the Power of the Sun. Solar energy is a light rain that pours down on us all day and night. Just because we don't see it during the winter months or behind the clouds does not mean its power is not radiating across the Universe.

In each cell and nerve of the body we have a spark of sunshine, a light that generates healing, positive health and, ultimately, a relationship with the Universe. As we breathe in and out we encapsulate the source of solar energy, and if you add the mind, thought and action, the benefits and results can be truly profound.

The image of the Sun, the feeling of its warmth, the memories it conjures of good times and holidays, literally uplifts our spirits. We don't need to be there to feel those benefits. Our brain is the home of the chemicals that create our emotions, and the body reacts accordingly to those stimuli. Thinking of sunshine changes our cells from flattened ones, as in depression, to full round ones, each a tiny sun throwing out positive vibrations. Is this so simple that its hard to accept?

Simply thinking about the concept of cellular healing changes the brain and then the body. Think yourself well is not a game of 'perhaps', but a science of 'certainly'. There is nothing more powerful than thought.

We know from both Yoga theory and the science of the brain that thoughts create emotions, whether we realize it or not. The study of both Yoga and Science are expanded on in *The Tao of Physics: An Exploration of the Parallels Between Modern Physics and Eastern Mysticism*, a book by physicist Fritjof Capra, published in 1975 by Shambhala Publications of Berkeley, California.

This was the first book I read after joining the Sivananda Yoga Vedanta centre in Canada. It seemed to me to be the bridge between my Spiritual endeavours and my analytical mind. In fact, I think that no matter what we believe, the facts are clear that Yoga is a Science as much as it is a philosophy.

So how do we get in touch with the deeper roots of Yoga theory? Only through Yoga practice. We are carried through life in the vessel of the body, so it is logical that it is the right place to start that Journey into Inner Space, with the flesh and the bone.

Consider *Surya Namaskar*, the Sun Salutation, as the bridge connecting the Earth to the Universe. Personally, I see the Human purpose as that bridge and our need to travel from Earth back to Heaven, the Divine. We forgot where we came from and our Yoga reminds us that our journey will take us back to the source of life, death, renewal and the Divine Consciousness.

The author Iris Murdoch asked, "What if we had no words? How would we think?"

My daughter replied, "We would use our emotions!"

Here is the question then. What came first?

After thousands of years even Yoga develops! It cannot and should not be held in a timeless capsule, but be allowed to grow and adapt as all things do.

People tell me it took courage to create another type of Sun Salute – the Sun Power Series. Really? Surely I am doing what all humans and visionaries do, finding action, thought and revelation in each moment of the day.

This translates into In-Spir-ation; the spiral of life and its mortal coil, *Kundalini*. This is the upward movement of *Prana* and the opening of the Thousand Petalled Lotus, *Sahasrara*.

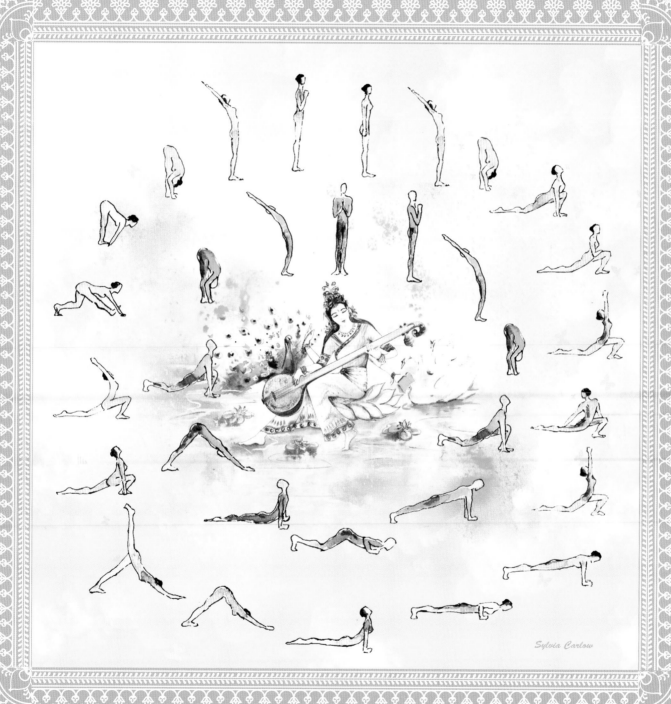

Sylvia Carlow

INHALE and EXHALE
Stand in *TADASANA*
hands down in *ISIS*

1

INHALE
Sweep hands over head, look at fingertips

2

EXHALE
forward fold
UTTANASANA

3

Photos courtesy of *Leicester Mercury*

INHALE
hands over head, look at fingertips

6

EXHALE
work into the hips
2 BREATHS

5

INHALE
Right leg back into lunge,
head back, chest lifted

4

EXHALE
Twist to the left

INHALE
Sweep hands over head, look at fingertips

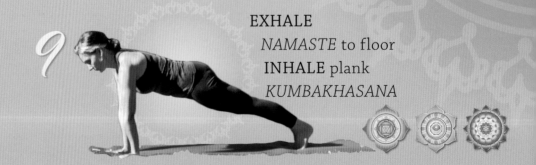

EXHALE
NAMASTE to floor
INHALE plank
KUMBAKHASANA

Photos courtesy of *Leicester Mercury*

EXHALE
Down dog
ADHO MUKHA SVANASANA

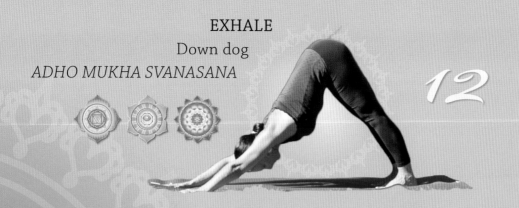

12

INHALE
Up facing dog
URDWHA MUKHA SVANASANA

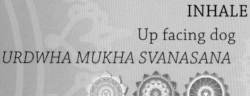

11

EXHALE
CHATURANGA or 8 point pose

10

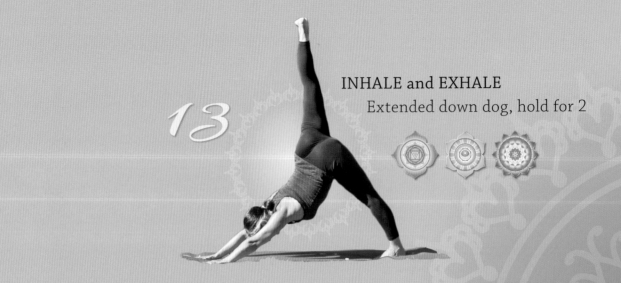

13

INHALE and EXHALE
Extended down dog, hold for 2

14

INHALE
Right leg forward into lunge
EXHALE
Work into hips

15

INHALE
Hands together into Crescent
Moon, then **EXHALE**

Photos courtesy of *Leicester Mercury*

EXHALE
Forward fold

18

and into Gazing pose

17

INHALE
Step forward

16

19

INHALE
Extended *TADASANA*

20

EXHALE
NAMASTE

Repeat on the other side, twisting to the right

Photos courtesy of *Leicester Mercury*

Yoga Asana

We are

the Bridge

connecting

the Earth

to

the Universe

AMN

A Daily Practice

A Daily Practice

How to fit some Yoga into your busy schedule

As a single Mother of four, and a very busy person, the idea of a Daily Practice was not only daunting but nigh on impossible! But was it?

I have always been a maverick, a person who is not afraid to walk my own path, alone if needs be. With this in mind I decided I would do what I had done since I was a young child learning the art of ballet, and that was to use any given time or place to try extending my legs or loosening my back! My younger brother often commented on the fact that my legs were always in the air!

I think that I have had a very privileged life and I am not thinking about material wealth, for I was born into abject poverty, but a richness of Love. How my Mother ever managed to get me to a ballet class still amazes me. She had four children too and as many jobs. Her hard work and vision for us culturally, politically and personally was that of opportunity and therefore a future. Her own dream was to be an actress, and back in the 50s ballet was not seen as a career, but a misspent youth! So when I showed a talent for the ballet she was going to help me and to give me the chance to become a dancer.

All around the house, in bed, the bath, cleaning the house or on the way to school I practiced my ballet. Pointing my toes on the bus, stretching my legs on the bed, reaching for the top shelf on my toes or arching backwards to pick a book off the floor. I walked with a book or two on my head to improve my posture and scrubbed the floor in deep lunges to open up my inner thigh muscles.

There was no end to my ingenious ways of practising ballet all day long.

Nothing has changed; I still do the same now. You are what you want to be but it takes some mental strength and good management skills!

Taking steps to get on your mat

I strongly believe that you can make time for anything you really want to do. There has to be a motivation behind our achievements. So if you want to include some 'me time' and some aspect of your day or week to self-practice then you have to allocate some time to do it. Easier said than done? Sure its tough but it's a case of looking at how you manage your day's timetable.

I always say to my clients that a little practice often, is worth more than allocating two hours a day to a gruelling regime. Those two hours are not sustainable, so you give up after a week proving to yourself that you really don't have the time!

Be realistic about your practice time or it's just another reason why not to get on with giving your self that much needed space in head and a release in body.

Aim:

Three things to consider when planning a Yoga practice and 'me time':

1. What time of the day, how long for and how often a week?
2. Is this do-able? Can I manage the commitment?
3. And is it sustainable? Can I keep it up?

Goal:

Planning a start and then progressing.

* I strongly suggest adding some meditation five times a week for at least five minutes. This is so profound in its benefits that it should not be ignored. Breathing rhythmically and deeply first to steady the mind and the nerves is the best start. Take a look at the section on Meditation (page 403) and choose one that resonates with you.

* Don't set goals that you cannot achieve. Better two minutes of mindful breathing than nothing; three rounds of the Sun Salute than nothing; and Yoga stretches are better than a marathon achieved once in a lifetime!

* Start by giving yourself a target of 15 minutes a day three times a week for your Yoga practice. Build this up to 20 minutes

* Increase to 15 minutes five days a week building up to 20 minutes. This is now the fitness level recommended for a daily regime to keep hearts healthy.

* Allow for recovery days. This means not exercising the same way as the rest of the week. So this could mean a brisk walk, a swim or a cycle ride with family or friends.

* Ensure you feel this is do-able; that you can maintain the regime and that you feel positive about it. If you feel under pressure, anxious or joyless at the prospect of your daily or weekly commitment, then take the pressure off and make it ten minutes a day!

* It's your life that you have to work with but if you feel that your heart isn't in it then look at the underlying reasons first and try not to procrastinate! What is stopping you doing something that will make you feel better?

* Once you start feeling the positive results of your simple, do-able, manageable practice you will wonder how you did without it!

* Everyone gains from your 'me time'. Your family, your work colleagues and your friends. Teach them how you took that very important step to self-preservation!

A Yoga Home Class Plan

Here is a home class-plan. It's a class that can last from 15 to 60 minutes.

* For a 30 to 60 minute session always relax to start with, to settle the rhythm of the breath and to focus the mind.
* For the very simplest session you need to include the basics.
* For your 15 minute session you can miss the relaxation but never miss out the sitting breathing, abdominal and alternate nostril breathing for 3 rounds.
* 3 rounds of Sun Salutations with a real focus on the breathing and enough to get your heart rate up!
* A triangle pose holding for 3 breaths on each side.
* A warrior pose II, hold for 3 breaths.
* A balance for 5 to 8 breaths.
* A twist for 5 to 8 breaths.
* A cobbler pose, hold for 3 breaths, pressing knees down with the buttocks active, lean forward for 2 breaths.
* Head to knee pose each side and hold for 3 breaths.
* Locust pose and or bow pose.
* An inversion of your choice.
* Relaxation pose for 5 minutes.

I have created a 60 minute session in pictures (starting page 328). Mix and match but remember the intelligent progression of poses. These warm up all muscle groups in preparation for deeper poses. Ensure you have a good slip free mat for your safety and comfort. If you are concerned about anything in your medical history, ask your GP/doctor.

Start with Sun Salute; never miss it out if you can do it! It's a cardiovascular exercise too.

Each muscle group is warmed up and stretched, released and strengthened. Blood is moved around the body and brain.

End with an inversion you are confident with or your legs up the wall with your bottom very close to the wall for support. This allows the blood to move from toes to heart and brain with ease and no strain on your back or neck. It's a perfect 'end of the day' pose!

Get out into the fresh air!
Open a window, get on a balcony,
practice in a park, or on a beach!
Be in touch with nature and the Natural You!

AMN

About 60 minutes

* Dynamic diaphragmatic breathing
* *Anuloma Viloma* – Alternate Nostril Breathing
* Sit and stretch
* *Surya Namaskar* – Sun Salute classical, 3 rounds (right & left is 1 round)
* Sun Power Series I – 2 rounds (right 1 round, left 1 round)
* *Virabhadrasana* I & II – Warrior I & II
* *Trikonasana* – Triangle pose
* *Vrksasana* – Tree pose
* *Natarajasana* – Dancer pose
* *Ardha Matsyendrasana* – Twist
* *Badha Konasana* – Cobbler pose
* *Janu Sirsasana* – Head to knee pose
* *Pachimottanasana* – The West pose
* *Salabasana* – Locust pose
* *Dharunasana* – Bow pose
* *Balasana* – Child's pose
* into inversion of your choice
* *Sarvangasana* – Shoulder stand
* *Matsyasana* – Fish pose
* Final relaxation, *Savasana* – Corpse pose

About 50 minutes

* *Savasana* – Corpse pose
* *Anuloma Viloma* – Alternate Nostril Breathing
* *Surya Namaska* – Sun Salute classical, 3 rounds
* Sun Power Series I – 2 rounds
* *Virabhadrasana* II – Warrior II
* *Trikonasana* – Triangle pose
* *Vrksasana* – Tree pose
* *Virabhadrasana* III – Warrior III balance
* *Ardha Matsyendrasana* – Twist
* *Badha Konasana* – Cobbler pose
* *Janu Sirsasana* – Head to knee pose
* Inversion/half headstand or
* *Viparita Karani* – Legs up the wall pose
* *Sarvangasana* – Shoulder stand
* *Matsyasana* – Fish pose
* Final relaxation, *Savasana* – Corpse pose

About 30 minutes

* *Savasana* – Corpse pose
* Breathing of your choice
* *Surya Namaska* – Sun Salute classical, 3 rounds
* A balance
* A twist
* A forward and back bend
* a simple inversion without stress
* Final relaxation, *Savasana* – Corpse pose

Establishing the Breath

Savasana – Corpse pose. Lie down, feet apart, arms resting away from the body, palms facing upwards, fingers naturally curled in.

Abdominal breathing. Close the eyes, place the hands on your lower abdomen. Ensure elbows are away from the body and placed on the floor. Breathe in slowly through the nose, visualising the breath coming in, past the chest and inflating the belly, then exhale slowly, allowing the tummy to deflate as the breath travels out through the nose. **INHALE** for 3 counts, hold for 1, and **EXHALE** for 4. Try this a few times until your mind calms down. Try *Ujjayi* breathing here, closing the valve at the back of the throat as you breathe out, making a soft sighing sound.

Once you feel the heart, breath and mind slow down, notice how you feel, then bring the awareness back to the body by moving fingers and toes and rolling head from side to side. Roll over before sitting.

Kapalabhati – Dynamic breathing. Placing your hand, palm facing your nose and mouth, blow out through your nose forcefully into your palm, feeling your diaphragm, the muscle under your ribs, contract. Then release the tummy to breathe in normally and repeat the forceful exhalation through the nose. Repeat this in and out pumping action at least 10 times before placing the hand down and repeating for another 10 to 20 pumps. This stimulates a good oxygenated blood flow to the brain as well as cleansing and strengthening your respiratory system. (see page 231)

Anuloma Viloma – Alternate nostril breathing. To calm and soothe the left and right sides of the brain. Block off the right nostril with the right thumb, **EXHALE** left, **INHALE** left for 4 counts, retain the breath for 16 counts, pinching the nostrils, **EXHALE** right for 8 counts, **INHALE** right for 4, retain the breath for 16, **EXHALE** left for 8. Repeat 3 rounds, beginning and ending on the left. (see page 236)

After *Anuloma Viloma*, inhale and extend the arms over the head, looking at fingertips. Lengthen the inner body as you lean forward onto the mat, keeping belly drawn towards the spine to protect it and breathe in and out for 2 breaths.

Come up onto hands and knees, making sure shoulders are directly over wrists and middle finger pointing straight ahead. Spread the fingertips. INHALE, tailbone up and raise the chin.

EXHALE; Tuck the tailbone under, pulling chin to chest, push hands into the floor to unlock the spine. Repeat – INHALE, raise the tailbone, chin up, EXHALE, tuck the tailbone under, pull chin to chest and release spine into neutral position.

Step forward to the front of the mat, either leg, and come to stand, avoiding any forward bends at this time, in case lower back is compromised.

Once standing, bring feet together, arms resting at the side and energise the thighs. INHALE, sweep arms forward and up, spreading the fingertips, palms forward, squeeze the buttocks, pushing them forward, gently arch back and EXHALE, hands in prayer. You are now ready to begin your Classical *Surya Namaskar*, followed by **Sun Power Series I**. (see page 310 for more detailed instructions)

Classical Surya Namaskar

Sun Power Series I

Stand 5 of your feet apart, middle toes pointing straight ahead. Energise the thighs and lengthen the tailbone. Place hands in **Inverted Prayer** or hold elbows if this is not possible. INHALE deeply as you gently arch your back, nose to the sky ...

EXHALE, forward fold, keeping the weight of the body towards the front of the feet to lengthen the hamstrings. Remain here breathing deeply and reaching the crown of the head towards the floor. Stay here for a minimum of 5 breaths, yielding rather than forcing this extension. INHALE to come up, reaching chin and chest forward to extend the hamstrings again, as in Figure 1 above.

Extend arms out to shoulder height, turning the right foot out, ensuring middle two toes line up with the knee cap. Turn the toes of your back foot in to prepare for ...

Trikonasana – **Triangle pose**. Looking along the right arm, INHALE, lift the arm and extend the ribs, EXHALE, lower the hand to grip either foot ankle or shin. Keep thighs pulled up, raise the arm above the shoulder, fingertips spread and turn the face to look towards the thumb and beyond. Protect the back of the neck by keeping the chin drawn in. Hold for 5 breaths. Any neck issues, please look to the floor.

Turn the head down to the floor, INHALE, reach the arm up and come back to standing. EXHALE into *Virabhadrasana II* – **Warrior II**. Ensure knee over ankle and thigh parallel to the floor. Back outside leg pushed into mat. Hold for 3 breaths.

Repeat on other side

Balances feet and hands

Standing in **Mountain pose**, feet together, arms resting by the side, bend supporting legs, take hold of right ankle with right hand, INHALE, lift heel up into groin, bring hands into prayer, focus the eyes on a spot on the floor and breathe steadily. INHALE, reach arms forward, thumbs crossed over the hands and reach up towards the sky pressing the side of the arms against the head. Hold for a minimum of 3 breaths. Those finding it difficult to balance, place right foot by left ankle putting the toe down when needed to maintain the balance. *Repeat on left side.*

Variation – Place right foot on upper left thigh, engaging buttocks, lengthening tailbone and placing hands in prayer position. Those finding this challenging, place foot on calf, hands on shoulders or prayer position. Hold for A minimum of 3 breaths. *Repeat on left side.*

Preparing for *Natarajasana* – Dancer. Extend left arm, bend both knees, place right foot in right hand and stay here for 3 breaths. If you are challenged, hold the wall or a partner until confidence is attained. *Repeat on left side.*

Moving into full *Natarajasana*. INHALE, raise the left arm, take hold of right foot and lean forward, raising the leg behind you, focusing the eyes straight ahead, hold for 2 to 4 breaths. Those challenged, lift the back leg, do not lean forward. *Repeat on the left side.*

Kakasana – Crow pose. Standing with feet spread (Mary Poppins style) lower yourself to the heels, knees open to the side, reach arms forward shoulder height, fingers spread, middle finger pointing straight ahead. Lower hands to floor minimum 20cm (12inches) away from feet, push elbows out to the side, grip elbows with inside of knees. Raise the chin and the gaze to the horizon and rock gently onto hands, pushing strength into the floor. Once confident, take weight onto hands lifting the toes off. If challenged, keep toes on floor. Hold for 3 breaths.

Ardha Matsyendrasana – **Half Lord of the Fishes – Twist**. From sitting, place right leg over left, leaning onto the left heel. IINHALE, reach the arms up, lifting the chin and gaze …

EXHALE, bring the left arm around the right kneecap hugging the thigh into the belly. Leading with the right shoulder and then the chin, take arm around the back or place hand on the floor, wrist against the lower back, pressing into the floor to lift the spine. Advanced students can bring left shoulder in front of the right knee, placing the hand on right knee or left foot. Breathe abdominally and hold for A minimum oF 5 breaths.

Counter pose. INHALE, place right arm inside right knee, turn to the left pushing up onto the left hip releasing hips and ribs. Come back to centre and repeat other side bringing left leg over right knee.

From sitting, INHALE, reach arms up, lifting chin and gaze and EXHALE into **Prayer**.

Badha Konasana – **Tailor pose**. Bringing soles of the feet together, walk sit bones as close to heels as possible. Placing thumbs on inside of feet, open them like a book pulling soles of the feet to the navel to open up the chest cavity. Breathe INHALE, then EXHALE, squeezing the buttocks and pressing the knees towards the floor. Hold for a minimum of 3 breaths. INHALE, release the buttocks, EXHALE, lean forward into a deeper extension and work your chest towards the floor. INHALE, reach forward to come up …

Forward Bends

Coming out of **Tailor pose**, place hands gently under the knees and **EXHALE** to draw the knees together. Hold for 2 breaths. Lean back into the hands before extending the legs forward.

Janu Sirsasana – **Head to knee pose**. Ensuring sit bones are level, extend left leg forward, drawing the right heel into the groin, keeping the toes of the left leg pointing to the sky.

INHALE, lift the arms up, raising chin and gaze. **EXHALE**, forward fold, holding onto foot. Those challenged, place a strap around the foot, holding onto both ends of the strap, reach forward to extend the back of the leg. Hold for a minimum of 5 breaths with eyes closed.

INHALE, reach forward to come to sit. **EXHALE**, twist to the right, bringing left hand to right knee, right arm resting on the floor behind. **INHALE**, back to centre. **EXHALE, Prayer** and extend the right leg out. Repeat this sequence on the other side, right leg extended, left heel pulled into the groin.

Preparing for forward bend. **INHALE**, raise the arms up, lifting chin and gaze ...

EXHALE into *Pachimottanasana* – **The West pose.** Forward Bend, first two fingers holding around the big toe. **INHALE**, extend the inner body. **EXHALE**, belly to thigh, chest to kneed, head to shin. Rock from side to side to loosen off the buttocks and ease deeper into the pose. Those challenged, please use the strap around the feet as before. Hold for a minimum of 8 breaths with eyes closed.

Counter pose. Lean gently into hands, fingers pointing back, pointing the toes ...

Ensure wrists are approximately 8–15cm away from buttocks, fingertips spread ...

INHALE, raise hips, let the head drop back fully, mouth closed, squeeze the buttocks, continue to raise the hips. Hold for 2 full breaths before gently lowering to the floor. Those challenged should keep knees bent, feet wide into table pose. Lower blood pressure? Keep your chin tucked into your chest.

After lowering the hips, come back to sitting pose, hands in **Prayer** and just breathe in and out, ending this series.

Back Bends

Bhujanghasana – **Cobra** – **back bend**. Lying on your tummy, draw the fingertips back towards the shoulders, raising the elbows to the sky. Forehead resting on the floor, heels apart to avoid irritating the Sacroiliac joints that can cause sciatica.

INHALE, stroking the nose and chin on the floor as you come up, pull the shoulders back, elbows in. Engage the abdominal cavity and attempt to bring hands off the floor to work the fine muscles of the spine. **EXHALE**, lower the forehead to the floor.

INHALE, stroke the nose and the chin along the floor, coming up as high as possible, pulling hands towards the hips. Keep the knees on the floor, though the hips will raise. Ensure heels are separated, buttocks active, chest lifted as you take 2 full in and out breaths. Lower gently to the floor, turning the head to one side or the other, whichever is most comfortable, resting the arms down by the side, resting for 2 or 3 breaths.

Push back into **Child's pose** (knees separated, toes touching, ease bottom into heels with forehead remaining on the floor for 15 seconds). Roll up to sit then lying down onto your back, feet and knees apart.

INHALE, push hips up to the sky into *Setu Bandhasana* – **Bridge pose**. Clasping hands together underneath the back roll from side to side pulling shoulders under, extending the arms. Press fist into the floor, chin into chest. Press lower leg into the mat, energising the thighs and buttocks, keeping knees over ankles to protect the knees. Hold for 3 to 5 breaths before lowering to the floor. Once lowered to the floor, release the hands, roll over onto your side …

Coming to a kneeling position concentrate on visualising a strong and confident pose and regulating the breath to help concentrate the mind.

Reach the arms out from the shoulders, fingertips spread, middle fingers pointing straight ahead. Lower the hands to the floor ...

Place the crown of the head in front of the hands, creating a tripod (three points on the floor). Pull the elbows in, pull shoulders away from ears, engage the abdomen, tuck toes under ...

INHALE, raise the buttocks to the sky, open the feet wide, keeping toes on the floor ...

Place one knee on the end of the elbow or arm, then the other until in a confident head and hand balance. Hold for 3 to 5 breaths before lowering the legs to the floor and remaining in **Child's pose** for a minimum of 15 seconds.

Shoulder stands

Lying on your back, knees up, feet apart, roll back and forth or simply lift the hips off the floor to come into ...

Ardha Sarvangasana – **Half shoulder stand**. Pull elbows as close together as you can, working your hands down towards the shoulder blades. Relax the face, jaw and belly, breathing abdominally before ...

Pushing up into full *Sarvangasana* – Shoulder stand. Remain here with eyes closed and concentrating on abdominal breathing for approximately 2 minutes to get a full blood flow from feet to head and back.

INHALE, and EXHALE, lowering the legs behind the head towards the floor into *Halasana* – Plough pose. Do not force the feet to the floor, but take them to where they are comfortable. If your feet are on the floor, keep legs straight, clasp hands together and extend the arms to the floor. Hold for 5 breaths, breathing into the belly and now into the back.

Those more advanced can come into a deeper pose drawing their knees towards their ears holding for 5 breaths, breathing into the back.

Lowering to the floor, vertebrae by vertebrae, use your arms as a brake so as not to hit the lower back onto the floor. Knees bent, feet apart ...

INHALE, lift into *Ardha Chakrasana* – **Half wheel pose**, hips high, holding onto ankles or heels if possible. If not, place a strap around the ankles, holding onto each end, before pressing the hips high to the sky, opening up the thoracic spine, gently pulling chin into chest. Hold for 3 breaths, squeezing the buttocks and energising lower legs and thighs. Ensure knees remain over ankles no matter what! Lock thumbs together, rolling from side to side to get shoulders underneath and arms extended along the mat ...

Lower the body onto the arms, release the thumb, spread the fingers. Walk the feet away extending the legs, feet together, toes to the sky. INHALE, lift and allow the head to drop down behind, elbows pressing into the mat, rest the top of the head gently onto the mat into *Matsyasana* – **Fish pose**. Make sure upper back is off the floor and buttocks remain on the arms. Hold for a minimum of 5 really deep breaths, as you can take in a third more oxygen than normal in this posture.

Slide the head and neck back to the mat, release the hands, clasp the back of the head, pulling the elbows in. Lift to look at the toes coming into a counter pose and ...

Slowly EXHALE to the floor, separating the feet, arms away from the body into *Savasana* – Corpse pose. Rest here for a minimum of 5 minutes watching the breath come in to the belly and watching the breath go out. Push all other thoughts from the mind by gently asking them to leave your space.

Bound lunge

Wide leg forward fold

Bound twist

Pigeon variation

Wide leg down dog

Variations

Tree variation

Crane variation

Warrior III

Inversion variation 1

Inversion variation 2

Inversion variation 3

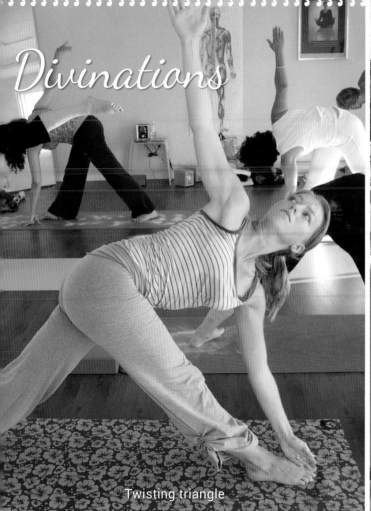

Divinations

Twisting triangle

Three legged dog

Extended triangle

Modified fish pose

Standing twisting prayer

Leg extended balance

Locust variation

Inspirations

Deep seated chair pose

Full bridge variation

Motivations

Locust variation

Sphynx pose

Full wheel variation

Bow pose

Camel variation

Yoga for Hard Times

Life on the Edge

Do you know you live life
in the finite expanse of the Universe?
Do you feel as though life is
a stream of random events?

Life is on the edge,
the edge of time and consciousness.
A moment of confusion, an error in judgment,
an opportunity missed, are all about life.

We sit still and wonder
at the world spread out in front of us.
The Silent presence behind us
a reminder that life has its own time and plan.

Without that Stone-Still Rock we are nothing.
We cannot know Peace without it.

The Rock is a reminder that we are alive.

The breath can change into wind
and howl and scream.
And yet it is always the breath.

Place your toe on the Edge of Life and Live.

You could fall.

But most likely you will fly.

AMN

Original photo by Lala Meredith-Vula

Yoga for Hard Times

Life, it can be both glorious and messy so here are some practical tips on how to deal with both. Just when you thought you were doing well, coping and moving forward, the carpet gets pulled from under your feet.
I call these testing moments 'God's Jokes'!

As part of this section, as well as using an affirmation and an action, please include the Daily Practice sessions we suggest (starting on page 327). Yoga poses activate almost every system in the human body. They mean that you are using your body to stimulate an oxygenated blood flow to your heart, muscles and organs and generally allowing yourself to actively participate in your own well being. Yoga stimulates the respiratory, digestive, skeletal, muscular, lymphatic, and endocrine system.

I think it is interesting to know that all Yoga poses target almost all systems of the body and especially the endocrine system. The human endocrine system is a group of important glands that excrete and secrete hormones that keep the body and brain balanced and working harmoniously. These glands are the pituitary, pineal, thyroid, thymus, pancreas, adrenals and gonads.

Hormones act on nearby tissues or are carried in the bloodstream to act on specific target organs and distant tissues. Diseases of the endocrine system can result from the over-secretion or under-secretion of hormones, or from the inability of target organs or tissues to respond to hormones effectively. Common diseases are overactive or underactive thyroid, diabetes from not enough insulin produced by the pancreas and adrenal fatigue where adrenaline is over excreted into the body due to high stress levels. It is for this reason that stimulating these glands means you are helping to keep yourself healthy in both mind and body. It's a 'win win' situation!

For further reading on anatomy and physiology, try to get a copy of the *World's Best Anatomical Charts*. Medical students use this comprehensive resource, as do my students!

The Fallen Angel

Yoga is a 'Sandstorm
of Inspiration,
an Oasis of Peace
and a Gentle Palm Tree
in Times of Trouble'

AMN

Your body is your calling card, it says who you are

Standing up for your-self, those shoulders tell a story!

If you walk into a room, a job or a relationship with your head buried in your shoulders then you are speaking very loudly!

What you are saying is, "I am a tortoise", "I am not worth looking at or noticing".

Changing how the outside world views you.

If you are who you say you are then no amount of words is going to change how people perceive you if in fact you don't believe it yourself.

You must try to emanate how you describe your personality, your skills and your view on life.

Gaining confidence from standing up straight.

Acting out words can have a physical response, such as 'chin up!' or 'pull yourself together', as opposed to 'falling apart.' Stand in front of the mirror and try to smile. It can just be a tiny smile and, just like the Sun coming over the horizon, it glows bright and is full of hope!

How this affects you and those who perceive you.

My Grandmother, like other people of her age and time, used euphemisms to help deal with life. They were often quite harsh, such as, 'Smile and the world smiles with you, cry and you cry alone'. I heard this when I was young and maybe it affected me but I do smile a lot even when I don't feel like it. Often I don't get a smile back, so that is tough, but eventually I believe in my smile and it becomes part of me.

My point is that we need to try and communicate and standing up straight is a simpler way than smiling. It confirms you are aware of your surroundings, the people you live with and the job you have. Your gentle but steadfast confidence will spread throughout your life. It's really for you that this is so important, not for others. Learned responses can be positive rather than negative so start to stand up for yourself!

A Daily Thought and Action

❋ Stand in front of a mirror with shoulders back and down, chin parallel with the floor, arms resting by your side, feet slightly apart.

❋ Breathe slowly and gaze steadily. Be tall and strong and still, like the mountain. You are not only the foot of the mountain but also the peak. Speak mentally or in a quiet voice:

I walk tall, upright and true.
I have courage and I embrace my confident Self.

Yoga for when you've overdone it!

Abusing our body when we drink too much, smoke or take drugs, expresses underlying issues we are trying to deal with. We are self-medicating. They are destructive habits; do you really have to give those up?

Yes you do! It's pointless believing that you are in control of your addictions. The truth is they are in control of you. The other interesting point is that *your* mind is the one controlling *you*. It is a known fact that we only need painkillers, cigarettes, drink, or whatever the substance you abuse yourself with, every four hours. So of you chain smoke you are choosing to do so as your body doesn't *need* it.

Addiction can be a genetic pre-disposition but even so you can give up, but you have to want to, *really* want to. Consider observing your mind, feelings and physical responses when you reach for the 5pm drink or that extra painkiller or cigarette.

Be in the moment. It can help you do these actions with mindfulness rather than mindlessness, that way you begin to take control of your life.

Eating and how to change our mood through our food

We know only too well that when we are exhausted and our adrenals are depleted we grab carbohydrates to boost us and give us a quick fix. We also know even better that this action has a dramatic and fast reaction. We go up and we drop down, hard! What our mind craves and what our body needs are two distinctly different things.

The best foods to grab are nuts, seeds, and red fruits, as these have lower sugar, and drink lots of water. Sound boring? Well it is if your mind wants you to believe otherwise. Have small tubs of mixed foods I call 'Tiramisu foods', a little comfort food. Take a look at our chapter Food and Mood (page 139), it may surprise you.

Simple things you can do to boost your Immune System

A large glass of spring water first thing in the morning and carry on drinking throughout the day, as each part of the body needs a certain amount of water to function.

The lungs alone need two full glasses to work efficiently, never mind the rest of the body!

Winter is often a time when people really get in trouble for not drinking enough water. Water infections are common for instance. Don't wait to get thirsty, you are already dehydrated!

I always light a candle at the table at breakfast and all other meals, it reminds us that our life can be still and the flame can represent all those we love and have, or those we have lost. I tell my children that they are the flame and that their light can fill a heart as well as a room! All these heating and warming thoughts as visualisations help keep us feeling tingling and alive.

Two minutes of silent thought on the breath allows us some inner peace; time to recharge and to spend time contemplating nothing but just being in the moment. Precious me time!

Rituals are important too. They can be as simple as a break in the morning for a walk around the block or afternoon with a book and a cup of tea.

A walk in the garden to relax the eyes and enjoy some fresh air, a park if you do not have a garden, or open your windows wide and breathe in the *Prana*.

Have a gossip with a friend! Gossiping and laughing releases endorphins – the 'feel good' hormones! Really! We all love it and that is why! Men could be encouraged to gossip more!

Spend a little longer in the toilet if you are mother of many or have a demanding job. Fill the smallest room with good, thought provoking books or magazines! Relax and enjoy the peace – hopefully no one will want to disturb you there!

Working so hard we don't know how to relax and so losing our identity because of it

I am the biggest culprit of this dilemma. I really did think that unless I was working so hard I collapsed each day or my body hurt all over that I wasn't working hard enough. As a ballet dancer, choreographer, drummer and fashion designer, all at the same time, I knew how to work myself to death and how!

It has taken me years of practising how to slow down my breath and so too my mind. By doing this I was able to 'make time' rather than 'spend time'.

As a career woman before having my four children and embracing the Natural mothering instinct in me, I honestly believed, 'I work therefore I am.' I was a person to really have fun, take chances and opportunities, but the lifestyle I was leading included too many negatives for my health. I had lost my joy of living a simple life

I gave life a chance and saved myself by finding my own path. I still work a lot, I am a very creative and driven person, but I take a coffee break out of the office, meet a friend at least three times a week and make time for talking to my children and spending time at home just pottering about. I switch off the phone, the computer is off all weekend now and I try to go for a solitary walk. I have plenty of time now I have slowed down. 'I am therefore I don't.'

Finding moderation in all things and learning to care about Ourselves

Moderation in all things is a great way to measure your life.

We do not need extremists in our world, religious, political or domestic. I have been a pretty extreme workaholic, and even Yogi, neither of these made me happy or others around me.

However it seems we need to learn the hard way. If you are excluding people from your life because they don't feel they can cope with your beliefs, then it does not mean you must drop your beliefs or your friends or family. I think we can meet people half way and practice *Ahimsa*, non-violence in word thought or deed. If we have to force our will on others to help us justify our chosen beliefs then it could be time to withdraw and consider how to be part of the world, but not to give up what we have worked hard to discover made our life more meaningful.

I can't give you any answers, only some personal experiences. I raised my children to be vegetarian and explained why as they grew up. But if they wanted to eat meat at friends' houses then that was their free choice. Interestingly they ended up with friends who liked the food they ate at our house and asked their mothers to add it to their menus. Choice is the most important part of freedom. Allow others to see your world by example not by force or judgement. Just an idea!

A Daily Thought and Action

❋ Open the window wide or a door to a garden, or outside world. You may wish to stand in a room that helps you be at peace.

❋ Open your arms wide and lift them up to the sky and say in your mind or with your voice:

I open up my life to others,
with joy and freedom as well as in Peace.

Yoga for stressful real – life drama

The Wedding, the preparation and the aftermath

Marriage is one of the biggest events in some people's lives and for that reason it is seen as one of the biggest stresses. It can take years to plan, organise and execute. It involves emotions and relationships, not only with a partner but also family and friends, and is therefore highly emotive!

After talking to people, it seems each couple has different priorities but similar stories about compromise. The choice of venue, who they invite and why is something the partners discuss a lot and even argue about. It seems to be a lot about 'doing the right thing' or about seeming to do so.

It is interesting that this incredibly important day is often built on tradition to the point of exhaustion and duty. Like all major events in one's life, they need time to be considered, and one aspect that is often overlooked is the purpose of these events. Marriage is still a life-long commitment when you decide to live with a chosen person, and back in my day the family, vicar and priest were all very much involved with the process. You were made to understand the enormity of the step and of its practical and spiritual purpose. If that didn't put you off then you were supported all the way to the altar!

The point is that like so many areas of our lives these days the day has become the focus, the dress, the venue, the flowers and food, and therefore the moral values are sometimes overlooked.

I have my own ideas of marriage as an institution but they are my own and will remain so, but I would like to think I could guide my children. A spiritual guide in our life at this time would be so useful, as long as it did not mean submitting to dogma of course.

Advice? Talk to your friends, close members of your family if you can. Ask a third party for help if you are experiencing doubts, as I do believe this is a normal part of the commitment itself.

I know many people who have a wonderful marriage based on respect, friendship and mutual support and it is a foundation they discussed during the relationship. I know that love is often talked of as the most important part but love is all of the above surely?

The aftermath is often the hardest time for both people. It's called the 'after wedding blues', I'm told. I certainly had them and wished now that it had a label because I may have been able to tell someone how I felt. There were feelings of nothing to plan, to focus on and to actively 'do'. Sad really but it happens. A dear young friend told me that she and her husband planned a three month honeymoon two months after the wedding so they were able to get back to a normal life but still have a wonderful adventure to look forward to. Great idea!

Moving homes through choice or circumstance

As well as the wedding, moving home is one of the other seriously stressful events in a lifetime. Moving seems to be a big preoccupation these days, unlike the past when people often lived in the same home their entire lives, with the property being handed down to one or more child. The expression, 'Home is where the heart is', is still one of the terms we use when choosing to move or being moved on. It helps us deal with the possible trauma it is going to entail. This expression was actually talking about the 'hearth', the fireplace, as that is where families sat to keep warm and to gain some light when candles were expensive and the only source if light.

If you have been through some particularly painful experiences in your life then one of them may have been homelessness. I squatted for some years in my youth because I had no job and no address meant I could not find a job and therefore could not afford a roof. A vicious circle indeed.

There is little comfort out there for the homeless. It is a degrading, frightening, and desperate situation and often one is left very vulnerable to predators.

I am hoping that as you read this it helps to put your own situation into some perspective and to consider if there is anyway you can help others. The Centre Point Project that was originally patronised by Princess Diana is for homeless young people. This amazing place has given hope and a lifeline to many youngsters, helping them to cope with life and to help them move forward.

Work on the belief that all will be well in the end as it is imperative you do not lose hope for long – so hard but so important.

On another note, moving may be just that, a move in the right direction!

Pregnant – happy or not

It can be one of the most wonderful pieces of news to discover you are pregnant, but it may also be somewhat of a shock or surprise. Whatever your feelings are, don't be scared of them. Let someone know how you feel, talk it out and certainly don't be self-critical. Be kind and accept that what you thought you would feel in reality has not transpired. Sometimes this is the biggest shock. We never know how we feel about anything until it happens.

Consider that the child will be with you in your travels over the next nine months. But if you decide that a child at this time is neither an option nor a practical reality then talk to professionals who can counsel you and help you make the right decision for you. They cannot tell you what to do but they will listen to you and with support they will be with you in whatever you decide to do for your life and its future. Timing is crucial here. Act sooner rather than later.

Bereavement from loss of any kind.

I intend to keep this very simple. There are three stages to bereavement, which is a part of ageing, terminal illness, death, divorce, redundancy and childlessness for instance. Those three intrinsic stages are: Denial, Anger and finally, Acceptance. Acceptance being the most painful stage I feel, as it too is an end in itself.

Learning to deal with ups and downs with equanimity

Talking with quiet confidence will always beat screaming with obvious insecurity. So what would be great is to be able to take everything thrown at us with the same balance of emotions. The best we can do is to do our best. Stop, be still, take it all in, then make a rational choice that suits all concerned. Sounds good but we all know that is not always how we feel; it's more about how we would like to deal with things. The Buddha did say that we have a split second where we can choose how we deal with a situation. I suggest you believe that to be true and give yourself a shaft of clarity, a dividing of the waves and then take the right action. Just a thought is enough to get this clarity.

A Daily Thought and Action

❊ Find a place where you feel safe and comfort-able. See this word? 'Able' to be comforted.

❊ Place yours arms around you and love who you are and embrace what you are dealing with, because it won't just go away without your help. Think or speak out the Serenity Prayer:

Divine Mother, grant me the Serenity to accept the things I cannot change, Courage to change the things I can, and the Wisdom to know the difference.

Yoga in the Work place – Home or away

Getting that new job and the fears of your first day

Getting a new job is a big deal these days and should in itself be celebrated. As someone who has always created her own jobs, I can only imagine what it must be like to start with a new set of people, rules, ways of doing things and its application. My best advice is to recall your interview and the fact that you got the job. Reinforce the confidence others had in you and progress from there. Introducing yourself to your new colleagues also needs some thought. Be confident in your posture, and smile when you introduce yourself. Practice this in the mirror or with trusted friends and family. After all, life is a stage and you are one of the characters, so introduce that character as one you think you can move forward with.

How to organise your time and your desk efficiently

Having a desk is like cooking. Clear up as you go along. Some of us are filers and others pilers, whichever one you are keep a logical system for how you keep on top of your papers. This could be that something akin to your desktop on your laptop.

Anything you are working on needs to be easily accessible so keep it visible. Prioritise your work, place it on the floor near your desk if you have to, that way you will need to step over it, so get it done!

Few of us have the luxury of a Personal Assistant, so create a simple system to help deal with paperwork or files on your laptop. "Never leave till tomorrow what you can do today", is what my Mother taught me. It works!

How to take time out without the boss knowing. Here are some simple Yoga basics you can do from your desk

Remember to breathe! Sounds obvious but as we get more pushed to deal with piling up 'to dos' we also pile on the stress. We stop breathing deeply and in so doing don't work as efficiently. Put a little alarm on the laptop or phone every 20 minutes. When it goes off, breath slowly and deeply, scan your body for any stress areas, such as shoulders, neck and hips. Get up and walk around, make an excuse to get a tea (herb is better), or extra toilet visits. This applies at home as much as at work.

Try the series of seated Yoga poses at the end of this chapter. These can be used on an aeroplane too.

Dealing with the people you work with to get productive results

Three practical rules here:

1. Listen to people's ideas;
2. Be listened to in the same way, with respect; and
3. Learn to cooperate by trying out an idea first. You may learn something.

A Daily Thought and Action

❖ Clear your mind of clutter. Do this by opening a mind door and asking anything you don't want in that space to leave. This may include, work, colleagues, the boss, your role as a boss, family and friends. Don't worry, you can always ask them back later! If you feel uncomfortable at your office work desk, go somewhere else, but try it.

❖ Now your mind is a minimal space, allowing you to breathe with conscious application, and to move your body in a simple yet beneficial way. Sit still, focus on one spot or close your eyes. Open your body up to stretching with your poses and choose at least six each time you take a break. Do these twice a day, minimum. On a daily basis try this affirmation with slow rhythmic breathing:

I am an open door, I allow things to come and go.
I am both clear headed and clear minded.
I have plenty of time to achieve my daily goals.

Yoga for a near-functional family Life

The new baby, dealing with tiredness, feeling low and those Great Expectations.

No matter how long you have wanted a child, had to fight to have one or had one unexpectedly, you will never ever be prepared for the reality. The reality is it's the hardest work you will do and not get paid for!

I had my four children at home and I think I was privileged to do so. The stress levels were lower than most births because I was at home and I was able to drop back into a routine smoothly and baby joined in. But wherever you have your baby it is still a huge re-adjustment.

The Mother of all mothers. How to do everything and still get your hair done!

My children fed from me every 20 minutes! I threw the clock away and decided that I would expect nothing, no 'me-time' ever and so if I got five minutes I was very grateful. When my first child was ten weeks old I ventured alone to the hairdressers. What a treat. Baby was left with Daddy. When I returned two hours later, they were both crying! So again, do your best but do give yourself the chance to do something for you. Learn to hand over even if it's challenging. The biggest mistake I made was to think I was the only one to be there for my first baby.

The Father, dealing with the feelings of being demoted and still trying to be superman

I have been married twice, three children with the first marriage; one with the next. Why oh why didn't I realize that the relationship needed more attention. I am not blaming myself solely, as it does take two, but I see where we both went wrong. If you have a child, it needs all of you, and it is easy to forget that your relationship needs attention too.

Dads are trying so very hard to live up to their new role and it's not the same as Mothers. We have nine months to prepare, and our body changes. It's visible to all. What has Dad got? Nothing physical – it's all mental. Fear, trepidation, and excitement.

All these feelings are very real indeed, but often forgotten for the new Father. This tiny bundle came into his life and turned it upside down. The feelings of helplessness and being put second can be very real for the new Father. They want to be everything – the protector, the provider and the Super-Dad!

A man needs to be needed for them to be at their best, so let them in. Say hello to them first in the morning, in the evening and at bedtime. Share the feelings of parenthood, not just the feeds and the nappies!

The single parent crisis: was it thrown upon you or was it a choice?

As a single parent I have had to do some real soul searching. Can we seriously choose to be a single parent or is it the circumstances we find ourselves in at that time in our lives that forces a solution? I know there are men and women who choose to go it alone but is it about choice or about what life seems to be offering us? When I look back at both my marriages I see them as successful but not fulfilling, but this did not include the children in my case. My relationship with them was and is wonderful, and part of how I wanted them to grow up helped me make the decision to go it alone. I had a disciplinarian Father who was also brought up in a disciplined way. We are Arabs and Father ruled the home. My English Mother was like the good fairy, trying to make things softer after the event.

Their personal life was very tough and as Human Rights activists it was impossible to keep others out of their relationship of course. I often wished they would divorce and stop the fireworks, so much so that I left home at 13. However, they did stay together, and after we children left it got better for them, to some extent. My Mother said that marriage problems and arguments were mostly about children and money. I can say now, "So true".

No matter your personal circumstances or reasons, it wont be the easy option. There may be violence to deal with, with a man or woman, and the fallout for children will be devastating. It may be that you just never found a stable partner to have children with and made a huge leap into elective single parenting, having a child with a sperm donor such as a friend or from a sperm bank. Very brave you may say but it's brave to have children and even harder to consider raising them alone.

Even as a single parent, I feel that it is the most rewarding of life plans, if that is what you choose to do or find life has chosen for you.

We can't choose our family but we can choose to interact

I need to keep this simple. We can't choose our family, but we can choose to try to get on. I can hear some of you say, "No way, its impossible!" I can also hear a lot of hurt in that statement.

There are so many painful relationships in a family dynamic that it may be too hard to find a way to start healing the rifts. I can relate to this and I can also say that anything is possible if you are capable of love.

You also have to want to mend things.

✽ Some family members shout to get you to hear them. Try listening.

✽ Some members gang-up against you. Step back and observe why. What do they get from it and what do you lose?

✽ Your siblings may exclude you from family decisions. Try asking them why, without prejudice.

✽ Some areas of family politics need your complete attention. You must do the work but if you do and nothing changes then accept you can't do any more.

✽ This is so tough, but to save yourself you may have to consider stepping out.

✽ The death of a parent challenges the dynamics of a family; the death of a sibling is a traumatic shift within it. Awareness of these subtle but potentially damaging shifts will keep you be clear-headed and honest about what may lie ahead. I had no idea that even the closest family members may show unfamiliar behaviour in these very stressful times. Be vigilant!

✽ A family crisis highlights rifts, past hurts, even jealousy and hatred to a parent or sibling, and emotions create havoc.

✽ Out of chaos comes calm; that is the nature of the Universe. Time to accept that our paths may be diverting us to some other place.

*People come into our lives for a Reason,
a Season or a Lifetime.*

A Daily Thought and Action

* Sit quietly somewhere you won't be disturbed. Switch off your phone, close the door and light a single candle. This symbolises Hope in my world.
* Draw your spine upward, shoulders down and back, then open your heart-centre. From being 'down-hearted' endeavour to be 'up-lifted'. Keep trying!
* Visualise the person or people you are angry at, hurt by or who exclude you. This is very challenging. It took all my strength to do this with one family member. Closing your eyes, softly breathe in and out to calm your emotional body and mind. Take your time.
* Now see them with your minds eye. Hold their face in your heart centre. This can take a while, as you will feel yourself tighten and resist. After all, you would rather they disappear than hold them in your heart!
* Send love to them, keep the image as strong as you can and try very hard to remain with that flow of love reaching steadily towards them. I found this to be so difficult. I learned that I do hold on to 'stuff' and that was an interesting shock.
* What has changed is you, your feelings allowed you to practice what you knew all along, as this affirmation explains…

To err is Human, to forgive, Divine

Yoga in your home space

I hate ironing! How to organise simple jobs with mindfulness

I hate ironing too! I used to watch my Mother up late doing this awful chore and made a mental note never to do it! How can it be avoided? Fold your clothes really well and smooth wrinkles out after they come out of the washing machine. Hang them up with care, either on a hanger or dryer, avoiding folding if possible. Never leave clothes in the machine after they have been washed, as the creases won't come out easily when smoothing them. If you have to iron shirts teach your users how to iron them themselves!

PS if you love it, then how amazing are you?!

Enjoying time in the bathroom to escape the phone, laptop or family!

Make time for a bathing ritual, even if once a month. Enjoy candles, essential oils, music, and darkness, anything that helps you switch off and opt out of the world for a while. You will wonder how you managed without it.

Don't have a bath? Then shower for longer then usual. Then light scented candles in the room and indulge in oils for your body afterwards. Enjoy!

How to provide emotional and nutritional nourishment in the kitchen, and to try not to be resentful with the people you feed.

Providing simple and nutritional food for you and your family is easy and cheap. Shop at your local market or swap home-grown vegetables with a friend, you could do something for them in return. Keep anger and frustration out of the food preparation; like anything, energy is left in the air. Try to be calm when providing nourishment, it means you are still practising your Yoga and practising *Ahimsa*, non-violence, in word, thought or deed.

Clearing your space and your mind for two minutes a day

Take your attention out of your head and into your body. Be still for two minutes a day. Find a practical time in your home or work place to 'opt out' for those two minutes. Sit, lie or even stand, empty your mind of the jobs you are doing and watch your breathing. Slow the breath down and you will slow your thoughts down. It honestly takes seconds to focus your mind; it's all in the slow breath! Inhale slowly into the belly and breathe out even slower.

A Daily Thought and Action

❋ Stand still, with feet hip width apart. Draw the shoulders down and back and keep the chin level. Close the eyes and visualise a firm floor supporting you and a steady heart.

❋ Allow yourself to steady the mind by focusing on your breathing. Now steady your body by noticing your mind. Ask your work colleagues, family and friends to vacate your space for two minutes. Afterwards invite those you want back into that space. It may be interesting to see whom you don't invite back in!

*I do not resent what I do in either my home or work.
But I recognize those people or actions that do me no good
and I aspire to let them go.*

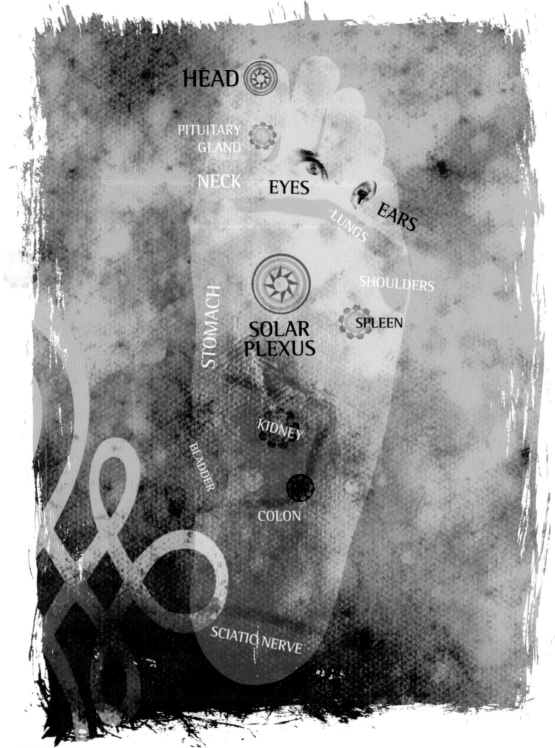

HEAD

PITUITARY GLAND

NECK — EYES

EARS

LUNGS

STOMACH

SHOULDERS

SOLAR PLEXUS

SPLEEN

KIDNEY

BLADDER

COLON

SCIATIC NERVE

Conclusion

❋ Establish three 'do-able and sustainable' things you can manage each day for your peace of mind and those around you!

❋ Look for signs of 'dis-ease' and therefore practice becoming 'at-ease'.

❋ Practice your Sun Salutations everyday and also try 'Seated Yoga' for home, work or travel, as well as for those less able, when you need to. But remember, simple actions like a walk in the fresh air is imperative.

❋ A gossip with girlfriends or a meeting with male friends to moan and groan all improve the release of those 'feel-good' endorphins!

Happy Feet. Keep them moving!

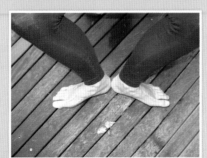

Seated Yoga

The Four Agreements

From the Toltec Tradition of ancient Mexico, this is an ancient recipe for a better life and a better you.

1. Be Impeccable with Your Words

Speak with integrity. Say only what you mean. Avoid using the word to speak against yourself or to gossip about others. Use the power of your word in the direction of truth and love.

Comment: Consider *Mauna* (non-speaking) when lost for words!

2. Never Take Anything Personally

Nothing others do is because of you. What others say and do is a projection of their own reality, their own dream. When you are immune to the opinions and actions of others, you won't be the victim of needless suffering.

Comment: Consider that suffering is optional.

3. Try not to Make Assumptions

Find the courage to ask questions and to express what you really want. Communicate with others as clearly as you can to avoid misunderstandings, sadness and drama. With just this one agreement, you can completely transform your life.

Comment: Transformation can happen in a moment.

4. Always do your best

Your best is going to change from moment to moment; it will be different when you are healthy as opposed to sick. Under any circumstance, simply do your best, and you will avoid self-judgment, self-abuse and regret.

Comment: Be uplifted rather downhearted in all you do or say; it will allow you to bring out your best.

Sleep is the ultimate reward of a busy and constructive day and ...

Peace of mind our hope

As in the words of St Augustine

'The Reward of Patience is Patience'

Never give up on yourself

Depression

Depression: The Human Kind

The Wikipedia dictionary definition of Depression is:
'Feelings of severe despondency and dejection when
self-doubt creeps in and that swiftly turns to depression.'

In Human terms it can be:

Melancholy, misery, sadness, unhappiness, sorrow, woe, gloominess, dejection, downheartedness, despondency, dispiritedness, low spirits, heavy-heartedness, moroseness, discouragement, despair, desolation, dolefulness, moodiness, pessimism, hopelessness, I've fallen into a depression, post-natal depression, etc. etc....

In Psychiatry:

It is a mental condition characterised by feelings of severe despondency and dejection, typically also with feelings of inadequacy and guilt, often accompanied by lack of energy and disturbance of appetite and sleep. Plural noun: depressions.

Clinical Depression:

This is caused by a chemical imbalance in the brain, and this is what most drug treatments are based on.

Original photo by Talitha Hepple-Newland

Depression is my dark place.

My depression is my old friend, always there.

I am alone and unable to remember who is in my life that cares.

I am invisible therefore worthless.

I hate myself.

I am unworthy of being loved.

I cannot love, as I have no real feelings.

I am so raw that I hurt all over.

I live in my head,

I am so angry and yet have no voice so I lock my feelings up inside,

AMN

In my own experience

There are so many variations for the explanation of depression that they blur into a 'depressive' mélange in my opinion. I also feel that these 'words' in no way reflect or truly illustrate the meaning or feeling of depression, as they are almost abstract in their reality.

In my experience, and I have plenty of it, I began to 'feel depressed' around the age of 14 and I saw it coming; it was a small black cloud I could see on the horizon, slowly but surely coming my way and it sat right over my head for some time to come. Even thinking about it now I fell heaviness in my heart. It is a black smooth stone, pulsing darkly, like my heartbeat but not flowing with blood, only fear.

These are a few of the very real feelings of those suffering from depression. I say suffering because that is what is happening. My depression began with a shock, a blow around the back of my head it seemed.

I had no foundations under my feet anymore and no walls to fall onto. The very things I thought were true had now been diminished to the realm of delusion.

I fell apart, I unravelled, and I dropped into a black hole without a bottom to it.

I was on a small black disc up in the blackness of the universe with no light, moon or stars. I had entered the Kingdom of Chaos.

I started having panic attacks soon after my 'unravelling' and these came in between my bouts of depression. In fact they were part of my depression but I did not realize this.

We all go through very bad times, either caused by events within our lives or outside. *But* we don't all get depressed.

Depression can land on you from a great height or sidle in beside you without you realising. It is insidious, terrifying, life changing and utterly soul destroying.

Many people with depression may also have some degree of anxiety too, which can include excessive worrying leading to the feeling of terror, heart palpitations, sweating, and stomach pains. When these complications happen, mental health symptoms can be more severe, and the road to recovery can be even rockier than when depression or anxiety occurs alone.

I know this to be true as
I was very confused for
some time, not sure why my
anxiety was not subsiding.
I realized my recent trauma,
divorce, had triggered panic
attacks beyond anything
I had experienced before.

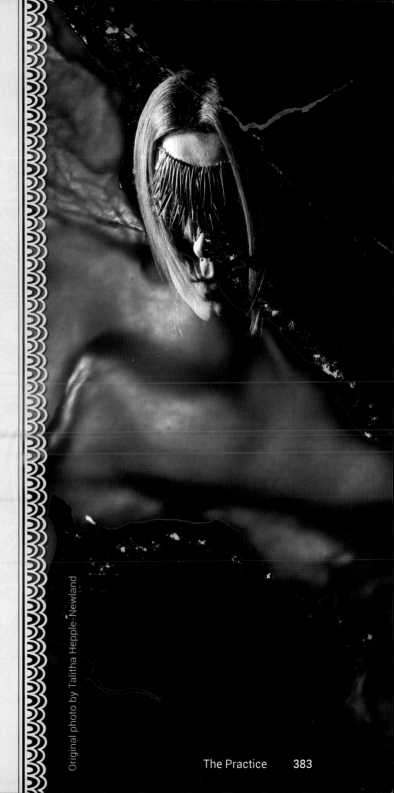

Original photo by Talitha Hepple-Newland

Help me understand what depression is

There are times when we all feel sad, hopeless or fed up; it's part of life. Depression is different. With depression these feelings don't just go away. They can last for months, even years, becoming so intense that carrying on with everyday life can become impossible.

Depression can be hard to spot. There are many different symptoms, some emotional and some physical. These are some of the most common, so if you've experienced four or more for most of the day, nearly every day for over two weeks, it might be time to talk to someone and visit your GP/doctor for help.

* Tiredness and loss of energy;
* Persistent sadness;
* Loss of confidence and self-esteem;
* Difficulty concentrating and making decisions;
* Avoiding others and becoming isolated and lonely;
* Not being able to enjoy things that are usually pleasurable or interesting;
* Undue feelings of guilt or worthlessness;
* Feelings of helplessness and hopelessness;
* Sleeping problems – difficulties in getting off to sleep or waking much earlier than usual;
* Finding it hard to function at work/college/school;
* Change in appetite;
* Loss of sex drive and/or sexual problems;
* Physical aches and pains;
* Self-harm;
* Thinking about suicide and death;
* Trying to commit suicide.

It's easy to blame ourselves but depression can affect anyone. You might feel guilty or frustrated that you can't find the motivation to keep up with things, and it can be especially hard to spot the symptoms if you've been feeling the same way for a long time. Many people find they also experience anxiety alongside their symptoms, so nausea, breathlessness and headaches are all signs that it might be time to get help.

Depression is common, and in its mildest form most people can lead a healthy and active life with the right treatment and support. On the more severe end, depression can be devastating and even life threatening, so don't go through it alone. Spotting the signs and getting help early can be vital, so talk to someone about it, hear their concern and visit your GP/doctor for help.

Are there signs you are living with depression?

Depression can make simple, day-to-day life seem impossible. It can take a huge amount of strength and motivation to manage basic tasks like getting out of bed and leaving the house. Things we take for granted like speaking to friends or reading a book can become exhausting, and some people start to feel anxious or ashamed about not being able to do the things they used to, especially if it means taking time away from work or college or school. There is growing evidence that children suffer from depression too and this is due in part to the pressure young people are under and the idea they are 'too young' for depression. Look out for eating disorders, patches where there has been hair pulling, self-harming and drug abuse.

Feeling and becoming isolated

It can be hard to explain our thoughts and feelings to others. When depression takes hold some people find themselves overwhelmed by emotions, while others feel cut off from them. This can make relationships difficult, and many people feel they have to hide what's happening. The more overwhelming our symptoms, the more isolated and lonely we can become. Left untreated, depression can have a devastating impact on our relationships, our work, our finances and our overall health, so it's vital to get help as early as possible.

You can manage depression with help

Most people with depression will get better with the right treatment and support. For some it takes months, for others it's years, and you might find that your symptoms go up and down, particularly during periods of stress or change. For many people, recovery is about being able to manage depression in the long term, so you're more likely to be able to prevent your symptoms from reoccurring in future or can stop them becoming unmanageable if they do. In the depths of depression recovery can seem unimaginable, which is why encouraging someone to get help isn't always straightforward. The good news is that things usually get better, and with the right support most people will go on to lead a healthy and active life. But there is help now if you can access it for yourself or children, friends and family.

Reach out This is so important if you can... write a list of people by your telephone, or in your mobile contacts who you trust will care that you are struggling. This has worked for me, because when I am really low I cannot remember that there is anyone out there I can call out to. This is the nature of depression and why so many don't ask for help.

Treatment for depression comes under three main areas and most people find it helpful to explore them in combination.

Self-help Such as reading about depression, its causes and cures, or by considering meditation or stress relief exercises and group work. This is usual alongside professional help.

Medication If you have decided with your doctor that treatment with an antidepressant medicine would be best for you, there isn't much to choose between them in terms of how well they work – they are all similar to one another. On average, about six in ten people with depression will respond to treatment with an antidepressant.

Talking Therapies The use of such therapies as Cognitive Behavioral Therapy (CBT). CBT is a talking therapy. It involves a series of sessions that last for between 30 to 60 minutes where you talk to a therapist. It is a way of learning about how you think about yourself, the world and the people around you and how your thoughts and feelings are affected by what you do.

Once you understand this, you can learn to make changes in the ways you think about situations and how you respond to them.

The 'Cognitive' part of the therapy is about how you think about things, and the 'Behavioral' part of the therapy is about what you do. So CBT is about changing the ways you think and how you act. After a while, these changes add up to make you feel better.

CBT isn't a therapy that delves into your past, trying to find causes for your emotional distress and symptoms. It concentrates on how you feel now, and the difficulties and problems you face now, and the changes you can make that will help you to feel better now.

When you have a condition like depression, it is very common to have a negative way of seeing the world around you and responding to anything that happens in a negative way. The world seems over-demanding and even minor problems can seem overwhelming.

CBT helps by teaching you how to break down these seemingly insurmountable problems into smaller parts. You can then see how these smaller parts are connected and how they affect you.

The smaller parts are:

Thoughts   What you think about the situation. Is it overwhelmingly difficult or are you able to deal with it?

Emotions   How you feel about the situation. Does it make you feel good or does it make you feel bad?

Physical feelings   Sometimes a difficult situation or emotional turmoil can cause physical feelings like dizziness, nausea, headache, shortness of breath, sweating, palpitations and so on. Does this situation make you have feelings like this?

Actions   What you do in response to the situation. Do you do something positive about it or do you just ignore it?

Each part can affect the others. How you think about a problem can affect how you feel physically and emotionally and what you do about it. Changing one or more of the parts can also change the others. So, if you change the way you think about a situation, or what you do about it, this can change your emotional response as well.

In depression, there is a vicious circle that connects your thoughts, emotions, physical feelings and actions. If a situation arises that you think about in a negative way, this is likely to make you feel even more depressed, perhaps give you a physical symptom like a headache, which makes you feel worse still, and your response is to do nothing about it because your negative thoughts tell you there is nothing you can do about it. Interpreting the situation in such a negative way almost always leads you to jump to unrealistic and unhelpful conclusions.

This can lead to a downward spiral that creates new situations out of nothing, that have the effect of making you feel even worse. You start to have unpleasant and untrue thoughts about yourself.

CBT helps you to break this vicious circle of negative thinking, feelings and behaviour. When you see these parts separately, you can learn to change them – and so change the way you feel.

The sessions are intended to help you to learn how to change your thinking and behaviour so that you can do it on your own, and work out your own ways of tackling your problems.

Give yourself a
Breathing Space

Zen Buddhist Meditation

How I ultimately overcame my own depression

I went through divorce for the second time and this time the fallout was the biggest trial and event in my life that challenged my ultimate salvation.

I worked very hard on what I call 'doing the work'. This means reaching out, taking action then applying what you learn every day, hour and minute.

It took me 18 months to read one particular book that leapt off the shelf and threw itself at me. The cover was black and dark grey – brilliant! Say it as it is! It was called *The Depression Book: Depression as an Opportunity for Spiritual Growth* by Cheri Huber.

I knew that this was it, what I had been looking for. I had spoken to a Zen Buddhist practitioner a few weeks earlier and we were discussing meditation. I was asking about how he meditated and what was the focus and technique in Zen Meditation. He said the breath was the key of course but the mind on the body was the turn in the lock. Staying focused on the breath and the body was so different to the Yoga-Hindu meditation I had used for many years.

There the focus is till the breath but also the use of a mantra, a sacred word that cleansed the mind of dialogue and washed the mind of thought.

This was interesting because, when in my depression and deep terror, I felt the body-pain clearly. I had fear rush through my body from my feet to my heart. It gripped my heart as if I was dying. Staying focused to the physical was hard for me at first but I read Cheri's book that assured me the terror would pass if I didn't try to stop those feelings. I worked so hard each day, step by often-painful step until I felt my life start to gain power and order.

It is now eight years since then and I have managed to see my depression coming. If you can manage to step away from your crisis, your behaviour and your actions and give yourself time to react appropriately then you are doing so well. I knew this and the rewards have been across my life. I am able to see the black horses galloping over the horizon and divert or sublimate them. They gallop off now!

The Simple Steps for when you are down or not:

1 Sit comfortably somewhere safe and private.

2 Place your sit bones on the edge of a Yoga block, meditation stool or cushion.

3 Legs should be crossed or kneeling on the block or cushion.

4 Place hands in your lap, right hand on top of left with both palms up.

5 Close your eyes and watch the breath. Allow it to flow seamlessly in through the nose and out.

6 Take a deep breath then let out an audible sigh. This will allow you to let go of any residue anxiety and lack of attention.

7 Notice your body, how you are sitting, where your legs ache, where the emotional pain is located. Is it in the belly, heart or back for example?

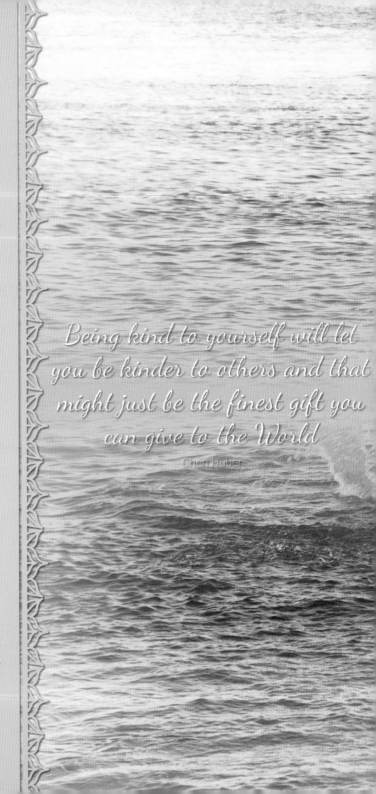

Being kind to yourself will let you be kinder to others and that might just be the finest gift you can give to the World

Cheri Huber

Original photo by Talitha Hepple-Newland

What to avoid:

❋ Try not to reach for a drink, a cigarette, food, talking too much or sex!

❋ Face the feeling in your emotional body!

❋ Its time to release yourself!

❋ Do not label yourself!

❋ Do not tell yourself you are hateful, unworthy or unlovable!

❋ All this is the mind playing with you.

❋ Control the internal dialogue by bringing your mind to where it feels the pain in the body!

❋ Be kind to yourself!

❋ Keep breathing!

❋ Breath is Life!

❋ Start living today!

Note to Self

good vibrations

The Power of Light

Our goal in living is to move towards the light. No matter what our life is, like a plant, flower or tree we reach towards that light. Each part of both our physical body and our Divine body is like the diamond buried deep within the rock. It exists in the dark and it takes your commitment, your work and endeavour to release that light from its depth. Your light is travelling in an upward direction. Each day you practice your prayer, *Asana*, spiritual reading and kindness, this light illuminates your road to the Divine.

Imagine the spine as the road to Enlightenment. As you travel, lights illuminate your path of spiritual development and you reach centres of concentration and energy that we call chakras. You cannot see chakras in the gross body but they are there and the colours and properties they have are very real indeed. Some of us need proof, by seeing these coloured energy centres, and some of us can accept the concept. Both are valid and should be seen as progress. The beauty of true Yoga is the element of individuality.

Each chakra works from the gross to the deeper layers of a human's consciousness.

The seven main chakras are the same colours as a rainbow. The spectrum and the seven colours red, orange, yellow, green, blue, indigo and violet are revealed when the white light is split. Unite these colours and they become One Light once again.

Swami Vishnu used to say that while we first place our feet on the path of Enlightenment, we need help to keep us there, so the Divine rewards us with visions, dreams and sight. Once we are on that path and our feet are firm, those rewards become simply the many miles we have travelled.

A teacher is such a light. When you attend *Satsang*, a meeting of like-minded people with your Guru, you are listening to someone who is talking from experience. You cannot understand the knowledge from a real point of view, only from an intellectual one. You could not say we are 'One' without trying to step into the heart of your student. Remember, we all have a story and to respect that suffering is not elitist, it touches us all and so does Happiness; it is a reflection of the light, so allow it to shine!

The Power of Light is all around you, not only from the Sun's rays or those of the Moon but from all we meet, teach, learn from or transform. Become the Light.

Walk a mile in my shoes and see we are one.

You need never see my footprints to know that I have been there.

You need not hear my voice to know I speak.

However, you do need to follow your light

to know you are on the right path to your Journey to Inner Space,

and the destination is your very own Self.

AMN

Darkness cannot drive out darkness, only light can do that
Hate cannot drive out hate, only love can do that.

Martin Luther King Jr., *A Testament of Hope: The Essential Writings and Speeches*

darkness

a Garden of Black Roses

light

the Crystal in your Mind

Meditation

What are the benefits of Meditating?

The benefits of meditating are numerous and progress is personal. Such as why we want to try it and what we want from it. The five top benefits in my opinion are these below, as they are the ones that make a lot of sense when relating the practice to our human life and our body and brain.

1. A sense of 'Self' and 'the feel good factor' is improved and lasting

Chocolate is a good substitute for the feel good factor and, though natural, has side effects like 'we love it too much!' So one way to get a 'natural high' is to increase the endorphins in the body. Many people have experienced this 'high' from all types of exercise.

Meditation also increases endorphin levels in the body. The word 'endorphin' comes from the two words, 'endogenous' and 'morphine'. Endorphins are small, protein molecules that are produced by cells in your nervous system and other parts of your body. The important role of endorphins is to work with sedative receptors that are known to relieve common pain. These flood the body any time we hurt ourselves or in pain from child birth for instance.

These analgesia-producing receptors are located in your brain, spinal cord and other nerve endings, which is why practicing Yoga is so good too!

Endorphins are not a single molecule but actually come in several forms, and can be anywhere from eighteen to five hundred times as powerful as any man-made painkiller. The best part is they are not addictive, but natural!

2. Sleeping better without the subconscious mind

A truly great benefit of Meditation is if you use an appropriately engineered 'brainwave meditation'; this is when your brain can be put into a brain frequency that actually replaces sleep. For example, two to three hours of sleep can be replaced when your brain is put into a certain 'meditation frequency' for 20 to 30 minutes. Often called 'Autosuggestion' or 'Yoga Nidra' meaning Yogic Sleep, this is when the conscious mind takes part in our deep relaxation and the subconscious mind remains in a state of non-action. The idea of power napping, or 40 winks, is not new. We have been doing this for centuries. It is a well-known fact that those with high IQ and tendencies toward genius rarely sleep as long as most of us. This is down to the way they are able to give total focus to one given assignment or job.

Autosuggestion

Autosuggestion is when we take our attention, or 'Mind', into a specific part of the body. By using the breath we exhale to 'let go' of both tension and anxiety. An in-breath is always a preparation, an out-breath a release. It is best to start by scanning the body with our 'inside eyes' to register where our own 'personal' tension lies. This is what is called mind-body awareness. This allows the thoughts to slow down to very little action and the brainwaves react too in the same way. Before long we have one thought, one breath, one mind, one body. The benefits are that on 'waking' we feel as though we have had a deep and restful sleep. It works! I know. I have an insane life, four children, and fabulously crazy job and don't sleep more than six hours. If I did not practice deep relaxation and meditation I would be certified and put away by now! Or so my children tell me! I used to tell them the same when they disturbed me in my meditation time; of course now they are older and wiser they simply join me!

3. Stress is lowered by decreasing The 'stress' chemical Cortisol

One of the best benefits of meditation is the reduction of the stress hormone cortisol which does significant damage to our body. Within our fast-paced society it is common for many people to have too much cortisol flooding their bodies. High levels of cortisol have been found to increase heart attacks, undesirable cholesterol, lower bone density, increase blood pressure, and it causes hyperglycaemia, suppresses a healthy thyroid and lowers immunity. Regular meditation noticeably lowers cortisol levels and reduces the risk for these diseases.

4. It helps to deal with Anxiety and Depression

I have had personal experience with both anxiety and depression. Depression crept into my life the first time when I was 14. My life seemed as though it did not belong to me and I had no understanding of ever being able to have a part in it. Life at home was strained and I had just gone to boarding school – I had received a scholarship to train as a ballet dancer. That part of my life was my life, but being at home in the holidays was hard for lots of reasons, one of them being that we were very poor and those at school were rich. I had not known till then that I was poor! One day in the holidays, with no local friends anymore as they had moved on, I saw a black cloud cross the room and sit above my head. Depression!

I entered my 'Dark Place' for the first time of many over the years to come.

I discovered meditation the first time when I was three and went to church with my Grandmother in Iraq. She visited our Syrian Orthodox church almost every day. I used to kneel next to her, intrigued by the quietness and deep sense of peace that came over her and then in turn to me. I loved the silence, the incense and the candles. The priests chanting seemed to be a calling from long ago. It's no wonder that Yoga felt so familiar when I discovered it and meditation.

My meditation practice changed me. I was able to step back from my depression and later my anxiety and control these overwhelming feelings. It has taken years but, like everything this is not just for now but a lifetime.

Regular meditation increases levels of the neurotransmitters serotonin and GABA, which are mood stabilizers. Lowered levels of GABA have been associated with increased anxiety, tension and insomnia. Lowered levels of serotonin are associated with depression. Increasing serotonin levels is one of the most significant meditation benefits, in my opinion, since so many people today use anti-depressants to influence serotonin levels. There is so much research now by both medical people and scientists as to the positive effects of meditation.

Makes me smile when you think that the Ancients just 'knew' about it and got on with it!

Meditation is truly simple truly profound.

5. Awakening our Intuitive side

With regular practice meditation benefits us emotionally. It puts many people in touch with a 'higher power' or 'higher Self'. This increases intuition, creativity, and purpose, and can change our perspective from viewing something as a 'problem' to instead viewing it as an opportunity for spiritual and emotional growth. These higher emotional states are a natural progression, because the mind and body are kept more balanced through the other physical and mental meditation benefits we have already seen. The 'Third Eye' Chakra is called the *Ajna* and is the window of inner vision. The pineal is located back from the point between the eyebrows and has a retina; hence the term the 'third eye'. So interesting and amazing to think the Yogis knew this long before brain surgery!

It is never too late to meditate and you can never be too young. Introduce it to your parents, friends and to your children and see the wonderful transformations they have in their lives.

Where and how do I start?

Begin with finding the right space in your home. Take your time to tune into your environment; in other words where do you feel relaxed and calm? There are obvious places that are not relaxing and calming of course, like the kitchen or hallway!

So think about where you feel good and where you go to be quiet or alone. Take the phone off the hook. Turn off your mobile phone, radio and television, as well as any unnecessary electrical equipment in the area immediately surrounding where you will be meditating, especially the fridge! The drone of a fridge is ever present and you don't notice the drone until the fridge stops!

Once you have found that place, create a central focus or altar. Here you can put things that you love and find beautiful and inspiring. These may include photos of inspirational people that you have read about or met. You may wish to have things around that remind you of the people you love, like members of your family who are not here with you at this time. Incense and candles have been associated with contemplation and meditation for hundreds of years, thousands even. These items are seen in all religions as well as in the therapy room or at times of celebration. We light candles to remember those who have died or who are lost and as long as the light burns we keep vigil for them. The flame's centre is still and the heart and mind know this and we hold our gaze here.

Why do we use incense, inspirational objects and candles?

'The mind is like a monkey', so say the wise, and it's true. It jumps from one thought to another, much like a monkey jumping from branch to branch. The idea of using incense is to help the mind associate with the smell and ritual of lighting the stick, to aid quiet contemplation and meditation.

If we go into a busy shopping centre, our mind is focused on looking for shopping and items to feed or satiate the physical body. Even then it can be hard to concentrate when there is noise, crowds and lots of mental and sense stimulation, such as the smell of coffee!

If we go into a church or sacred place, then we enter a very different energy space. We can feel this as soon as we walk through the door; the air is still and almost thick with prayer and the thought of spiritual grace and fervour. The same can be said of a library. I love the library because it's the mind here that is still as well as the body, and the thickness in the ether is mental thoughts at their most focused. When my children used to sit and study I would feel very centred and happy, the house was quiet yet productive, and their minds were doing what they are good at, learning.

A hospital has another type of energy. Here there are thoughts of loss, fear, pain and often grief but then there is also recovery, relief and new beginnings. But we still would not run around or shout, as the ether insists on some decorum and respect for those ill or desolate and for those helping them to heal.

So what we are realising is that each space or place has an energy that helps the mind associate with a particular function or action of the body, the mind or outcome. This is why we create such a space in our home.

So each time you enter the space, light your candles for your eyes, the incense for your nose and look at your inspirational photos or objects for your touch, then all of this ritual aids the mind to prepare for your meditation practice.

As you continue to meditate in that same space, the energy there begins to reflect the energy of your mind. Still mind, still breath, still action, still heart, still here ...

AMN

Starting Your Meditation Practice

Why meditate anyway?

Meditation has been seen in the west as rather an odd, almost cultish practice. Associated with the likes of the Beatles and their Transcendental Meditation Guru The Maharishi Mahesh Yogi. His demure and humble image was screened across the world and people thought the Beatles had lost their minds! The truth is, they had found their minds and discovered that the mind wasn't them, but a tool they could use to make their lives clearer and more purposeful!

Did you know that the whole aim of Yoga postures (*Asanas*), is to be able to sit still and comfortably with no pain in the body, so you can meditate?

If we just think about the spine for a moment and its anatomical structure, then we can see it's like a road with a few hills and dales but it is going straight upwards; this is what I call the direct lift to The Divine.

AMN

Preparing your Body

It is traditional to sit for meditation. This can either be on the floor cross-legged or sitting on a low stool if hips are tight. It would not be alright to lie down on your back or on your tummy. The reason for this is the energy flows to the crown of the head, and its journey upwards via the spine needs to be unhindered. Collapsing on either side of the body inhibits the correct function of the lungs, and this means we are not receiving the benefits of our breathing. Allowing the back to drop forward onto our diaphragm (the dome shaped muscle under our ribs) means that this special muscle, that aids the inhalation and especially the complete exhalation of stale air, is almost disabled.

Consider your posture during the day. Are you walking with a straight back? Are your arms resting by your side while you stand, are they forward (your pelvis is pushed back), or are your arms behind your shoulders (hips pushed forward)? Correct sitting poses start with correct standing.

Look in a mirror and notice the level and height of your shoulders and the hips too. Start to become of aware of how you carry yourself throughout the day. This is also closely related to your work and your perception of yourself.

The ribs are attached to the mid-spine and come around to the front, protecting the lungs and heart. Here they are fused at the sternum, creating a shield, like armour. When we let our spine collapse, then the road upwards is a lot more difficult and the capacity to breathe fully is also hindered.

We have all seen the image and power of the seated Buddha. We don't always know why, but it inspires calm and compassion. We don't have to be a Buddhist to appreciate its serenity and we are curious to the reason why too. If we go back to the things that remind us of peace and quiet and help the mind associate with those qualities, then it's the same feeling with The Buddha. The pose helps us to focus easier and to imitate the serenity it inspires.

Start By 'Acting out' the Positive

Meditation enlivens your whole system, cleanses the mind of thoughts that drain and replaces them with pure light. Hence you become the words of the song from REM:
Happy shiny people, holding hands!

Try this exercise by letting your body respond to the words, Sitting in a comfortable sitting pose, react physically to these words: 'down-hearted', 'uplifted', 'half-hearted'. Amazing how easy it was to describe with your body the connotations of these strong and powerful words. Only one of them is a positive word and yet it's probably the most unfamiliar one. Try to start your day by standing tall and saying the word UPLIFTED! It really will change not just you, but the world outside your mind.

Meditation is your birthright. It is not an elitist practice and only for those who are learned scholars, Priests, Swamis or Shamans. Meditation is simple to learn and may be difficult to keep up, but after all we are learning that the mind is not who we are, but a tool to use when we need it.

Sleep and the World will sleep with you.
Wake up and the World sees your Presence.
AMN

Abstract Brain changes in Meditation

Meditation is a complex mental process involving changes in cognition, sensory perception, affect, hormones, and autonomic activity. Meditation has also become widely used in psychological and medical practices for stress management, as well as a variety of physical and mental disorders. However, until now there has been limited understanding of the overall biological mechanism of these practices in terms of the effects in both the brain and body.

There is growing evidence to show that meditation can make people healthier and happier. It may even increase life span, alter brain structure and change personality.

Now mainstream medicine is beginning to take notice of meditation's effects. For example, mindfulness-based cognitive therapy (MBCT), which is about 80 percent meditation, has been approved in Britain for use with people who have experienced three or more episodes of depression.

MRI scans of long-term meditators have shown greater activity in brain circuits involved in paying attention. Long-term meditation can also cause changes in the actual structure of your cortex, the outer layer of your brain. Brain regions associated with attention and sensory processing have been shown to be thicker in meditators.

Studies suggest that meditation can help you to train your attention and focus, even in the midst of distractions. For instance, when disturbing noises were played to a group of experienced meditators undergoing an MRI, they had little effect on the brain areas involved in emotion and decision-making.

About 10 million people meditate every day in the West, and many more in other parts of the world.

Brain Training: Activating the Amygdala

The amygdala manages connections and responses between several regions of the brain. It's directly involved with emotional well-being, the fight-or-flight response and fear conditioning. A recent study suggests that the amygdala also plays a role in the complexity of social life.

Activating the amygdala in a positive way stimulates higher order mental processes. This can improve creativity and intelligence while elevating positive emotions.

The amygdala also processes feelings on the opposite end of the spectrum. We receive 'bad feedback' whenever we perceive something as negative. It causes a strong emotional response that often leads to instinctual reactions. The emotional feedback is a good thing because it's quite useful for letting us know when we are consciously creating a desired outcome, or just reacting.

By noticing the difference in thought processes you can consciously control the direction in which the amygdala sends its impulses.

We can *choose* to stimulate the amygdala forward, turning on the reward centres for positive emotions. When the amygdala is stimulated forward it is sending signals to the frontal lobes. This is where the brain handles cognitive functions such as long-term decision making and appropriate social actions. These functions can play a major role in determining levels of success and happiness.

When the amygdala signals backwards it is inducing a fear response. It is a state handled by the lower-level reptilian brain, responsible for base instincts. Needless to say, thinking motivated by this part of the brain is not well suited for modern society.

These responses, both positive and negative, are hard wired. However, because of how clever we humans are, we can consciously control our responses, taking charge of our reactions to the environment.

Stimulating the amygdala with regular practice can help you enter a psychological state of flow. In this state you can easily overcome problems and disregard distractions. Being in flow results in a single-minded focus and joy that comes from losing yourself in productive activity. Trivial issues don't slow you down when you are actively engaged and living creatively.

Practicing meditation, living creatively and being positive are some things you can do to improve your amygdala's responses. Certain practices may take more time and effort, but the outcome is incredibly rewarding.

There are plenty of engaging exercises you can do to stimulate positive responses. Any time you use imaginative thought processes you're stimulating the frontal lobes. The image on the previous page shows precisely where the amygdala is located in the brain.

Here are a few exercises you can do to ignite your imagination and activate those frontal lobes:

* Picture the amygdala inside your skull. Now imagine that it's glowing with soft blue light. Imagine the light surging into your frontal lobes and gently setting off billions of neural pathways.
* Recall a frustrating situation. Imagine feeling relaxed and in control in this situation. Can you consider another solution to your problem in this resourceful state?
* In your mind's eye imagine a feather gently tickling the surface of your amygdala.
* Imagine meeting your idol. What questions would you ask them? Try to create a vivid mental picture of this meeting. Maybe your idol can provide some answers that will surprise you.
* Everyone has issues in their life that sometimes seem unsolvable. What would you do if you didn't have to deal with those problems? Imagine how you would feel if you knew how to solve those problems.

Hopefully you enjoyed some of these exercises. Get creative with them; you can come up with some of your own to achieve a similar effect.

Any time you engage in creative activity you are activating the frontal lobes. Using your imagination trains the amygdala to reward you for this positive behaviour. Please continue to act on those creative impulses. The pleasure you receive for being creative is Mother Nature's way of saying, "Keep going, you're headed in the right direction".

Some of the Brain areas that are stimulated in Meditation

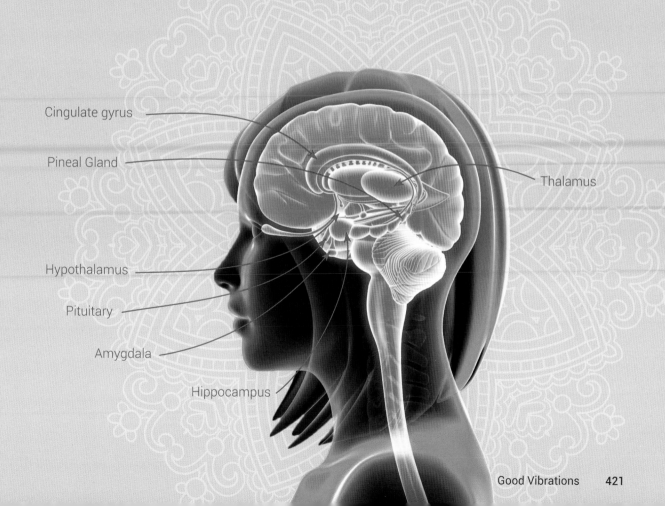

Cingulate gyrus

Pineal Gland

Thalamus

Hypothalamus

Pituitary

Amygdala

Hippocampus

The Pineal Gland, what an eye-opener!

We were all born with our 'third eye' open, but through identification, egoism, and want for control it has been closed, because our culture cannot survive with it open.

What does this say? Does the pineal gland actually contain a retina, cornea, and pupil, literally making it an eye?

The pineal gland doesn't actually contain a retina, cornea or pupil in the way our eyes do but its cells greatly resemble retinal cells. Other than producing melatonin and serotonin, the pineal gland also contains photoreceptive cells (sensitive to light). Why would we have such a receptor within our brain? Because our souls are coherent light and are not bound by our bodies.

The pineal gland (also called the pineal body, epiphysis cerebri, epiphysis, conarium or the 'third eye') is a small endocrine gland in the vertebrate brain. It produces the serotonin derivative melatonin, a hormone that affects the modulation of wake/sleep patterns and seasonal functions. Its shape resembles a tiny pine cone (hence its name), and it is located near the centre of the brain, between the two hemispheres, tucked in a groove where the two rounded thalamic bodies join. It is also thought to have been a light and motion sensing organ.

The pineal is shaped like a pinecone, and pinecones are a sacred symbol in certain religious establishments. The triangle is also sacred and represents the pineal gland and it is more important than most believe.

This extract is from an article in the *New York Times*:

'Modern medical dissection has already discovered that the front section of the pineal gland is equipped with the complete structure of a human eye. Because it grows inside one's skull, it is thus said to be a vestigial eye. Whether it is a vestigial eye or not, our community of cultivators has reservations. Yet modern medicine has, after all, already recognized that there is an eye in the middle of the human brain. The passageway that we open targets exactly that location, and this happens to agree completely with the understanding of modern medicine.' Zhuan Falun (English, Page 51, the 3rd translation edition, The Universe Publishing Co., NY)

In recent years, scientists gradually discovered that the mammalian pineal gland is photo sensitive. However, the mammalian pineal, unlike that of other vertebrates, is not thought to be directly light sensitive. Melatonin, the principal product of the mammalian pineal gland, acts as an internal representative of nighttime.

Scientists have already realized the structural similarity between the pineal and the retina. The pineal was simply called 'folded retina'. A variety of genes that are only expressed in eyes are expressed in the pineal gland as well. The pineal gland not only has photoreceptors, but also has a complete system for optical signal transduction. That is to say, if there is a light-transducing passageway, a pineal gland is capable of detecting light.'

Prof. Lili Feng

Change your Mind

We all know that Yoga does wonders for the mind. Even those new to *Asana*, *Pranayama* and meditation feel an increased mental stability and clarity during, as well as after, practice. Due to sophisticated brain imaging technologies, neuroscience is proving what teachers and practitioners have known for thousands of years – that Yoga and meditation can literally change your brain.

What exactly is going on up there? Take a look inside and glean a basic understanding of brain anatomy and function which will serve as a useful road map for your Inner Journey. On the physical level, the right hemisphere controls the left side of the body, and the left hemisphere controls the right. On the level of the subtle body, *Ida Nadi* (the lunar energy channel, cool breath) is connected to the right half of the brain, and *Pingala Nadi* (the solar energy channel, fire breath) is connected to the left side of the brain.

Nadis are the energy channels very like the Meridians in Chinese Medicine. These are cleansed and stimulated by such breathing techniques as *Kapalabhati* (see page 231), a dynamic diaphragmic breathing exercise that stimlates oxygenated blood flow to the brain, and *Anuloma Viloma*, alternate nostril breathing which calms and soothes the right and left side of the brain.

A student of the great Indian poet Kabir once asked him, "Kabir, where is God?"

His answer was simple:

He is the breath within the breath.

Right-Brain Functions

Casual *Free*

Intuitive *Creative*

Visual *Colours*

Non-verbal

Imaginative

Emotional

Holistic

Divergent

Subjective

Random

Simultaneous

Adventuresome

Spatial *Analogue*

Sensory *Tactile*

Synthetic *Relational*

Words of songs

Left-hand control

Left-Brain Functions

Systematic *Directed*

Logical *Rational*

Factual *Words*

Verbal

Propositional

Rational

Linear

Convergent

Objective

Sequential

Successive

Cautious

Digital

Abstract *Symbolic*

Parts *Detail*

Tunes of songs

Right-hand control

YIN
Feminine

YANG
Masculine

Three Easy and Sustainable Meditation Practices

We have learned that ritual and repetition train the mind into behaving, so it knows that these things we do each day are 'Meditation Time' rituals.

Prepare to Meditate

* Clear your immediate space. You are creating a Sacred Space to use as your Sanctuary or 'Time Out Place'.

* Light your candle and incense and switch off all other lighting if practising in daylight.

* Put your chosen meditation shawl around your shoulders and front of your body. Traditionally we meditate very early in the morning or late in the evening, these times can be cool or even cold.

* Take a block, cushion or rolled up mat and place your sit bones on the first third of it. This helps tilt the pelvis forward to aid the spine to lift upwards, especially around the lower back.

* Sitting comfortably, place the back of your hands on the end of your knees, keeping the elbows bent towards the hips, and bring your thumb and first finger together, extending your other fingers out in Chin Mudra.

Candle Gazing – Tratak

Tratak is the perfect start to meditation and can be practiced at any age. In India this is the first meditation introduced to children, as it is easier to focus the mind on a flame than to ask them to try to clear the mind of thought. The concept can be difficult to grasp. This technique is said to be excellent for the eyes, as well as clearing the mind's path to stillness. Meditation can be very hard to achieve if you are very stressed or agitated but Tratak is achievable and rewarding.

The candle captures your sight and draws it into a one-point pointed state. I believe that the eyes are the steering wheels of the body and mind. If you move your eyes (like a wheel of a car) to look at the things around you, or to engage with an activity, then the mind is moving too and in turn the mind moves the body so neither are still.

The light from a flame is taken in by the eyes and generates energy. The lens of the eye concentrates the energy of the light and heat of the flame onto the retina. The retina then conducts the light and energy through the optical nerves to the lobes at the back of the brain. This energy through the eyes now increases in the pineal gland and improves its function. The pineal gland is at the back of the head and feeds on light and heat energy. It is the only gland that is receptive to light, even though it is encased in bone. The pineal gland is known as the 'Third Eye' (Ajna Chakra point – purple/indigo) residing between the eyebrows, and converts light into the electromagnetic energy responsible for the entire body's glandular system. Flooding the pineal gland with light stimulates its development and functioning. This allows the opening of the 'Third Eye' and *Ananda*, the feeling of bliss.

Yoga and Hindu scriptures say
that practicing Tratak develops
greater intuition and that the
past, present and future all begin
to appear with equal clarity
and equanimity.

How to Practice Tratak

I suggest that the flame is kept about 12 to 24 inches from the face and at eye level. Begin by taking a few deep breaths, then focus your eyes on the flame, keeping your gaze unblinking for as long as you can. You may start to feel tears develop in the eyes. Producing tears is said to have many beneficial effects such as cleansing them and releasing stress. Keep your eyes focused, gaze gently at the flame, not the candle. Let your eyes rest on the flame.

You will find tears flow and sting; close your eyes. You will see the affect of the flame in your eyes and mind. Focus on the flame's 'image' with closed eyes and notice how it may be changing. It may glow very brightly and then grow dim, only to glow brightly again. Bring your attention to the space between and just above the eyebrows, to the Ajna Chakra, the 'Third eye'. You may feel deep peace and distance from your body. Allow that feeling to spread through your entire being.

After the flame has faded from your mind's eye, slowly open your eyes. Do not look at the flame. It is recommended that you face any direction but south when opening the eyes. It is also recommended that you gaze at the greenery of a living plant or flower for a moment. Since Tratak increases the heat and light energy in the eyes, you may want to use a drop of rosewater (or a similar natural eye drop) in each eye to refresh the eyes. Ideal times for Tratak are sunrise and sunset or the hour midway between sunset and sunrise.

When pineal function is restored to its peak, the body begins to respond with new balance as nerve energy begins to flow evenly through both halves of the brain, body and spinal cord. The upward rush of energy creates a feeling of bliss. The opening of the pineal gland takes time and does not happen overnight. Regular and persistent practice of Tratak will bring greater awareness of the visual realm, a relaxed state of mind, enhanced brain wave function, and a deeper knowledge of the Self, all leading to the path to Enlightenment. And it's really easy to do!

If thoughts crowd your mind
simply let them pass by like clouds in a blue sky.

AMN

Breath Awareness Meditation

Working with students for so many years has challenged my ability to help as many of them as I can to start meditating. As Yoga is about realising, understanding and embracing the breath then this has always seemed a good place to begin.

To Prepare

Sitting comfortably, place the back of your hands on the end of your knees, keeping the elbows bent. Bring your thumb and first finger together and extend your other fingers out in Chin Mudra. Imagine a golden thread from the top of the head to the sky above. This will help to keep you upright. Draw your ears away from the shoulders and open the chest. Imagine your heart is a light and let it shine out.

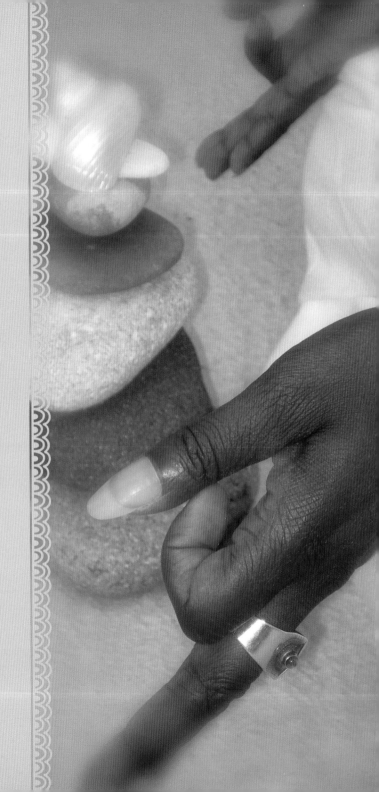

To Begin

Close your eyes and bring your attention to the breath. Follow it by using your inside eyes, through the nostrils, down past the chest and into your belly. Do the same as you watch it come back and out through your nostrils again. Try this a few times, just observing the breath. Notice how the mind begins to settle down as you do this. Your aim is to be conscious first of the mental chatter and then to be aware of how your mind quietens with the discipline of the breath.

You can use these techniques at any time of the day, especially when you notice you have stopped breathing while performing a task in a stressful situation, like feeling you don't have enough time to do it. To avoid getting into this place, take time each day, when it's appropriate, to take one or two minutes to watch the breath. You could be about to drive, to start a project, go to the dentist or tackle a situation you are feeling is difficult, like talking to someone about your feelings, needs or issues.

Observation of the breath is simple once you realize you never gave your breathing any attention ever, unless it stopped from shock, strain, fear or pain.

Give your Self
the gift of breathing
Deeply
Sweetly
and
Wholeheartedly!
AMN

The Mind and the Breath are interdependent;
they cannot be separated.

Active Mind – Active Breath

Just try for a moment to think of something that makes you particularly angry — a person, incident or unresolved situation. Close your eyes and enter the drama, acting out your role in it. Take a few minutes to notice that your breathing has changed because of what you are thinking about.

Now imagine your head is full of moving snowflakes and see them melt as they fall into your belly where your breath is settling. You may want to use the image of sand in an egg timer as the sand moves from the top to the bottom, or rose petals fluttering into the belly and resting there in the pelvic bowl. These images help to slow down the breath and in turn the mind's chatter also diminishes.

Meditation takes many forms and one is simply to slow down the breathing as a way to slow down thought.

Still Mind – Still Breath

Japa Meditation

Meditation is a Spiritual First Aid Kit for the Soul, to help us to discover that the mind is not our Master but indeed a tool for helping us deal with life's ups and downs.

Japa Meditation is the repeating of a Mantra, usually in Sacred Sanskrit, which is known to have a vibrational frequency that resonates throughout every cell and nerve of the body. These vibrational frequencies clear the Soul of debris and drama, clearing pathways to new ideas and giving us a deeper understanding of what our lives mean to us.

Japa Meditation is regarded as one of the most effective forms of meditation. It helps calm the mind and clears the path to a peaceful mind by soothing it from problems and worries that cloud it from time to time.

Known since the ancient times, Japa Meditation has been practised by all religions such as Hindus, Christians, Muslims, and others to allow them to experience peace, calmness, and order in their minds and life.

Reminding ourselves that the mind is a tool for all, Japa Mediation, or repetition of a mantra, has been passed down from one generation to another as a living testament to the need for controlling the monkey-mind and even more now than in the past, as life gets faster and technology dominates our lives.

Meditation involves focusing the mind on one thought by giving the mind a single job, either watching the breath or co-ordinating the breath with a mantra such as INHALING, "OM", EXHALING, "OM". This pushes all other thoughts away and absorbs the mind in the thought of the mantra, giving the mind no space to reap havoc!

It is important that the words/sounds/vibrations used are not words like kitchen or vacuum cleaner! These have vibrations of course but not ones that elevate our consciousness. Mantras can also be any word that evokes a sense of calmness, inspiration, and even respect, such as repeating the word 'Peace'. This has been proved to have the softest and deepest of vibrations that heal, rather than harm, the Subtle or Astral Body (as opposed to the physical body).

Yoga is based on the principles of *Ahimsa*, non-violence in word, thought or deed. So when we were children and our elders suggested that, "Sticks and stones may break our bones but words would never hurt us", did not realize that words penetrate our consciousness, our very deepest selves and leave wounds that never heal, unless we know how to heal them.

There are two ways to practice Japa Meditation

One is audible Japa Meditation known as Vaikhari Japa, which includes repetition of mantras in whispers and even audible pitch. The other is the silent or mental Japa Meditation, which is also known as Manasika Japa. This form is extremely powerful as it completely focuses the mind, and once it is mastered tends to halt any outside influences from unsettling the mind.

The Mind can be experienced as a lake

The aim of meditation is to attempt to still the lake so it looks like glass. Each time we allow a thought to create drama it's like throwing a pebble into the lake. The ripples move away from the centre and out to the edge of the lake. These ripples then begin to move back to the centre, hence Karma, 'as you sow so shall you reap'. Thoughts can be loving, and powerfully so, but they can also be dangerous, not just for others but for ourselves.

For so long we have lived in Slavery to our minds
Redemption Song, Bob Marley

How to Practice Japa Meditation

You are What You Think, Say and Do.

Usually the best way to practise Japa Meditation is by sitting cross-legged on a block or cushion as before (see Preparing your Body on page 415) and chant the mantra by passing a single bead of the Mala rosary through the first finger and thumb of the right hand.

❖ Sit up straight, legs crossed or other;

❖ Left hand in Chin Mudra;

❖ Place first bead between finger and thumb;

❖ Pass a bead on your in breath, pass the next bead on your out breath.

❖ Each breath and passing of bead should have an OM spoken mentally, or any other given mantra.

There are other methods, but for me, I have found teaching this method to my clients and student teachers has been easy to adopt and with good results. In Indian tradition, the right hand is seen as pure, to use for eating food for example, and the left for cleaning the anus and genitals and therefore not conducive to the practice of raising our vibrations. This can be challenging for left-handed people in more than one way, physically and mentally, and I often have to reassure them that this is not like being at school when being left-handed at one time was seen as 'bad' or the 'devil's hand'.

As we meditate each day, we are building a strong foundation in our personal lives, in our work ethics and Spiritual Practice.
Each stone is a pillar reaching up towards a stable and purposeful life.

AMN

What are Mala Beads?

Mala Beads are a string of 108 beads. The root bead, often with a tassel, is bead 109. These single beads, pushed through the first finger and the thumb, are also accompanied by either a breath or, as in Japa, with a mantra mentally chanted or quietly whispered. Children particularly like the whispered version – it is never too early to learn to meditate!

Having a physical action to go with the mental action really does establish concentration, perseverance and dedication, and ultimately a purpose.

Why 108 Beads?

Honestly, there are at least 108 reasons! Below are some of them that have been given for having 108 beads on a mala, as well as a few other points of interest. None of these reasons are more or less true than any others, but you may notice that the number 108 seems to be like a road map of reality in general, and for the Human Being especially.

108 Reasons

A selection I thought might be interesting and useful and others just mind-bending!

1. **9 times 12:**

   Both of these numbers have been said to have spiritual significance in many traditions: $9 \times 12 = 108$, also $1 + 8 = 9$.

2. **Powers of 1, 2 & 3 in mathematics:**

   1 to the 1st power = 1; 2 to the 2nd power = 4 (2×2); 3 to the 3rd power = 27 ($3 \times 3 \times 3$). $1 \times 4 \times 27 = 108$

3. **Harshad number:**

   108 is a *Harshad* number, which is an integer divisible by the sum of its digits. *Harshad* is from Sanskrit, and means 'Great Joy!'

4. **Desires:**

   There are said to be 108 earthly desires in mortals...indeed and the rest!

5. Lies:

There are said to be 108 lies that humans tell...I wonder.

6. Delusions:

There are said to be 108 human delusions or forms of ignorance... interesting!

7. Anahata:

Heart Chakra: The chakras are the intersections of energy lines or Roundabouts and there are said to be a total of 108 energy lines converging to form the Heart Chakra. One of them, *Sushumna*, leads to the Crown Chakra, and is the path to Self-realisation...'I know who I am'.

8. Sanskrit alphabet:

There are 54 letters in the Sanskrit alphabet, 54 × 2 = 108. Each has masculine, *Shiva* and feminine, *Shakti*.

9. Pranayama:

If you can meditate enough to have only 108 breaths in a day, Enlightenment will come. I do believe you can make time by slowing the breath and then the mind can perform with clarity all it needs to deal with on a daily basis.

No matter what the meaning of 108, it is important that if a Mala is used to count Mantras then make a commitment that the Mantra is spoken, whispered or chanted with sincerity, devotion, feeling and full attention.

AMN

Visualisations

Visualisations for Heart and Soul

My Personal inspirations: the ROSE-HEART and the CHAKRA GARDEN

The Rose–Heart: A Story about Love and Forgiveness.

The Rose is the universal symbol of Love. No love story, romantic interlude or happy ending would be complete without the Rose's image. As in Shakespeare's *Romeo and Juliet*, it would not matter what it was called because it would still smell as sweet. For many centuries the Rose has been depicted in religion, the arts of courage, on an emblem of loyalty and as part of prayer. It has been nature's priest or priestess, a goddess among flowers and shrubs.

This visualisation came from a vision that I experienced when my heart was breaking. I was in so much pain that my heart had turned to stone. I cannot remember anything about the events that led me to this place. All I knew was that I could never love again and never forgive. Love and forgiveness are close relations. It is really very hard to love someone if you cannot forgive them, and there are people in your life that deserve both your forgiveness and your love, and that includes your body.

The smell of the Rose will transport the Soul to a world where Love has the perfume of the Rose, Forgiveness is as soft as its petals and its thorns are the swords of Redemption.

AMN

I was expecting my first child and intuitively knew that I had baggage I needed to let go of. I remembered my own childhood and how I had not understood some of the things my parents had done or said and how there were secrets that I was not privy to. As I grew up and became a Mother myself I began to realize that some things cannot be said or understood by a child in its wider context. So I forgave my parents and I forgave me for thinking badly. In fact I had stood in ignorance.

The person I chose to help me work some of this out with was a very special woman who massaged my unborn child and me. All my children love to be massaged and they are over 20 now! It has always been a way to communicate without words, and I think this is why I chose this medium to let go with.

I could communicate with my heart without words. During the hour's session I was able to relax and found that I could feel my inner body responding as much as my outer body. She suggested I place my awareness in my Heart Centre. I can honestly tell you that my whole body screamed, "No!"

My friend asked me to try again and to bring my awareness and thoughts to my Heart.

Under no circumstances was I going to let go of my stone, because it kept me down and rooted to the spot, paralysed with fear. Like a stone holds you down in the water. I was happier to drown than to let it go.

AMN

This was so hard but I also felt I had been given an opportunity to release my heart from its stony prison.

* So I breathed very slowly as directed.
* I saw with my inside eyes my breath weaving its way with the *Prana* to my injured heart.
* I visualised that the colours of my breath and Prana were pale blue and opaque white.
* I remained breathing slowly into my belly and back out through my nose for a few minutes.

Stay with the breath.

* My mind began to respond and I could feel my heart beat become a rhythmic flowing pulse.

Stay with the breath.

When my friend thought I was ready she asked me to look at my heart. This was difficult but I kept my inner eyes on my heart.

I was shocked to see that not only was it a stone, but a dark place. My heart should be a healthy red surely?

* I had to breathe harder and longer and slower.

Stay with the breath.

Suddenly, with no precipitated thought to trigger it, I could smell the fragrant intoxicating perfume of a Rose, the strong perfume from roses that I smelled as a child. An uplifting, relaxing, falling-into-memory that I found I could not resist.

* I breathed and saw the rose was a perfect soft pink and was tightly budded.
* I knew what I had to do and it took all my will power to go on and do it.

I willed the bud to release its glory by unfolding its wing-like petals and as it did so I became small just like Alice in Wonderland.

The petals held me like a baby and the smell was so overpowering that I could hardly breathe for its perfume.

Then I took a Deep Breath and as I sighed
I acknowledged that my Heart had opened.

AMN

What had I learned?

I learned that to forgive and to love is not easy, but that we must make a contract with our 'Self' to try to live up to our own expectations of a good person and a good life before we ask others to do the same.

How to use this Rose-Heart Meditation

Think of a person, persons or situation that has caused you great pain and has not been resolved. Take your time, try this, don't just read this and close the book. Picture their face or the scene in your mind's eye. Take your time here because when I did this for the first time I did not want to look at them, not even in my mind's eye!

Once you can see them clearly, place them in front of you and allow the Rose to open in your Heart and send rays of Love and Forgiveness out to them. The colour here is your own colour and the Rose too will be of your own intuitive choice.

Keep the image of their face and the ray going out to them for as long as you can manage it. Once you let go of the meditation take some deep releasing breaths and smile. Open your eyes and take a moment to see how you feel.

Of course you have realized that the person, persons or situation have not yet changed but you have! The next time you see them or find yourself confronted by old wars and wounds, how amazed you will feel when you realize your heart is still open!

The Chakra Garden: A Place for Us

A Visualisation for Children and vulnerable Young People

This visualisation came to me many years ago while I was running a training course in the Rocky Mountains in Canada. This part of the world is stunningly beautiful; its silent majestic mountain range creates a temple around the lower lands. All mountain ranges have their own unique personality. I can remember arriving after a long flight and road journey and thinking how still these mountains were.

While I was working there I was asked to do some Yoga with children who had Down's Syndrome, some learning difficulties and others had mild Cerebral Palsy. Of course I said yes. I had very little warning to prepare anything and at that time had little information on the children either, who ranged from age 11 to 16. They arrived by a small bus, looking rather confused but happy enough.

We ushered them into our Yoga studio and asked them to sit down and face another child. They were very excited and chatting a lot amongst themselves and being typical children! Some of the carers were really happy to join in, except one who sat on a chair and watched. I felt uncomfortable about this at the time and should have said something. This woman had a very loud voice and, rather than speak to the children, she raised her pitch till it felt as if she was shouting. She told me I would never calm the children and not to take it personally! I took a deep breath and walked to the front of the studio. The studio, though on the small side, had wonderful full-length views of the Kootenays, one of the mountain ranges of the Rockies around the town of Kimberley. I had no ideas at that time as to what I was going to do with these lovely children, but to be honest I rarely worry, I just let go.

The children and carers took a while to settle down and as I scanned the room I could see that some of the young people had already found some inner space.

I took a long slow breath, looked around at my wonderful surroundings and asked for some help. Within seconds my mouth had opened and the following words came out.

Hello everyone, my name is Anne-Marie and I am so happy to see you all here today. We are going to go on a journey in our minds and have a lovely time together this afternoon.

Please lie down and find a comfortable space. Let your feet come apart and your arms rest by your side. Turn the palms towards the sky and if you can, please close your eyes.

We are going to go to a beautiful garden today with our mind and enjoy the colours, sounds and the smells there.

Before we go there, notice the sounds in this room. Then notice the sounds outside. There may be birds and insects or a car or plane. Take your time to listen. Your breathing has changed and it's getting much quieter.

Take some slow breaths and feel your tummy get bigger like a balloon as it fills up with your breath. Then breathe out even slower. Watch the breath move out though the nose and in through the nose.

In your mind I want you to walk out onto the grass under your feet. Look down at your feet and notice that you don't have any shoes on and your toes are feeling nice as they move in the grass. The grass feels cool and there is still early morning dew on it. Start to walk slowly, still looking at your feet, and notice there is a path in front of you. Look at the path as you place your first foot on it. What does it feel like? Is it warm, is it cool? Is the path made of stones or wood? Take your time.

As you walk along your path, start to look ahead of you and see that there is a garden and it seems to be a secret place as it has a wall around it. What is the wall like? Is it tall or low, flat stones or round ones? What colour are they? Are they grey or brown? This is your wall, one you made. It is very special so look at it carefully and notice everything about it, like the moss growing on it or small plants growing in it.

As you walk closer to the wall you notice a door or a gate in your wall. Lift your hand up and take a look at your hand, see it lift up and push against the wood. Slowly push the door open and take a look at your beautiful garden. The grass under your feet is very soft and cool and the grass tickles your toes. You feel very happy in this garden.

I would like you to turn to your right and walk towards a large group of red roses. They are in full bloom and smell heavenly. Get close to them and get your nose as close as you can. Now take a deep breath though your nose and let the perfume fill your head and your heart with red roses, then imagine these roses falling into your lower tummy and feel really safe.

After spending some time there turn to see the next small-planted area where there are lots of orange daisies. They are dancing happily in the breeze of the morning and the warm sunshine. Get close to them and smell them, they smell like vanilla and orange cream. Take a big breath through your nose and let that orange vanilla smell move down into your navel and feel really happy.

Let's walk now to the next bed of flowers and here we have tall yellow lilies. Their heads are standing tall so that they can reach the Sun. They look like the rays of the Sun as they stand there lifting their faces. Get close to them and let their golden faces shine on your face like a million smiles. Breathe this yellow into the part above your navel and let the yellow shine. You feel really peaceful.

Now let's walk over to your little forest of green trees, these have silver trunks and emerald green leaves that jingle like coins on the tree. Listen to their sound. It's a tingling jingling sound and the green leaves are moving happily together. Look up into the branches of the jewelled green leaves and the silver tree trunk. Let the green rest in your heart and say to yourself, "I love me!" It feels so calm here and loving.

You have just noticed that there are lots of small blue flowers that have big petals and they seem to have a white diamond in the middle. These cornflower daisies are shy flowers and they are very kind. You will have to come down to your knees to hear them talking to you. Bring your ear very close to them and listen. Can you hear them say 'we love you, we love you, and we love you'. Let their blue colour rest in your throat. You are feeling all soft and sweet inside.

We are standing up now to walk to those purple flowers on that bush. They are big flowers and when you look inside you see they have a yellow centre that looks like an eye. Look at the eye and feel as though you are falling into the purple petals and the yellow eye is very kind and clear. Watch your breathing as you are in those purple flowers and let the purple rest on your forehead. You are feeling very tall and brave.

You have just noticed a bright white light in the shape of a ball coming up in the sky. You can see it coming up over your wall. This is the pale morning Sun rising to wake us up. Let the white light rest at the top of your head. You are feeling at peace with the world.

Take a big deep breath and begin to move your toes and fingers. Roll your head gently from side to side and give yourselves a stretch on the floor. Bring your knees up and then roll to your side. Curl up there before you come to sit up with crossed legs. Start to open your eyes very slowly and put a big smile on your face. Look at the friends around you and say hello!

What happened next?

The children were so calm that for some time they did not speak. They looked wide-eyed and rested as if they had woken from a deep sleep. Then they looked for their friends and radiated love and well-being. Wonderful! The loud teacher was also speechless but for another reason all together!

As with any meditation, visualisation is also one of the best ways to ease stress and tension in our lives. When practised without force or expectations, and if possible on a daily basis, then visualisation helps our minds become peaceful, allows us to manage our life strategies better and evokes some happiness from within.

Sacred
Sounds

Kirtan: Chanting of Sacred Sounds

The Theory and Practice

Chanting is an aspect of Yoga that people find confusing at first. It seems to be nothing but singing in a strange language. I think we may all have had the experience of being (or feeling like) the one person in class that didn't know what they were doing! The rest of the group seemed to be enjoying the experience and you felt uncomfortable?

Kirtan, as this chanting is known, is a relevant and natural part of Yoga. We all enjoy listening to the voice, especially when the heart is in it, but we may not be able to 'sing'. The beauty of chanting is that it is rather about the quality of the voice, not the ability.

Kirtan is about the 'content and the motivation' behind the voice.

Why is it that these strange sounds produce such reactions in people – joy, devotion, and even tears? This needs some simple history behind the chanting.

Chanting in the traditional style is done in Sanskrit

Sanskrit is an ancient language and is the root language of the 'Indo-European' family of languages.

Most languages evolved by a process of naming and consensual recognition. This means that as a language forms, the primitive person would use 'ug' for tree and the rest of the tribe would use this same sound as a matter of convenience in communicating with each other. Most languages don't follow any logical order or formula because they are made up of primitive sounds that then become a language. Sanskrit does not follow this pattern.

Sanskrit is a consciously evolved language

When we make a mental picture in the mind of an object or concept, it has an actual 'vibration'. This vibration has to come into the physical as speech in order to communicate the idea of the object or concept. Sanskrit does not follow the rule of random naming of an object or concept; it uses the vibrations of the human vocal chords as closely as it can to the mental vibration. Consider that we are replicating a subtle vibration into a gross physical vibration.

Vibrations are in everything, no matter live or an organic object like a stone or wood. Consider the opera singer reaching top 'C' and the glass shattering; this is because the frequency was the same. When soldiers cross a bridge, they break rank so they don't possibly hit the same frequency as the bridge and it begins to break. An earthquake is the same.

Sanskrit was not formed by primitive cultures but by people who had an astounding and innate knowledge of the workings of the Human mind and body.

To share Vedic Chant is to share an experience of silence through
listening, a process of healing, and a link with nature,
the deeper Self and the Divine.

TKV Desikachar

He who knows the secrets of the sounds,
knows the mystery of the whole universe.

Sufi Master Hazrat Inayat Khan

In the beginning was the word and the Word was with God,
and the Word was God

Paul 1.1 – Bible

or THE SOUND WAS OM

In the beginning there was Brahman with whom was vak (speech),
and the word is Brahman

Vedas

Everything is word

Shabda Brahman – *Vedas*

By sound vibration one becomes liberated

Vedanta-sutra 4.22

Question So, what difference does it make if we use the word 'blah' for a stick or the Sanskrit sound '*Danda*'?

Answer Well, when the Sanskrit word is sounded properly, it vibrates in the mind at the same frequency as the actual object or concept. Everything animate or inanimate, whether actual or conceptual has a vibration.

It is this 'property' that makes the Sanskrit so important in chanting or even just speaking the Sanskrit names in a Yoga class.

PERSONAL COMMENT: there are now Buddhist centres in the UK that are run by the Chinese who are anti Dalai Lama. They have tried to malign his work and lineage. These Buddhist centres chant in English and therefore the vibrational properties are lost. Look out for these places and try not to be caught up in their practices. These sects are called Nagarjuna Kadampa.

What is the Subtle Vibration we experience in Kirtan?

What we are chanting is not just 'hey look at that stick let's pick it up!' The chantings are of a very high spiritual nature. They are concerned with the concepts of goodness, mercy, patience, balance of Mind, perfection in all aspects of material and spiritual endeavours.

The importance of Sanskrit in these types of chanting is that when you make the Sanskrit word with your mouth and voice, you are also reproducing the vibration of the concept or idea itself in your mind. The more you chant sacred sounds, the more your mind is full of positive compassion and action.

Like attracts like and so the mind. Think of iron shavings and a magnet; those tiny single iron shavings draw together to become one as they get nearer to the magnet. So chanting does this with our thoughts, bringing to one point, and as a group singing together we become very powerful.

We are Good Vibrations; we are made of song; sing with Sincerity and an Honest Heart.

Jaya Ganesha Jaya Ganesha Jaya Ganesha Pahimaam
Sri Ganesha Sri Ganesha Sri Ganesha Rakshimaam

ॐ नमः शिवाय

Om Namah Shivaya

Pronounced as Aum Num-ha Shi-why.

Om Namah Shivaya is known as the great soul redeeming mantra and the five-syllable mantra.

It means 'I bow to Shiva.' Shiva is the supreme reality, the inner Self. Shiva is the name of your true identity – your Self.

According to Hindu mythology, there are three Gods who run this creation: Brahma, the Creator of the Universe; Vishnu, the Preserver; and the Shiva, who in the end destroys the Universe. Among these three Gods, Shiva, though considered a destroyer and maker of chaos, also symbolises our inner Self, which remains intact even after everything ends.

Living a Life

Affirmation

We, The Lotus Bud of Perfection

Is it possible that we can be both a human and a Divine being? Is it conceivable that we can become greater than our thoughts, to aspire to 'Be' rather than to simply exist?

The word 'Bud' is one of those words that show up in our minds not only as a word but an image. The power behind the bud itself is pregnant with potential. It is full of anticipation, of hope and wonder. What will it turn out like, what colour, shape, smell? Its greatness lies in its cultivation, its roots and water quality, as well as its genetic make-up.

Do we construct bars around our own potential created from fear of failure or from the fear of success? Succeeding in life means we have to take responsibility for our actions, whereas failing allows us to blame our circumstances on someone or something else.

Greatness is dormant in us all
no matter how we were cultivated, nurtured or taught.
We are simply waiting to be awakened.
Wake-up NOW and Smell the Lotus!
AMN

Which one do you fit into?

On the Run

'On the Run' is always in a hurry. If something has to be done it must be done as soon as possible. You have a lot of responsibility, very high expectations for yourself and others and very little patience.

Yoga tip Try to spend even five minutes a day thinking about how to calm your mind. 'More haste, less speed' means staying focused on the moment and not tomorrow. Breathe into the belly, inflating it like a balloon, and exhale through the nose slowly until you feel calmer and more centred. You will achieve twice as much without the ulcer!

The Worrier

'The Worrier' worries about everything; you make mountains out of molehills. The Worrier often suffers sleepless nights as you have too much on your mind, you find it hard to relax and have low self-esteem.

Yoga tip Keep all things in proportion and remember you only need to take one day at a time. Make a list of your priorities and work on each one in turn.

Before you sleep, listen to your breathing. If it is erratic it means your thoughts are crowding you. Relax each muscle in turn, from your feet to your head, telling them to release and let go. By concentrating on each task your mind has no time for other thoughts!

Workaholic

'The Workaholic' puts a career before anything else in their life including relationships, socialising and family. They work very hard, enduring long hours, as they are predominately focused on moving up the career ladder.

Yoga tip Get out and give yourself at least one night a week for personal work, on your Self. By the 'Self' I mean the inner world that you have little time for.

The inner world gives you a perspective on the things that really matter, like your long time investment in your happiness. Happiness is a way of finding contentment in life not easily found. Something like a local Yoga class will keep you in contact with your neighbour and community and will keep in touch with grass roots.

Night Owl

'The Night Owl' works irregular hours and finds their work commitments clash with a social life. You may find yourself waking up sluggish due to irregular sleeping patterns, which can throw the body clock out of sync. The Night Owl can easily fall into routines of eat, sleep and work, letting exercise, leisure and her social life fall by the wayside.

Yoga tip OK, this is a tough one because although a lot of people work nights, most of the world doesn't. But you know, with a little more creative effort you may be able to find an early morning Yoga class that you can go to after a shift, then food, then bed! You will be able to meet people like you and have some special time for yourself. You may be surprised to find there are others out there like you. A class will release tension from the body, help you detox and create a more positive energy that will see you cope with the life you lead.

World on Your Shoulders

'The World on Your Shoulders' is balancing many responsibilities including a job, family, husband, finances etc. She is very routine focused but has very little time to herself and has a habit of putting everything before herself.

Yoga tip Now this is an easy one for me, with all the above and more! This is where you need the 'Head Space' that will keep you sane. Find a short course in Yoga, that will give you the confidence to practice at home, if that is all the time you have. Once you have the tools of life and sanity/survival you will be a happier and nicer person. If the pivotal point of the home should collapse where will the family be? Looking after your health is looking after your family too. They will also respect you more than if you behave like a doormat. Find time for the real you inside the mother, wife and breadwinner!

Party Animal

'The Party Animal' puts his social life before anything else, he wants to have as much fun as possible before he gets too old. His job may be of great importance to him, but is secondary to his social life. Late nights and early mornings can soon begin to take their toll.

Yoga tip OK party animal, you want to have as much fun as possible before you get old. HA! Did you know that drinking, smoking and crazy sleep patterns are aging you quicker? Alcohol ages your face and destroys your liver and kidneys. Smoking creates wrinkles sooner and creates a grey tinge to your skin because of the depletion of oxygen in the bloodstream etc. Then again you know all this, so look into your deeper Self if you dare and see what it is you are really running away from. Stop the abuse and you can still party without the aids to help your self-confidence. Tough but true; I've been there! Find a Yoga class quick!

The Last Minute person

'The Last Minute' man or woman excels under pressure, but leaves everything to the last minute, meaning that everything has to be done at once, causing stress levels and blood pressure to increase.

Yoga tip You can still excel under pressure without the stress, by pacing yourself. Why do you do things last minute? Because you have always done it that way. It's what we call in Yoga, creating grooves. We create good grooves or bad; these can be changed. We walk past the cake shop one day and decide to get one. Next day we think, "Oh that was nice lets have another." We have created a groove. We could just as well have walked past the vegetable store or the gym and created a positive groove by doing a positive action.

Change your way of thinking; find a way to start a job sooner; keep the mind focused and find you have more time, not less, and your body is responding accordingly!

Originally published in Natural Magazine.

The West has dictated how we practice Yoga in the 21st Century.

We practice Yoga in a studio, gym, healthclub or a space at home.

Yoga is as natural an exercise system as is washing your body to keep clean.

Get outside whenever you can.

You may have a garden or terrace; you may have a small balcony, so get out with your mat and express yourself.

No outer space?

Open the window and let the outside in.

Natural You

From Luminous Birth
to Golden Years

From Luminous Birth to Golden Years

We are sentient beings and we live in a world of sentient beings.
Sentient beings are, in principle, aware of Self and others.
They witness themselves and others.
Our ability to see others and ourselves depends on our ability to be Open-Hearted.

The Heart is not simply a pumping organ that keeps the body alive, it is also known as the Seat of Compassion, Empathy and Love.

The simple and well-known phrase, 'she was broken-hearted', refers to the emotional heart, where resides the pain of rejection, betrayal and loss. Open-hearted is the open door to meeting another 'like-felt' soul. Here is where compassion is centred and where the Rose blooms.

Compare this then to hatred, which also likes to dwell in the heart and can grasp and suffocate it of all that makes us sentient. Consider the phrase, 'he was hard-hearted', and we have a strong image of a stone, crystallized tears or evil, switch this word around and it spells 'live'.

So what affects do love, hate, grief, joy, betrayal and loyalty have on the heart?

It is a known medical fact that severe stress puts an inordinate strain on the physical heart. Stress is big business these days and that is partly due to people being more informed and encouraged to monitor their own health but...

Heart to Heart Resuscitation

Too much stress ages you!! It destroys cells, drys up your skin, stops the natural process of absorption of vitamins and minerals from your food and all together ambushes the body and leaves you exhausted.

Stress has a major impact on the heart, raising the blood pressure and keeping it there, stops you relaxing and getting good recovery time such as sleep. Heart attacks are very real and are a long-term process of abuse. This is not only from food, drugs or alcohol, but also from a deeply troubled mind. Look to finding some way to let off some of this pressure.

Talk to your heart before your mind and ask it to speak to you. Having a heart to heart with your own compassionate voice really helps. Give your heart the time it needs to function to its optimum and time for your life to find its rhythm.

Part of the action towards a healthy heart, physically and emotionally, is accepting issues around subjects such as betrayal, loss and anger. 'We need to talk about it', is a great way to start!

Being young, staying youthful and living to your full potential is the best tonic for defying gravity. A love for living will keep your cells vibrant, whole, and full of sunshine!

Getting too old too soon is a real fear for most of us, so I suggest you give your heart the love and attention it deserves, from good food to love and compassion....

Open Heart Surgery!

What is 'being' young and what is 'being' old?

'Being' suggests that we choose to be something and act out that being. 'I want to be full of life', 'I want to be happy'; these statements are our own thoughts vocalised.

Growing up and getting older are a state of mind as much as a state of body, and this is proved scientifically by observing the brain's responses to positive thought and action, as opposed to negative.

I have met old men in the body of a ten year old and six year olds in the body of an 80 year old. How we are bought up, and the blue print we are born with, shapes what and who we are. True, but this does not mean we cannot or do not change throughout the process of 'being' human, because we can and do.

'As soon as we are born we begin to die', is a happy note from many Yogi sages. If we continually think this then don't we become it? We are what we think after all.

The secret of Youth is Yoga

This is not a misguided statement, it is a fact. Think yourself young!

I saw my Mother practice Yoga up until she could not walk. Even after being diagnosed with terminal cancer, with five months to live, she managed a stupendous *Ardha Chandrasana* – Half moon balance!

How? I believe it was through the Power of Thought and the ultimate strength of her heart and her love for life. She had been practising for many years and her mind went into an auto-response,. Our muscles have memory as we know and her *Samskaras*, those grooves were deep.

You can never be too young to start practising Yoga either! Start teaching your own children, nieces, nephews, wards and friends' children the benefits of meditation, stretching and strengthening the body and stimulating the brain. Play games by acting out the poses, using animal names for instance, which stimulate the opposing sides of the brain and encourage true deep connected breath.

Stress is normal and it's the motivator to get you 'up and doing'.

Good Vibrations

Ask Anne-Marie . . .

Ask Anne-Marie . . .

. . . about establishing breathing techniques

✱   **What are the Four Modes of breathing?**

1. **Clavicular:** Clavicular breathing relates to the clavicles (collar bones), and because it is a shallow inhalation, it is the most inefficient type of breathing as it uses only the uppermost lobes of the lungs.

   During **Clavicular breathing**, air is drawn predominantly into the chest by the raising of the shoulders and collarbones and simultaneously contracting the abdomen during inhalation. This requires a lot of effort and maximum amount of air can be drawn this way only for short periods of time.

2. **Thoracic:** Also known as shallow breathing, or chest breathing, Thoracic Breathing is the drawing of minimal breath into the lungs, usually by drawing air into the chest area using the intercostals, rather than using full lung capacity via the diaphragm. Shallow breathing can result in, or be symptomatic of, rapid, irregular breathing and hyperventilation. Most people who breathe shallowly do it throughout the day and are usually unaware of the condition.

   NB: **Empowered Thoracic Breathing:** expanding the chest and rib cage maximally on inhalation so that the intercostal muscles reach their outermost limits of isometric tension. This mode of breathing is necessary in certain postures, such as spinal twists or when *Uddiyana Bandha* (pulling the navel towards the spine), is engaged, because the abdominal area will be constricted and abdominal breathing will be limited.

3. **Abdominal/Diaphragmatic:** The diaphragm is a dome shaped structure that not only assists in breathing, but also acts as a natural partition between our heart and lungs on the one hand, and our stomach, spleen, pancreas, liver, kidneys, bladder, and small and large intestines on the other. The top of the diaphragm actually supports the heart, while the bottom of the diaphragm is attached all the way around our lower ribs and connects also to our lower lumbar vertebrae. When we are breathing fully and deeply, our diaphragm moves downward as we inhale and upward as we exhale. The more the diaphragm can move, the more our lungs are able to expand, which means that more oxygen can be taken in and more carbon dioxide released with each breath. On inhalation the abdomen swells and on exhalation the abdomen is drawn in towards the spine to force air out completely.

NB: **Yogic or 3 Part breathing:** this is a technique also known as the 'complete breath' because the three chambers of the lungs, beginning with the lower lungs, then moving up through the thoracic region and into the clavicular region are fully utilised.

4. **Paradoxical:** empowered chest breathing carried to extremes is called paradoxical breathing. It occurs when the abdominal wall moves in during inhalation rather than out. Therefore it is a paradox, not logical.

❉ What is Ujjayi breathing?

Ujjayi breathing is characterised by the soft, sibilant roaring sound made by slightly closing the glottis as breath is drawn in through the nostrils and released. It is often translated from the Sanskrit to mean 'victorious breath'. It is a strong internal breath and cleans the throat of mucus and the Vishudda Chakra of emotional blocks.

❉ Why do we use it as part of all our practice?

Ujjayi breathing helps to create heat (*Agni*) and oxygenises the blood to the muscles. It also helps to still the mind by bringing attention to the rhythmic sibilance of the breath, which in turn aids focus and inward attention, moving the student towards a more meditative, conscious practice. It also helps to encourage and maintain abdominal breathing, which is more beneficial and efficient for performing *Asanas*.

❉ What is Kapalabhati and what does it mean, literally?

Its literal translation is 'head/skull shining' breathing.

❉ What are the benefits of Kapalabhati?

Kapalabhati is a *Kriya*, or cleansing technique, used to purify the body. In this case, it helps to expel waste carbon dioxide from the body and, because it is cardiovascular, brings fresh, oxygenated blood into the body. It tones and massages the internal organs, expands lung capacity and improves the respiratory and digestive systems.

❉ When should Kapalabhati be avoided?

If you suffer from high blood pressure, glaucoma, hiatus hernia before surgery, are pregnant or suffer from any heart conditions then this is dangerous! Even toothache means it should be omitted from practice until its better, as the blood flow upwards will swell the gums. Do not practice with a headache either.

❉ When do we introduce Kapalabhati?

Kapalabhati is introduced no earlier than week 3. This gives new students ample time to learn and establish abdominal breathing before employing this diaphragmatic technique at a more advanced level in *Kapalabhati*.

❋ Why is this NOT suitable for pregnancy?

Because *Kapalabhati* is an intense and powerful diaphragmatic breathing technique, it places pressure on the abdominal area, thus is not suitable for pregnancy.

❋ What are the benefits of Anuloma Viloma?

Soothing, balancing, relieves stress on the body and mind, regulates the breath and is a useful aid to meditation.

❋ Is Anuloma Viloma good for a beginner or not?

Yes, as it is a gentle and calming technique that enables the beginner to develop competency and awareness in abdominal breathing. It also balances, as well as stimulates, the right and left hemisphere of the brain, body and breaths.

❋ How do we teach this and how many rounds?

For beginners *Anuloma Viloma* is taught by establishing a suitable sitting posture, then by closing off the right nostril with *Vishnu Mudra*, inhaling through the left nostril for a count of 2, closing both nostrils and retaining the breath for a count of 8, releasing the right nostril and exhaling for a count of 4. The process is then reversed, right nostril to left, to complete one cycle or round. At least three rounds are performed. **Intermediate** ratio is inhale 4, hold 16, exhale 8.

❋ When should we introduce the Bandhas?

The *Bandhas* are introduced once the student has become familiar with the basic breathing techniques. They should not be introduced until the student has reached an intermediate level of practice, especially in the case of *Uddiyana Bandha*.

✻ What is a Bandha?

A *Bandha* is an internal muscular 'lock' or contraction that seals energy, *Prana*, in the body when performing *Asanas* or *Pranayama*.

✻ Describe the three locks

1. Root Lock: a contraction and uplifting of the perineum and pelvic floor muscles (corresponds to the pelvic diaphragm);
2. Abdominal Lock: an inward and upward pull of the abdominal cavity towards the spine (corresponds to the diaphragm); and
3. Chin Lock: bringing the chin downward to rest on or towards the chest or sternum (corresponds to the vocal diaphragm).

✻ What are their Sanskrit names?

The Root Lock in the perineum area between the anus and genitals is the *Moola Bandha* and is activated by drawing up this area. The Abdominal Lock, activated by pulling the internal lower pelvic muscles up and in, is the *Uddiyana Bandha*, and Chin Lock is *Jalandhara Bandha*, activated by drawing chin down and chest up.

✻ How would you use them?

Moola Bandha: Once the breath is retained, lift up the pelvic floor muscles, particularly the perineum, or for the less experienced, contract the sphincter and genitals.

Uddiyana Bandha: Once the lungs are empty, draw the abdomen strongly up and inwards towards the spine and hold until ready to take a controlled, deep inhalation.

Jalandhara Bandha: While retaining the breath, extend the spine upwards, lift the chest and draw the chin down towards the chest, creating a stretch on the back of the neck (and on the spinal cord itself). If you have any neck issues then avoid this, as it will pull the spinal cord, particularly around the back of the necck.

Ask Anne-Marie . . .

. . . about Surya Namaskar, Sun Salutations

❋ **What is the meaning of Surya and Namaskar?**

Surya, in Sanskrit, means 'The Supreme Light' or the Sun. *Namaskar* means 'salutation', and is an expression of humility, denial of the ego, in the presence of that which is greater then our small 'self'.

❋ **Is the Surya Namaskar an Asana?**

No it isn't because this is a flowing series, one pose to another. *Asana* means 'steady' and there is only one hold in the series, in the Plank, and this is so you gain momentum for the rest of the series.

❋ **What is the exact meaning of the word Asana?**

Asana means 'steady' referring to one's centredness in a posture.

❋ **Can you give me an example of an Asana?**

Virabhadrasana I – Warrior I is a true *Asana*, needing to be held for several breaths before coming out of the posture, as is *Vrksasana* – Tree Pose.

❋ **Why is the Sun Salute at the start of the class?**

The Sun Salutation postures are a cardiovascular exercise and will generate heat within the body. This in turn warms up all the major muscle groups, stretches ligaments, and prepares the body for further activity. It extends and flexes the spine and synchronises the mind, body and breath for later *Asanas*.

✳ Sun Salutes are 'Cardiovascular'. What does this mean?

This refers to the heart, lungs and blood vessel system of the body and relates to the body's ability to take in, transport and utilise oxygen. The salutes stimulate a good energised blood flow and raise the heart rate.

✳ What are the 12 key poses in the Sun Salute?

Stand with feet together at the end of your mat, body is in good posture, arms by the side.

1. EXHALE *Tadasana* – Mountain pose in prayer,
2. INHALE Extended *Tadasana* – Mountain extended into an arched back
3. EXHALE *Uttanasana* – Forward fold
4. INHALE Lunge right leg back
5. RETAIN THE BREATH *Kumbakhasana* – Plank pose
6. EXHALE *Astanga Namaskar* – 8 point pose
7. INHALE *Bhujanghasana* – Cobra
8. EXHALE *Adho Mukha Svanasana* – Down dog
9. INHALE Lunge right foot forward
10. EXHALE *Uttanasana* – Forward fold
11. INHALE Extended *Tadasana* – arching back
12. EXHALE into Prayer position in standing pose

The Sun Salutes are 12 basic poses but without stopping. The sequenced series means you flow from one 'pose' to the other with each posture synchronised with either an in or out breath. I call this 'Dancing on the Mat'.

It can take years to master, so no hurry!

What is the meaning of Agni?

Agni translates as 'inner fire' and is one of the five elements, or *Bhutas*, consisting of Earth, Air, Fire, Water, and Ether, the atmosphere around us that holds memories. *Agni* is created as we practice this classical series, by raising the blood pressure. No need for heated rooms if practiced properly!

What is the meaning of Astanga Namaskar?

This means 'eight points of the body'.

What are the eight points of the 8 points pose?

Also known as *Astanga Namaskar*, the points are: two feet, two knees, two hands, chest and chin/forehead. This stimulates the natural curve of the spine, allowing a deeper extension in the lower back and opens the chest in an almost perfect pose for the back.

In what way does the Sun Salute stimulate the spine?

The Sun Salutation sequence accentuates the natural curvatures of the spine, flooding it with freshly oxygenated blood, sending much needed nutrients to the nerves and cells around the spinal cord.

Is the Chaturanga (Crocodile pose) a progression from the 8 Point pose?

Yes, the next step is to keep in plank, lowering through the arms. Keep the elbows in, touching the side of the body, bottom activated and tucked under. Keep legs locked out and neck in line with spine. This is a 'Yogi's choice' for your practice if you are ready to progress to a more dynamic sequence, such as in the Sun Power Series I.

Astanga Namaskar, 8 Point pose

Accentuates natural curves of the spine

Chaturanga, Crocodile pose

Photo courtesy of Leicester Mercury

Ask Anne-Marie . . .

. . . about Adho Mukha Svanasana, Down Dog

Downward Facing Dog (*Adho Mukha Svanasana*) is a semi-inversion that stretches the whole of the back of the body.

This is such a challenging pose to achieve! Once mastered, it is the hinge pose to almost all poses. It opens the shoulders and chest cavity and helps to develop your upper body strength.

While practising, it will encourage a good blood flow to the heart and brain and is dynamic in nature.

The best way to achieve it, or at least to work towards the best possible pose for you and your experience, is to start from a good Plank pose (*Kumbakhasana*).

❋ **I find the down dog very hard. I can't get my heels down and my shoulders and arms seem weak. How can I get the best from this pose?**

This is the most common of questions when it comes to this pose. It all seems so hard to get right and too tough to enjoy!

My advice is to start with the plank pose. This will target all the muscle groups you need to get a good down dog. A plank is a flat piece of wood and that is how it must look! No dropping the hips or lifting the bottom. The crown of the head must lead the pose and the ankles need to be over the toes joints, not in front or behind.

To achieve this pose you need to 'feel' all the muscles of the arms, legs, back and torso engaged. The idea of only engaging core muscles is misleading as you need to also engage the external muscles of the torso to protect your lower back!

Once you have gained some strength in your upper body, legs and torso then the down dog will be achievable.

What are the specific instructions and teaching points you use when teaching down dog?

I ask that you start in plank when learning to master *Adho Mukha Svanasana*.

Begin by **INHALING** and...

* On an **EXHALE** lift your hips/sitting bones up to the sky
* Make sure you hands are your shoulder width apart.
* Spread and extend your fingers tips, pressing the pads of your hands into your mat.
* Middle fingers pointing directly ahead; not the index finger as this will turn your hands outwards and put some strain on your wrist joint. Long term this can create wrist problems, and then elbow, then shoulders too.
* Ensure again that your hands are in line with your shoulders.
* Lengthen your arms by pushing into and away from your mat.
* Flatten your shoulder blades and rotate your deltoids outwards; this will bring your inner elbows towards the sky and help engage the back muscles.
* Keep your ears lined up with your upper inner arms, don't drop or lift the chin, remember your neck is part of your spine.
* Lift the front of your body towards your spine encouraging length in your spine and space from ribs to hips.
* Pull up your quads and lock your kneecaps. If you are very tight in the hamstrings then bend the knees and push your tailbone up to sky to begin the process of stretching out your lower back.
* Keep your feet and toes together to really lengthen your lower leg muscles. If your feet are apart you will only open the top of the legs and hips.
* Gently press your heels towards your mat with an energetic emphasis on the outside edge of your feet, keeping your big toes and little toes connected to your mat.
* This will stabilise your ankles and in turn correct knock-knees and help open your hips.

✳ **NOTE:** It doesn't matter if your heels do not reach the floor, as they will if you continue to release tension in the ankles and lengthen your hamstrings and lower leg calf muscles. Walking your feet in shortens them!

✳ Continue to tilt your sit bones up to the sky to stretch your hamstrings.

✳ Breathe deeply, rhythmically, evenly and soften your face.

✳ Hold the pose for a minimum of 5 to 8 breaths.

TO EXIT THE POSE TO REST: drop your knees to the floor and sink back into your hips, knees open and rest forehead on the floor or arms. Stay for 15 seconds

Ask Anne-Marie . . .

. . . about Warrior I & II and the Triangle

The Warrior poses

❋ **Why are these called 'Warrior' poses?**

Warrior poses mean just that: they have originated from Indian martial arts and were part of the moves used for spear throwing, shooting arrows and sword work.

❋ **What is the Warrior pose's main aim?**

The Warrior pose's main aim is to open the hips, encourage movement of blood to the lower part of the body, and to strengthen the legs.

The Warrior poses are particularly good for men's health. As the hips open through a strong emphasis on the groin area, fresh oxygenated blood is focused in this area. The blood floods the respiratory, lymphatic and reproductive system.

Men's health

The prostate gland, situated deep in the internal lower male body, accessed through the anus, is one area where men are vulnerable. Prostate cancer is one of the biggest killers of men from the age of 50. I like to use this pose to talk about men's health issues and to highlight the need for men to start taking care of themselves. Men only classes are a good way to help men open up. We do tend to focus on women's health more but as Yoga attracts more men daily we have an opportunity to introduce men's health.

Can they be adapted for the new and less able?

Yes, by lessening the depth of the pose such as bringing feet into a smaller stride

Give an example of a modification?

In a modified Warrior I, the practitioner would keep their hands on the hips instead of raising them above their head if they have shoulder issues for instance.

What part of the anatomy do they target?

Warrior poses target the lower body around the groin and therefore help keep the prostate and reproductive system healthy in a male. For women their reproductive system is also flushed with fresh blood, carrying away any toxins and feeding nutrients to that area.

Why is technique of the essence in this pose?

Warriors are strong, dynamic poses, therefore health and safety is a key consideration. Knees and lower backs may be compromised without good alignment.

Which parts of the body are most at risk and why?

The knees and lower back can sustain injuries if this pose is not performed correctly. If the knees are not in correct alignment then they are at risk and this can also stress the lower back.

Where should the knee be in Warrior pose?

The front knee should be directly over the centre of the ankle, with all points of the foot making contact with the floor.

How should the foot be placed and in relation to what?

The front foot should be placed at a 90° angle to the underside of the thigh, with the middle two toes lining up with the kneecap.

✳ In Warrior I, where should the hips be?

The hips should be facing directly forward to the front and positioned under the shoulders.

✳ In Warrior II, where should the hips be?

The hips should be open to the side, in the lateral plane and directly sat beneath the shoulders.

✳ How should the back foot be placed in all Warriors and why?

The back foot should be strong and straight, the outer edge of the foot pressing into the mat. This is to ensure the safety of the knee is not compromised and that the pose has a solid foundation from the back foot.

✳ In Warrior I, when the arms are raised, what should the alignment of the shoulders be?

The shoulders remain directly over and in line with the hips.

✳ In Warrior II, where is your vision directed?

Vision is directed over and past the middle finger of the outstretched front hand.

✳ In Warrior II, how should your arms be placed?

The arms are in line with the hips in Warrior II and should be extended to your side from your shoulders, parallel to the floor. Shoulders sit directly in line with the hips.

Take a look at the arms; are they in front of the body or behind? If so correct them, to extend from the shoulder.

Virabhadrasana I – Warrior I

✳ **In all Warriors the thigh is parallel to the floor. How important is this and where is the pressure placed in the thigh, out or in?**

The parallel positioning of the thigh to the floor is to open up the groin and hip, and protect the knee. The pressure is directed to the inner thigh to ensure the knee is turning out over the little toe.

✳ **What should the belly be doing as you hold this pose?**

In Warrior pose, the belly is soft but drawn upwards long, passive and empty, thus activating *Uddiyana Bandha*.

✳ **What is the difference between a Warrior pose and a lunge?**

In a lunge the hips drop deeper. A Warrior pose is a stable pose with the hips and pelvis remaining in line with the shoulders, body weight centred; whereas in a lunge the body weight shifts away from centre, i.e. towards the front leg, to deepen the pose and open up the hips further.

Virabhadrasana II – Warrior II

Parsvakonasana – Lunge

The Triangle

The Triangle (*Trikonasana*) is a geometrical pose. There is a real issue with students not understanding the mathematical triangle and that it has no bends or curves in it.

Here are some interesting questions asked about it.

❋ ## I am told to make a side bend to reach my foot in the triangle. Is this correct?

No, this is not correct and is to do with not observing the rules of mathematics and geometry. A triangle has straight sides. To keep from bending, don't lower hand to the floor if you have to collapse the spine or bend the knees. So the correct instructions to achieve the best pose are to ask the student to 'extend' or 'reach' to the side. This is then a lateral extension and not a side bend.

❋ ## Why is the Triangle often linked to the Warrior poses?

If we look at the anatomy of the *Trikonasana*, we need to be conscious of where we feel the pose stretching our muscles. As we come into the lateral extension, our knees need to be pulled up by applying the thigh muscles, the quadriceps. This in turn will allow a safe stretching of the inner thighs, adductor muscles. These we use to bring our legs together. By stretching them they are learning to extend. It can pull and be felt strongly; this is a message that they are working to extend.

The Warriors are deep openers for the hips and the inner thighs, so it is logical to practice a Triangle before a Warrior, as these can be very powerful indeed.

The logical progression from one pose to another is imperative to safe stretching.

❋ ## Should all my leg muscles be engaged?

Yes, engage all leg muscles but also your gluteal muscles, buttocks, and the core muscles too! Don't drop your body; think about the lines of a triangle.

Where should my arm be when it is extended above?

The arm should go directly up to the sky, and needs to be balanced over the shoulder. Watch out for it going behind you as this can put a lot of strain on the shoulder joint. Think about the thumb over the nose, look at it then take your eye along past the thumb. If your shoulder hurts, or is injured, drop it to sit along the side of the body or place hand on hip.

My neck hurts if I keep it looking skyward. What can I do about this?

This is a good question! If you have pain, strain or feel dizzy, you need to turn your face to the floor, but don't drop it, keep the neck lined up with your spine. If you feel dizzy it may be that you have low blood pressure, it may be worth seeing your GP/doctor to get this verified.

How do I get the best alignment?

If you were to look at the Triangle from the side, rather than the front of your body, you would see it's a very slim shape. There is no bottom sticking out and no head in front of your leg. So all you need to do is push your hips forward to your front of body and then push your back up against an imaginary wall. Keep your neck lined up with your spine and don't put your chin up. This way you will achieve the true geometrical shape of the triangle!

How long should I hold the Triangle for?

I advise 3 to 8 breaths depending on your experience.

Ask Anne-Marie . . .

. . . about Balances

"Why can't I balance?"

I run many Balance workshops and that question is the title. It is the most common question I am asked about balances and this is the one area of Yoga that seems to really matter to a student. Achieving a successful balance, whether on the feet or hands seems to mark a milestone in the progress of that student.

✽ **Do my feet make a difference to my balances?**
What if I have weak ankles, flat feet or bunions?

Yes, all those issues will make a huge difference to your ability to balance, as they will literally 'knock you off balance'.

The root of a balancing pose comes from the ankle, that is the foundation of the pose. If you have flat feet then your ankles will roll inwards. This action means your knees will knock together and in turn the hips are inwardly rotating, the lower back compressed.

If we cannot stand up straight then we wont be able to distribute our weight evenly in one place or on the surface we stand on.

Bunions are both painful and difficult to work with. Having an enlarged toe joint will pull you off balance just by the nature of the swelling and where it is. The big toe is an intrinsic part of achieving a balance. Imagine not having a toe? You would not be able to balance. So the use of a sliver of cork between the big toe and the next toe as you walk around the house can help ease the opening of the toe joint. If there is severe pain then don't force this. It may be that surgery is your only option. Try using the toe separators you can buy to paint your nails with ladies. Men stick to the cork cut in half lengthwise!

What can I do to help improve weak areas of my feet and ankles?

Trying some simple exercises can strengthen weak ankles. Fetch a tin of beans or any tinned food and place the tin on its side so it can roll. Try sitting with sit bones on the edge of a hard chair and with a straight back. Place your right foot onto the tin and push the tin away from you with your foot until the toes point. Use all the muscles in the leg. Then roll the tin back towards you until the heel drops down towards the floor. This will stretch the foot muscles and back of the calf and also strengthen the foot, instep and ankle as you push the tin away. Do this rolling action 10 times to start with, building up to 20 and repeat on the other foot. Try this twice a day for a week. Monitor your response when balancing. I had to do this when at ballet school to improve my arches ready for pointe work.

My hands and wrists as well as upper body are weak. Can I ever perform a hand balance?

Yes of course you can! You need to strengthen the arms, hands and wrists by simply doing your Sun Salutes! That amazing series builds up your strength and stamina. It is, as you know cardiovascular and so increases your heart rate, but also works the heart muscle and abdominals too. All these areas are needed to do a simple hand balance like the Crow (*Kakasana*). Even if you don't take all your weight onto your hands for some time, just trying is working the right muscles for the job!

In *Kakasana* (crow pose), your feet are your hands.

Big toes are your thumbs; little toes are little fingers.

Heel is the heel of your hand. Ankles are your wrists.

Your arms become legs. Deltoids are your buttocks.

Don't fall into your hands. Push out of the floor.

You need to fly, so keep your head up and lift from the heart!

What are the benefits of a balance?

The benefits of a balance are myriad. The legs work hard if you are on one leg. The foot roots into the floor and so, if you don't keep the four points of the foot rooted, then the ankle moves too much and trying to keep a balance becomes very hard work indeed.

The Tree pose (*Vrksasana*), is an obvious one to use to illustrate its focus in the body. After coming down from the one-legged tree pose, your leg feels huge and heavy and tired! A lot of blood has moved to that supporting leg and it really does swell up. So it feels like a tree trunk!

Blood is pushed up to the heart just through the effort of holding the posture. A balance forces the mind to be still and concentration is proved to be part of the achievement of any balance.

You balance everyday in all you do,
whether at work or at home.
Reaching to a top shelf,
stooping to pick something up,
carrying your shopping or a child;
it's all about balance.

❋ What role does the mind play in being able to balance?

The mind is all that balances are about. The mistake people make is to anticipate failure. When you try to put your trousers on, don't you balance on one leg more often than not? When you reach for the top shelf of your kitchen, don't you balance on one leg or on your tiptoes? The mind is not focusing on you balancing but on getting something done.

Try this: Stand on one foot and start swinging the other leg back and forth, smile, breathe, enjoy and have fun! What happened? Write it down!

Expectations are what throw people off balance.

My philosophy for my classes and students is:

* ❋ Practice with an open mind.
* ❋ Do not judge or force the pose.
* ❋ Do not say you cannot achieve a balance, confirming your worst fears!
* ❋ Focus the eyes on one spot at a low eye-level not high,
  as this can lift the chin and pull you backward.
* ❋ Breathe slowly and your mind will slow down.
* ❋ Steady mind, steady pose.
* ❋ Smile from the inside!

Ask Anne-Marie . . .

. . . about Twists

✳ ### What is meant by the expression 'connecting to the breath in posture'?

The Twist (*Ardha Matsyendrasana*), is one of the most difficult poses to achieve comfortably but is the best to feel how the breath and the mind work together. It is not easy to get into this pose but there are many modifications that help you to ease into it. Once you have settled in, the breath takes over and the mind melts. It is my personal favourite to practice if I want to remind myself why Yoga is my life. The pose, the breath, the mind all blend into one; you feel so released emotionally that it is a pose you can hold longer then you imagined you could.

Each Yoga practice should become a fluid and creative meditation, with the breath and movement indistinct from each other. You experience them as one action, inseparably intertwined. You will instinctively 'breathe as you move – stretch as you breathe'. Full awareness of your breath brings a clarity of attention and consciousness that transcends the intellectual mind and accesses bodily intelligence as a means of exploring and understanding our bodies. The breath can lead your movement into and out of a posture, endowing each *Asana* with a dynamic energy and yet, simultaneously, a meditative quality. It is concerned with being alive! Breath is rhythmic, nourishing and sustaining. Throughout our Yoga practice, connecting to the breath will deepen the experience and, with increased awareness, the breath can be directed to wherever it needs to go, where energy, oxygen or *Prana* may be lacking. Our movement is initiated or inspired by the breath and is surrounded by breath.

❋ Why does the Spinal Twist illustrate the expression so beautifully?

Ardha Matsyendrasana (Spinal Twist), requires full attention and awareness on the breath to deliver its true benefits. Breathing abdominally can, initially, relax the body and prepare it to move into the posture. For the twist to happen, space in the abdomen is needed, so a shift to empowered thoracic breathing allows space to be created in the abdomen to deepen the twist. Continued deep, empowered thoracic breathing (lower and upper chest) transforms the twist into a meditative posture, with the breath massaging internal organs and moving though our inner body like nothing else can. In the spinal twist therefore, the breath embodies the technical, exploratory and spiritual aspects of the pose and sustains us whilst we deepen and then exit the posture.

❋ How can you convey to your students the essence of 'connectedness'?

Each one of us is a miraculous cellular community comprising trillions of cells that all evolved from just one cell; a micro-universe. What we know as the human body is made possible by the intelligence that lies within these cells to assemble structures and perform their specialist functions, that give rise to our consciousness; a consciousness that is the individual expression of the universal consciousness (*Purusha*). The practice of Yoga helps us to create and hold a stillness that is ever present within us, yet not consistently experienced. Connecting with this stillness, this intelligence, this consciousness affords us a deeper understanding of our own Self, a micro-universe within a greater universe; infinity focused in a body. To connect with the breath and the stillness within is to connect with the bliss, the unity and eternal beauty of Life itself.

One drop of water contains the universe.
One cell contains the universe and in turn our body and mind reflects that internal universe.
Uni – together, Verse – song

Sing together

AMN

What does a teacher mean when they ask you consider the 'feeling of a pose' rather than simply the technique?

An *Asana* is not a mechanical contortion that can be achieved with a distant, distracted mind. It is a fully conscious expression of the body's natural potential, which cannot be understood on the level of mind as a concept or through intellectualisation. The essence of *Asana* is about sensing, asking permission of the body, communicating and co-operating with the body; that means the musculoskeletal body, the neuroendocrine body, the organ body, the nervous body, the fluid body, and the cellular body. There is an enormous intelligence that interconnects for each of us to make the simplest of movements. The feeling of a pose is therefore developing an awareness of what our bodies are communicating to us when performing an *Asana*. It is conscious-awareness and intuitive. It is about 'being', rather then 'doing'.

As a teacher how can we adapt spinal twist for people with serious back problems?

The spinal twist should not be done be people with a serious back or spinal injury. However, modifications for lesser back problems include: the use of a block to lengthen the spine and improve postural alignment, keeping the supporting leg/legs stretched in front and simply bending the other leg and keeping it on the same side or crossing it over if flexibility allows. Alternatively, a supine twist could be performed.

As in pregnancy, on occasion a student's tummy will not allow for a deep twist so what do you suggest for that student?

The pregnant student could fold their right foot into their thigh, left foot outstretched, and twist from this posture, keeping space in the abdomen. Alternatively, a supine twist could be performed.

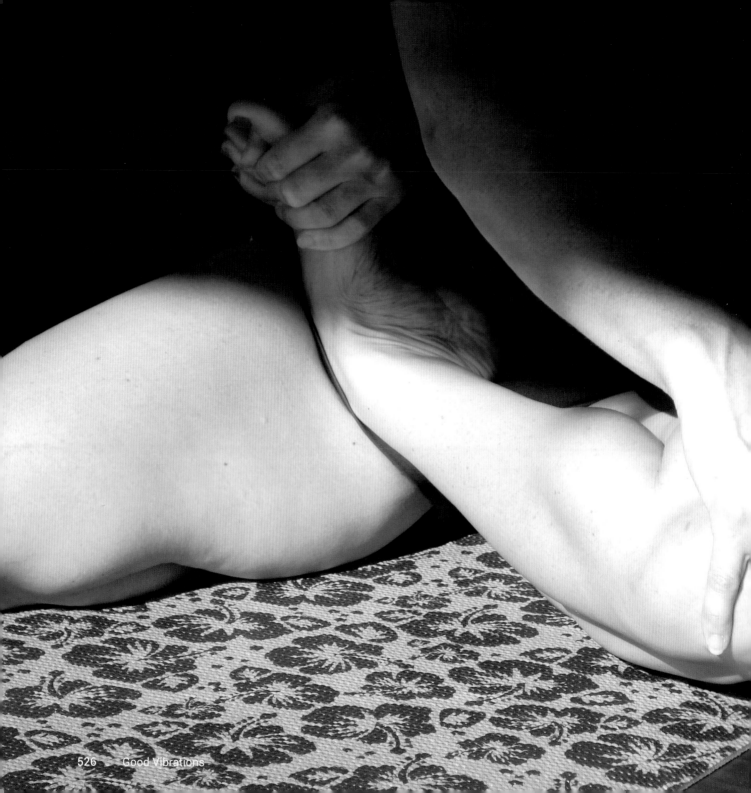

If a student is struggling and you have forgotten to give an alternative, do you try and force them into the pose?

No. A student is never forced into a pose. If there is time, bring them out of the pose and modify, adjust or provide an alternative for them.

Why would you make sure you have an alternative for the student

An alternative is important because the spinal twist is a challenging pose and it is essential to make all students feel included and allow them to access the benefits of the pose that have been described through a simpler or modified posture.

Is it possible that we sometimes humiliate a student without due care and how can we make sure that does not happen?

Yes, because people are naturally sensitive and sometimes vulnerable, assuming a challenging pose can be performed by anyone is potentially humiliating for an inexperienced or differently able student. A teacher must ensure that students understand that *Asanas* are not a 'one-size-fits-all' phenomenon. It is a teacher's responsibility to make students feel at ease with the principle that modifications and alternative postures are perfectly normal as they explore their own unique bodies. A Yoga practice is a personal journey of exploration and the teacher is the 'tour guide' to help students have the best possible individual experience.

Give an example of a full twist

A full twist, a very challenging and advanced pose, is *Paripurna Matsyendrasana* (the Complete Lord of the Fishes). The difference between the half spinal twist and the full spinal twist is the placement of the foot. In the full spinal twist the right foot is positioned between the left thigh and the abdomen. This creates a much more intense pressure on the internal organs of the body. Proficiency in the Lotus pose is a prerequisite for the full spinal twist. Its difficulty rating is 38 out of 60 in B.K S. Iyengar's 'Light on Yoga'.

Why do we always sit to the left to begin a twist?

The first twist should always be to the right as this stimulates the ascending colon, which helps with elimination. To achieve this is dependent on sitting to the left to begin.

Explain the organs involved in this pose, the left and right organs

The organs involved on the right hand side of the body are: ascending colon, gall bladder, pancreas, liver (right lobe) and the right kidney. On the left hand side: liver (left lobe), descending colon, spleen, pancreas, and left kidney.

Breathing is the key to getting the best from the Twist poses and it's worth understanding the 'Four modes of breathing'.

Explain what happens to the breath during the Spinal Twist

To enter a spinal twist, inhale to extend upwards, and exhale to move into the twist. Upon the exhalation the rib cage contracts and facilitates the turn into the twist. Once in the pose the breath is forced upwards into thoracic breathing, expanding the rib cage sideways, front and back. The breath is smooth and natural into the chest to create space in the abdomen.

Describe the benefits of practising this pose

Twists wring out the body and help to release enormous amounts of tension. When the musculature organs relax again after a twist the area becomes flooded with fresh, oxygenated blood and nutrients, which is cleansing and deeply nourishing. The spinal twist, in particular, *Ardha Matsyendrasana* (the Half-Spinal Twist), exerts a lateral tilt in the dorsa-lumbar and lumbar sacral area and this extension of the pelvis at the hips can be a deep physical/emotional release. It gives the internal organs a squeeze, removing toxins and delivers fresh oxygenated blood to them and, importantly, it stimulates the endocrine system.

The Spinal Twist is an important posture for the Viscera, the internal organs in the main cavities of the body, especially those in the abdomen, e.g. the intestines because the pose massages and squeezes blood out of the internal organs, improving circulation and maintaining their healthy function.

The Emotional Body

This pose can also help release emotional tensions held within the 'memory' of tissues and cells. It may be surprising to know that spinal twists are also good for slipped discs because they open up the vertebrae and stop compression, though not to be practiced if you are in pain with it! Best do a seated one and twist from the waist only.

Endocrine and Chakras

The Twist stimulates both the Endocrine (see page 564) and Chakra System. Notice that the chakras align with the endocrine glands, which is interesting as the function of these systems relate to the chemical body as well as the emotional and subtle body.

*So do the chemicals produce emotions
or the emotions create the chemical secretions?*

Ask Anne-Marie . . .

. . . about Forward and Back Bends

Forward and back bends need to be carefully practised with the muscular and structural body in mind. Logical and intelligent progression must be heeded if no strain to the lower back, groin or hips is to be experienced.

Start with opening the inner thighs and groin as in Tailor pose. This pose will also begin to slowly warm up the lower back and hips in preparation for the deeper and more challenging forward and back bend.

❋ **Should we start with a back or forward bend?**

Always begin with the forward bends as this set of postures will start to warm up all the correct muscle groups in safe preparation for the more dynamic and extreme back bends.

❋ **What is the best sequence for a forward bend series?**

Bhadrasana, Tailor pose, *Janu Sirsasana*, head to knee pose, and finish with *Pachimottanasana*, the West pose, hence intelligent progression of postures from warm up to deep extension.

❋ **What is the Sanskrit for Tailor pose?**

As ever, Sanskrit is often translated loosely, and in this case Tailor pose can be called *Baddha Konasana* or *Bhadrasana*, Butterfly pose, as they both open the hips and groin, and lengthen the inner thighs' adductor muscles. It may also be called Cobbler pose as both the Indian tailors and cobblers sit in this position when working.

Why is this pose a good preparation for forward and back bends?

This pose is a great 'warm up' for the lower back, the lumbar spine, as well as rotating the hip flexors.

The hip flexors are the group of muscles around the ball and socket joint as well as those that extend into the glutials and piriformis. These muscles include the iliopsoas group, which consists of the psoas major and iliacus muscles, and the quadriceps femoris group, which consists of the rectus femoris, vastus intermedius, vastus lateralis, and vastus medialis.

This pose 'eases' the body into a forward bend without stressing the lower back or hips. The beauty of this pose is you can work deeper and deeper as your body progresses, using the head as a 'weight' and of course focus on the breath each time you extend deeper. It should never be practised 'cold'!

Would Janu Sirsana help me progress to a full forward bend?

Performing *Janu Sirsasana* (Head to Knee pose), opens one hip and lengthens the hamstring on the other leg but it must precede *Pachimottanasana* as part of the logical progression of postural sequences. It will also continue to work the hips and the lower back without force or strain.

What is your 'Golden Rule' for forward bends?

I have developed a simple set of 'rules' with all my teaching methods and this works well when understanding the alignment of the spine and most importantly in a forward bend.

When moving forward into the bend:

* Move belly to thigh,
* Chest to knee,
* Face to shin,

In that order

Why does Pachimottanasana translate to 'The West Pose'?

'West Pose' is so called because it stretches the back of the body. In Indian culture the West is traditionally associated with the back of the body and the front as the East.

You are as young as your spine is flexible.

❋ **What major muscles group is engaged in this forward bend?**

The legs, particularly the quads, to stretch out the hamstrings, the hip flexors and abdominals.

❋ **This pose is also known as the 'youthful pose'. Why is this?**

This relates to developing flexibility in the spine and hamstrings maintaining an agile and fluid body, associated with youthfulness.

❋ **Should the head be lowered in this pose?**

You can lower the head to increase the stretch on the spine but only if the belly is reaching to the thigh: belly to thigh, chest to knee, face to shin.

If you are not able to get your belly close to your thighs then lowering the head to the knee does not stretch out your hamstrings but will put strain on your upper shoulders, neck and lower back. It is better to use a strap around the pad of the foot, which will give your arms some length and then aid your back to lean forward to get the best out of the pose. Practice this by bending your arms as though you were riding a horse.

❋ **Why should the shoulders be pulled back and away from the ears while practising this Asana?**

Pulling the shoulders away from the ears opens the chest, which facilitates better breathing, but most importantly, if the chest is closed it will round the upper thoracic spine. In a forward fold the intention is to lengthen the spine. Pulling the shoulders back activates the spinal muscles and encourages the front of the body to also lengthen, rather then collapse in a heap.

Why should the feet be kept together and knees to the sky?

To isolate, target and activate the hamstrings. If the legs and feet roll open then the exact muscle group you need to target are released and we flop forward with no benefits achieved.

What is the Sanskrit for Inclined plane/Reverse plank?

The Sanskrit name is *Purvottanasana*, and is the 'counter-pose' to the forward bend/West pose. Legs are kept straight, toes pointed to floor and the hands pointing away from buttocks to open up the chest and roll shoulders back.

It can also be performed as the Table, with knees bent and the feet planted mat-width apart. Keep the knees over the ankles, shoulders over the wrists and head dropped back if you don't suffer neck issues or low blood pressure. If you do suffer with either then keep your chin firmly tucked into the chest.

Why is the Inclined plane practiced after forward bend?

It is a counter-pose to the sitting forward bends. A counter-pose is a contraction of the muscles where there has been an extension, or an extension of the muscles to counteract a contraction.

Why is it so important to keep the wrists under the shoulders as you lift into Inclined plane?

The alignment of the wrists under shoulders supports the joint. If it is out of line it will go out of joint and a strain is likely to occur.

You keep the mouth closed in this pose. Why is that?

Keeping the mouth closed disengages and retracts the hyoid bone. This works the muscles in the throat to support the windpipe and the cervical spine. If the mouth is open, the hyoid floats and much of the support described is lost.

❋ Why should a pregnant student not perform the Inclined plane the normal way?

There is too much pressure and weight on the back from the weight of the abdomen's extra contents. This puts a strain on the joints, hips and spine. Best to sit cross-legged, lean back into hands and arch the back. This is considered a passive spinal stretch.

❋ What is the Sanskrit name for Cobra pose?

Bhujanghasana.

❋ Explain which muscles are used for Cobra.

The back muscles, including the deep muscles of the spine, the erector spinae, abdominals, triceps and biceps, and neck muscles.

❋ Explain how important is the use and placement of the shoulders?

The shoulders must be away from the ears and positioned directly over the wrists. This ensures correct support of the joint, thus preventing strains of the joint.

❋ Give an example of a back bend in late pregnancy.

An example of a safe back bend for pregnancy is a seated cross-legged back bend. The hands on the floor behind them support this back bend, fingers pointing away from the back, arch back to release only the cervical upper, the thoracic middle back and not the lumber lower back. This lower back area is weakened as the tummy expands and abdominals are stretched.

❋ What organs are stimulated during the Cobra?

The kidneys, abdominal organs, digestive organs as well as the heart and lungs are stimulated during *Bhujanghasana.*

Is Cobra OK for those with neck problems?

Yes, if the head is not bent back but kept level and looking straight ahead.

Where should the legs be in Cobra? Together, apart, or both ways depending on the depth of the pose?

The legs should be slightly apart so the heels are allowed to fall outwards to protect the SI joint – sacroiliac. Pushing the heels together compresses the SI joints and causes sciatica if continually practised in this way.

When doing a sequence of three Cobras, where and when do you inhale or exhale?

Inhale to come up, retain the breath and exhale to come down. Make sure you come up a little first time, and take the hands off the mat. This will make the fine muscles of the spine work as well as the major ones such as the Latismus Dorsi.

What is the Sanskrit for Camel.

Ustra means 'Camel' in Sanskrit; *Ustrasana* is the Camel pose.

What are the contra indications for Camel pose?

Contra indications for the Camel pose are injuries to the lower back, spine, or neck and also in pregnancy. If you suffer from low blood pressure then this must be practised with the chin pulled into the chest and the tops of the back of the thighs gripped and elbows pulled in so the bend is not extreme.

What muscles are engaged in this pose?

Lower back and back muscles, thighs, hip flexors, and abdominals.

❋ What organs are stimulated?

The kidneys are stimulated, abdominal organs, digestive system and the heart and lungs. So anyone with high blood pressure that is not medicated needs to perform a very moderate version.

❋ What can you gain from regular practice?

This pose increases spinal flexibility, improves posture, and aids digestion; it is also very energising and opens the heart chakra, as do all backbends.

Tailor pose

Head to knee pose

West pose

Inclined plane

Cobra pose

Folded tailor pose

Pigeon pose

Extended camel pose

Ask Anne-Marie . . .

. . . about Inversions: Headstand, Shoulder stand, Plough and Legs up the Wall pose

If you do not know Tadasana, you do not know Sirsasana at all, though you can stand on your head.

B.K.S. Iyengar

❋ **What are the benefits of an inversion?**

As the quote here explains, if you are unable to stand correctly in *Tadasana* (Mountain pose), then you won't really get the essence of *Sirsasana* (The Headstand), even if you are on your head!

Inversions celebrate the defeat of gravity, and once achieved to a good level they will feel light and uplifting.

Inversions revitalise the whole system, reversing the effects of gravity and flooding the brain with nourishment. *Sarvangasana* (The Shoulder Stand) strengthens the nervous system and emotions by stimulating the thyroid and parathyroid glands, which regulate metabolism as part of the endocrine system. The lymphatic and digestive systems are also stimulated.

Elevating the legs, as in *Viparita Karani* (Legs up the wall pose), also improves circulation, venous return, and lymph drainage, all of which nourish cells in the face muscles and skin, relieve strain and fatigue in the legs and feet, and stimulate intestinal sluggishness, improving digestion and elimination.

These postures evoke calm, quiet an over-stimulated brain, and soothe the nerves. In addition to all these benefits, *Sirsasana* also strengthens the neck, shoulders and arms and stimulates the pineal and pituitary glands of the endocrine system.

❊ What are the benefits to the Endocrine System?

The Headstand has a beneficial reconditioning effect on the entire endocrine system, enabling it to withstand greater stress and strain. It stimulates the system as it bathes and nourishes the glands with refreshed blood, in particular the pineal and the pituitary glands. Our health, growth and vitality depend on the proper functioning of these two glands that control the chemical balance of the body. The pituitary is the master gland and plays a very important role in regulating menstruation and pregnancy. Inverted postures regulate the functioning of this master gland. (See page 564 for more on this.)

❊ What are the benefits to the Lymphatic System?

The Headstand importantly increases circulation and drainage of lymphatic fluid. Lymph returns to your heart via the veins, is dependent upon muscular movement and gravity to facilitate its return. Thus, in the Headstand, lymph fluid is relieved from the legs and ankles and with regular practice prevents the build up of fluid in the legs and feet. Because the lymphatic system is a closed pressure system and has one-way valves that keep lymph moving towards the heart, when upside down in Headstand, the entire lymphatic system is stimulated, thus strengthening your immune system.

Salamba Sirsasana
Supported Headstand

Sarvangasana
Shoulder stand

Halasana
Plough

Viparita Karani
Legs up the
wall pose

❋ What are the benefits to the Central Nervous System?

The central nervous system consists of the brain, spinal cord, and a complex network of neurons. 'Nervous tissue is responsible for sensing stimuli and transmitting signals to and from different parts of an organism. Neurons are the basic unit of nervous tissue'.

The nervous system is responsible for sending, receiving, and interpreting information from all parts of the body. It monitors and coordinates internal organ function and responds to changes in the external environment.

The Headstand stimulates the nervous system and increases and enhances mental alertness and clarity; an effect felt after performing the pose, which lasts throughout the day. The posture increases blood and oxygen supply to the brain, refreshing and rejuvenating neurons. This serves to calm the brain and helps relieve stress and mild depression.

The Headstand, though a centreing, calming and soothing pose,
is also mentally challenging and can be both enlightening
and fearful in equal parts!

❋ What are the benefits to the Respiratory System?

Sirsasana strengthens the lungs and helps promote healthier lung tissue. When standing or sitting upright, gravity pulls our fluids earthward and blood saturates the lower lungs more thoroughly. The lower lung tissue is thus more compressed than the upper lungs. As a result, the air we inhale moves naturally into the open alveoli of the upper lungs. Unless we take a good, deep breath, we do not raise the ratio of air to blood in the lower lungs. When we invert, blood secretes the well-ventilated upper lobes of the lungs, thus ensuring more efficient oxygen-to-blood exchange, healthier lung tissue and oxygen consumption.

Correct performance of the Headstand helps the spine become properly aligned, improving posture, facilitating good breathing and reducing muscular stress. The inversion rests the lungs, which feel refreshed. The vital capacity increases as the lungs learn to breathe against the pressure of the body organs resting on it in the posture.

❋ How does it improve blood circulation?

Blood circulation to the brain is improved in *Sirsasana*; cells are rejuvenated and the brain, being the seat of intelligence, is stimulated. Inversions exercise the heart and encourage venous return.

One of the advantages of the Headstand is that the increased blood flow to and from the heart makes the heart pump stronger, increasing cardiac output, resembling the cardiovascular activity achieved while exercising. Interestingly, inverting your entire body in the Headstand lessens the strain on your heart. Normally, your heart works against gravity persistently to ensure that freshly oxygenated blood makes its way up to the brain and its sensory organs.

Sirsasana **also helps to relieve varicose veins**. With varicose veins, the valves in the legs are weak and they don't fully close after the blood flows up, this is the reason blood flows back into the legs and expands the veins over time. These veins swell and become painful. The Headstand gives the valves some help to stop the blood flowing back into the legs and relieves the swelling for a while. Regular practice of legs up the wall will do the same, as in *Viparita Karani*.

❋ What are the benefits to the muscles?

Sirsasana strengthens the muscles of the neck, arm, shoulder and abdomen, and also helps to align and strengthen the spine. Because the whole weight of the body is supported, the upper body and abdominal muscles are engaged to create stability in the pose. Headstand also tones the muscles in the legs.

❋ What are the benefits for vital organs?

The counteraction of the force of gravity in inversions allows the internal organs to reposition themselves and find new space. Also, the weight of the internal organs massages the lungs, increasing vital capacity as the lungs learn to breathe against the added weight.

❋ What are the benefits for digestion?

Headstand tones and cleans digestive organs and helps to increase *Agni*, gastric fire, producing heat in the body, which in turn improves digestion. Additionally, the weight of the abdominal organs on the diaphragm encourages deep breathing, which gently massages the internal organs. By reversing the pull of gravity on the organs, especially the intestines, it helps to cleanse them by releasing congested blood in the small intestine and colon. Fresh warm blood invigorates the cells and overcomes problems of the liver, kidneys, stomach, intestines and reproductive system. The change in posture enhances peristaltic contractions and aids good elimination, and can help alleviate constipation.

Opens the mind

Inversions challenge your mind so you have to face fear when first learning it.
Because of this they help to create a sense of self-awareness
and will develop self-assuredness.

We are born head-first in a classic birth
and the Headstand will make you feel a little lost, without boundaries
and prepare you for a
'World turned up-side down!'

Ask Anne-Marie . . .

. . . about Matsyasana, The Fish Pose

✳ **Why do you suggest practising the Fish pose after the shoulder-stand or semi-inversion?**

The Fish pose is the 'counter-pose' to the shoulder-stand, and should always have some sort of similar opening for the chest, extension of the neck and deep breathing to expand the lungs. During an inversion, internal organs are forced to drop towards the diaphragm, the dome shaped muscle under the ribs.

I consider that this posture can also be performed as a single pose for self-practice, especially after a hard day at the desk! However, without the benefits of the shoulder-stand or semi-inversion, such as half shoulder-stand supported by a wall, you may not 'feel' the results of practising it quite as deeply. The reason? It's so important to stimulate the spinal cord, the digestive system, endocrine and lymphatic systems and this feels so rewarding after the shoulder-stand.

✳ **What are the benefits of this posture?**

The chest opens, shoulders are pushed back and the heart space is open. The pose creates space for the lungs to expand and take in up to 30% more oxygen and so bringing fresh oxygenated blood into the heart and brain. The arched back stimulates the back and neck via the central nervous system.

❋ **I have low blood pressure and it makes me feel sick. Why?**

Low blood pressure means your heart is unable to pump sufficient blood to the brain when the head is tilted back. As the neck tilts back it constricts the arteries that supply blood to the brain. This can feel like you are fainting or may feel some nausea.

Anyone suffering from low blood pressure should practice this with the head supported on either a block or a blanket. The chest and thoracic cavity can still be opened and get all the benefits of the head back by pressing through the arms. Better still, have the thoracic cavity lifted with two blocks, a rolled blanket or small bolster...not a big one! Ensure legs and feet are relaxed.

Fish variation for wrist and hand issues

Supported Fish for shoulder issues

Supported Fish for low blood pressure and/or neck issues

❋ **Why is it called Matsyasana?**

The look of the pose resembles a fish. The ribs resemble the gills and if you consider this fish has been tossed onto the beach, then it needs to breathe very deeply indeed to survive and hope to be thrown back into the sea!

The Hindu deity Vishnu is said to have turned himself into a fish (*Matsya*) when the world was going to be destroyed by a flood. Vishnu as *Matsya*, carried the great Hindu sages to safety in a boat, and preserved their wisdom for mankind.

This is a must for children who often sit badly, for those suffering from breathing problems as it makes breathing deeply easier, and for panic attacks and anxiety as it again aids full chest and abdominal breathing.

Matsyasana is probably one of the
most liberating postures for
the Human Being,
even if it is called the Fish!

It allows us to breathe
without restriction,
and to live out of water
from whence we came!

Ask Anne-Marie . . .

. . . about Anatomy Basics

What Muscle Groups are targeted in a Yoga session?

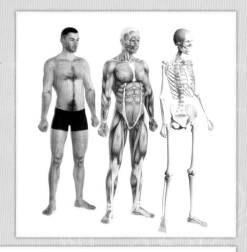

Lets start with ...

✳ Sternocleidomastoid

✳ Where is this muscle located?

This muscle is located on both sides of the front of the neck. It is a two-headed, strap-like muscle.

✳ How would you recognize a weakness in this area?

A weakness shows up in difficulty raising the head when lying down. The head would turn towards the weaker side. Neck extension also increases to form an 's' curve.

✳ What injury in this area would upset balance and structural alignment?

Extreme whiplash.

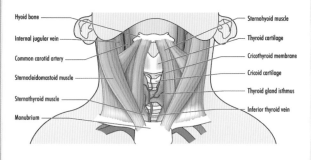

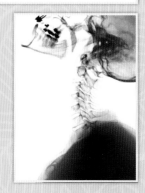

The Deltoid

❋ Where is it located and what is its action?

This is a three-part muscle located at the shoulder. It has anterior, lateral and posterior sections. The deltoid abducts the shoulder and flexes and extends the arm.

❋ What common ailments may affect this muscle?

The deltoid caps the shoulder and draws the arm away from the body, lifting the elbow. Weakness will make it difficult to raise the arm. Lung problems such as bronchitis, pleurisy, pneumonia, congestions and flu will usually affect the deltoid.

❋ How would you recognize a weakness in this area?

Difficulty holding the arm out to the side.

❋ What is a Yoga pose that would help?

Inclined plane (*Purvottanasana*), and/or Downward Dog (*Adho Mukha Svanasana*).

The Glutes

The Glutes are made up of the Gluteus Maximus and Medius, both on the upper body muscle layer, and then the Minimus located as part of the deeper muscle group.

The Gluteus Maximus muscle is located in the buttocks and is regarded as one of the strongest and largest muscles in the human body. It is connected to the coccyx, or tailbone, as well as other surrounding bones. The Gluteus Maximus muscle is responsible for movement of the hip and thigh.

Such actions as standing up, climbing stairs, and staying in an erect position are all aided by the Gluteus Maximus.

If there is pain when getting up to a standing position or lowering to sit, this could be caused by Gluteus Maximus syndrome. This is a spasm in the Gluteus Maximus muscle. The pain usually goes once sat down, and affects only one side of the body.

Other causes of pain can be an inflammation of the tendons or friction between the bones, tendons, and Gluteus Maximus muscle; these conditions are referred to as either bursitis or tendinitis. Anything described as 'itis' means inflammation.

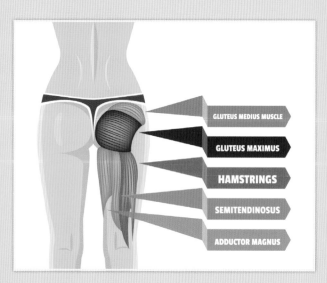

Treatments for these disorders include physical therapy or anti-inflammatory pills or injections. Physical therapists may try to put pressure on the joint of the Gluteus Maximus muscle and coccyx, or recommend exercises to reduce pain and improve the range of motion.

Try the twist pose sitting and the supine (lying down) twist. Make sure that in down-dog you tilt the pelvis and tailbone to the sky to encourage a 'pelvic tilt' to stretch out the hamstrings and gluteus.

❈ Hamstring

❈ What does 'hamstring' mean, literally?

To 'draw together the back of the leg'. (*hamme* [Ger] – back of leg + *stringere* [Lat] – draw together)

❈ Where is it located and what is its action?

The hamstrings are located on the inside and outside of the thigh. They flex the knee and extend the thigh.

❈ What are the name of the three parts of the hamstring?

From medial to lateral, they are: semimembranosus, semitendinosus, and Biceps Femoris.

❈ How would you recognize a weakness in this area?

'Knock knees' or 'bow legs'. Also, tight hamstrings prevent people from touching their toes whilst keeping their legs straight.

❈ Which Yoga pose would help?

Warrior III pose (*Virabhadrasana* III).

❋ **The Quadriceps, the large muscle group on the front of the thigh**

   ❊ This is made up of four parts. What are they?

   Rectus Femoris, vastus intermedius, vastus medialis, and vastus lateralis.

   ❊ What is its action?

   To extend the leg through the knee joint and flex the thigh.

   ❊ How would you recognize a weakness in this area?

   Difficulty straightening the knee and flexing the thigh.

   ❊ Give a Yoga pose to help with the weakness

   Chair pose (*Utkatasana*).

❋ **How do muscles enable the body to move?**

The primary function of skeletal muscles is to produce movement through the ability to contract and relax in a co-ordinated manner. They are attached to bones by tendons. The place where a muscle attaches to a relatively stationary point on a bone, either directly or via a tendon, is called the origin. When the muscle contracts, it transmits tension to the bones across one or more joints and movement occurs. The end of the muscle that attaches to the bone that moves is called the insertion. Muscles work together, or in opposition, to achieve a wide variety of movement. There are four functional groups:

1. Agonist/Prime mover: This is the muscle that contracts to produce a certain action around a joint. For example, the hamstrings are agonists when you flex your knee.

2. Antagonist: The Antagonist is a muscle that relaxes while the agonist contracts. The antagonist produces the opposite action about a joint. For example, the quadriceps is the antagonists to the hamstrings when you flex your knee. When you extend your knee, the quadriceps is the agonists and the hamstrings are the antagonists.

3. Synergist: Most movements require the action(s) of synergists, muscles that assist and fine-tune the action of the agonist, preventing unwanted movements, and which can be used to produce the same action, although generally not as effectively. For example, the biceps brachii is the prime mover for flexion at the elbow, while the coracobrachialis and the brachialis help the action.

4. Fixator: Other muscles act as fixators that stabilize the origin of the agonist to allow the prime movement to occur more efficiently, for example the muscles of the scapular.

How do we stretch our muscles?

❋ **Once your muscles have reached their maximum through stretching, what is stretched next, and by how much? What will result in over stretching?**

Once the muscles are warmed and at maximum length, it is the ligaments that stretch next. This stresses the tendons because they are not meant to stretch. Ligaments can only stretch up to 6% increase over normal length. Any further stretching will result in tearing and injury.

❋ **Name a sport that makes the body vulnerable to the above?**

Gymnastics.

❋ **What is Connective Tissue and what is it made up of?**

Connective tissue surrounds muscle fibre and is comprised of collagenous and elastic fibres as well as a base substance called mucopolysaccharide, which acts as both a lubricant and a glue.

Connective tissue is also related to fascia, an extracellular, fibrous network that surrounds and connects muscles. It can be made up of adipose tissue, areolar tissue and deep connective tissue. It is like a biological fabric and glue that holds us together.

What is a ligament?

Ligaments are fibrous connective tissue structures that connect one bone to another at the joint. They stabilise the joint and enable mobility.

What are the names of the three types of flexibility?

Static, dynamic and ballistic.

Describe some of the elements of the mental and emotional aspects of flexibility and tension?

Tension in the body is very often associated with an emotional cause: trauma, distress, or simply a habitual posture that has, over time, affected the balance and alignment of the body. Such emotional tension can be held in the body, in muscles, just like a repressed memory can be locked in the mind. Our psychology and physiology are closely related: smiling can sometimes help lift your mood, and standing more upright feels much more positive and energizing than stooping. The near instantaneous effects of our amygdala in response to stressful situations can flood the body with a potent bio-chemical mix that can hijack our rational mind. This is the case with anger or fright and we can often carry the remnants of that chemical infusion around with us long after the activating incident has passed. In fact, through memory and imagination we can usually recreate the same conditions.

All of these psycho-physiological reactions will store in our body, causing tension. Tension, in turn, limits flexibility, not just of movement but also of our attitude and thinking. It is quite common to see young teenagers who have deeply furrowed brows as a result of adopting an aggressive approach to life and carrying a 'chip on their shoulders'.

The fascia and tensegrity of the human body renders it a 'tension distribution system', both mechanically and emotionally. Physical forces are dealt with by the system as a whole and, the better the balance of the body, the better it copes. If tensions have pulled the body out of alignment – which is frequently the case – then held tensions could be limiting and problematic. Yoga can help to release such tensions physically, and as a consequence, mentally and emotionally too. Once tension in, say, the shoulders, neck or hips, is released, an emotional release may occur too, helping to restore the body to a state of relaxed poise and balance.

(further information at www.anatomytrains.com)

Should you use stretching as a warm up? If not, why not?

No! Stretching is not a warm up and can result in injury if muscles are stretched 'cold'. Connective tissue surrounding muscles needs to be warmed to produce increased flexibility and safer conditions for stretching.

How could you warm up?

The Sun Salutes! At least four rounds; right and then left being one round. Also gentle jogging for five minutes helps to raise core temperature by 1°–2°.

When is the best time to stretch?

When the muscles are warm, i.e., core body temperature has been raised by 1°–2°. Generally, it is easier to stretch in the afternoon/evening because the muscles have been in action throughout the day and have a greater range of movement.

❋ **What are the names for the various types of stretching?**

The seven different types of stretching are:
1. Ballistic stretching;
2. Dynamic stretching;
3. Active stretching;
4. Passive (or relaxed) stretching;
5. Static stretching;
6. Isometric (static) stretching;
7. PNF stretching (Proprioceptive neuromuscular facilitation).

❋ **Here are two types of stretching and their function that I consider useful to know about.**

1. Dynamic stretching: Dynamic stretching uses speed of movement, momentum and active muscular effort to bring about a stretch. Unlike static stretching, the end position is not held. Dynamic stretching avoids bouncing motions and incorporates more sport-specific movements. Arm circles, walking lunges, kicking actions are all dynamic stretches. Dynamic stretching is performed before competitive sports and helps to reduce muscle tightness.

2. Active stretching: Also known as a 'static-active stretch' and is one where you assume a position and then hold it with no assistance other than using the strength of your agonist muscles. The tension of the agonists in an active stretch helps to relax the muscles being stretched (the antagonists) by reciprocal inhibition. Static stretching is the opposite of dynamic stretching. The muscle groups are stretched without moving the limb itself and the end position is held for 10–30 seconds for 1–2 stretches per muscle group. A martial artist raising her leg up to an opponent's head and holding it there is a good demonstration of static active flexibility.

Can you give me one type of Yoga static stretch and its function?

Janu Sirsasana (Head to knee pose) is a type of static stretch. This pose is a hamstring stretch, where one leg is outstretched in front, while the other is bent with foot into the groin, knee open to the side. As you lean over that leg, the quadriceps are contracted on top of the thigh to support the hamstring stretch underneath the thigh. There is no movement of muscles therefore it is static.

What do the terms Isotonic and Isometric mean?

Isotonic is a muscle moving, such as extending the arm back and forth. Isometric is like static stretching where the muscles are working but not moving. Easy to remember that 'tonic' means lively!

What pose would illustrate a hip, spine, or leg stretch?

A pose that stretches the spine is Extended Triangle pose (*Utthita Trikonasana*).

This lateral flexion and extension also includes a rotation of the hips. This posture helps to lengthen and strengthen the spine and associated muscles, which increases flexibility. This is also a great inside leg stretch, targeting the adductor muscle.

Describe how a ball and socket works.

The biggest range of movement by the joints is provided by a 'ball-and-socket' joint, in which the spherical head of one bone lodges in the spherical cavity of another. It provides full range of movement in all planes, at the hip and shoulder.

In the shoulder joint, the humerus fits into the socket of the shoulder blade. Because the socket is shallow and the joint loose, the shoulder is the body's most mobile joint. The hip joint is less mobile than the shoulder, but it is more stable. The ball of the femur's head fits tightly into a deep socket in the hip bone. A rim of cartilage lining the socket helps grip the femur firmly. The ligament binding the two bones is among the strongest in the human body.

Don't move, I'm stretching!

❋ **Where would you find a pivot joint and what movement does it allow?**

In pivot joints, movement takes place around the vertical axis, like the hinge of a gate. A more or less cylindrical articular surface of bone protrudes into, and rotates within, a ring formed by bone or ligament, e.g. the joint between the radius and the ulna at the elbows allows the round head of the radius to rotate within a 'ring' of ligament that is secured to the ulna.

❋ **Give three reasons why a synovial joint may not move in the normal range.**

The range of movement of a synovial joint can be limited by:

1. Injury: caused by trauma resulting in damage or inflammation.
2. Osteoarthritis/rheumatoid arthritis: caused by degeneration of the cartilage and/or inflammation.
3. Lack of exercise: helps speed the exchange of used fluid in cartilage with nutrient-rich synovial fluid, and it helps build bone density and muscle strength, keeping joints, bones and muscles healthy.

Weight-bearing exercise compresses or squeezes your cartilage of the relevant joints. The compressed or squeezed cartilage oozes out some of its fluid, containing wastes. When you release the pressure, the joint soaks up fresh fluid.

❋ **In terms of movement, describe:**

1. Extension: To straighten, stretch out, or bend backwards away from the foetal position.
2. Rotation: The movement around the axis of a bone
3. Plantar flexion: 'Plantar' – the bottom of the foot – flexion, is the movement which increases the approximate 90 degree angle between the front part of the foot and the shin.

What are the fused and non-fused vertebrae and their relationship to 'poor posture' or a 'bad back'?

The diagram below represents the regions of the spine, namely: cervical, thoracic, lumbar, sacral and coccygeal, along with the number of vertebrae, indicating those sections that are fused – the sacral and coccygeal sections.

As a Yoga teacher, I would remind students that studies show that back pain is primarily caused by our poor living habits. I would also advise that Yoga is an excellent way to strengthen and protect the back from too much stress and strain. Yoga creates good muscle tone, especially for the abdominal muscles, which is vital for a strong back and helps to straighten out lordosis, over curvature of the lower back (as if the bottom were sticking out).

One of our poor living habits is slumping on ergonomically poor sofas. The muscle imbalance that causes slumping begins as children; we have to round the spine to reach the back of a chair. Eventually, the muscles of the front body become short and tight and the muscles of the back body become weak and over-stretched, causing the spine to curve backward and the head to poke forward.

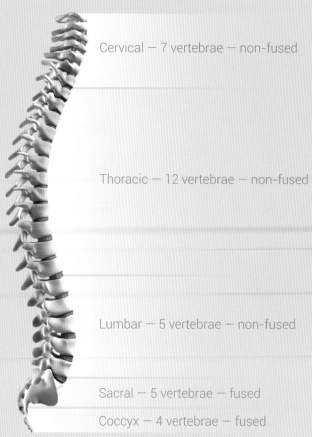

Cervical — 7 vertebrae — non-fused

Thoracic — 12 vertebrae — non-fused

Lumbar — 5 vertebrae — non-fused

Sacral — 5 vertebrae — fused

Coccyx — 4 vertebrae — fused

This slump of the mid-back – the thoracic spine – is called a kyphosis. Kyphosis can also be addressed through a well-balanced Yoga programme.

To prevent back pain it is best to avoid undue stress on injury-prone back tissues whilst strengthening the muscles that support them. Yoga provides strengthening postures and relaxation to achieve both of these.

Posture and alignment are key factors in our health. An energized body exudes confidence and there is a better biomechanical transfer through the body systems that can help to reduce the likelihood of injury. Yoga is a preventative medicine that has a powerful and positive effect on posture, alignment and ultimate lifestyle. The basic advice from a Yoga teacher to a student would be to work on developing and aligning the 'plumb line' through postures such as Mountain pose, seated poses such as Staff and Half-lotus, and Cobra and Locust. These can all help to develop better posture and attain the alignment of ears, shoulders, hips and ankles through stronger leg and back muscles as well as a rolling back of the shoulders.

❋ What are the Spine's curvature disorders?

There are three main types of curvature disorders of the spine:

1. Lordosis: Also called swayback, the spine of a person with lordosis curves significantly inward at the lower back.
2. Kyphosis: Kyphosis is characterized by an abnormally rounded upper back (more than 50 degrees of curvature).
3. Scoliosis: A person with scoliosis has a sideways curve to their spine. The curve is often 'S' or 'C' shaped.

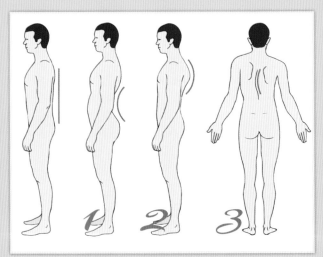

What is the simple anatomy of the heart?

The heart is a muscular organ that pumps blood to all the tissues in your body through a network of blood vessels. The right side of the heart pumps blood through the lungs where it picks up oxygen. The left side of the heart receives the blood containing oxygen and pumps the blood to the rest of your body.

Your heart has four chambers and four valves that regulate blood flow:

* Left and right atria: Chambers that receive blood returning from your body through your veins.

* Left and right ventricles: Chambers where blood is pumped to your body through your arteries.

* Mitral valve: The mitral valve controls the flow of oxygen-rich blood from the left atrium to the left ventricle.

* Tricuspid valve: The tricuspid valve controls the flow of oxygen-poor blood from the right atrium to the right ventricle.

* Aortic valve: The aortic valve controls flow of oxygen-rich blood from the left ventricle to the body.

* Pulmonary valve: The pulmonary valve controls flow of oxygen-poor blood from the right ventricle to the lungs.

✳ What is the diaphragm and its function?

The diaphragm is the prime mover for inhalation and exhalation. It is a large, thin half-dome shaped muscle that separates the thoracic and abdominal cavities, sitting just under the lower ribs.

Inhalation

On inhalation, the diaphragm moves down/contracts, expanding the chest and creating a negative inspiratory pressure in the thorax that draws air in through the trachea. Contraction of the diaphragm also gently massages the abdominal organs.

Exhalation

On exhalation, the diaphragm moves up/relaxes and expels air from the lungs.

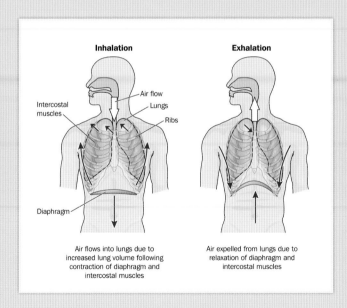

Note: The medical explanation of the action of the diaphragm is correct but the function and action seem to conflict. As mentioned on page 224, Yogic breathing is not to be confused with Thoracic breathing.

✳ **Can you show me the endocrine system in a simple way?**

The adrenal glands affect the body's response to stress and play a major role in the body's fight or flight response.

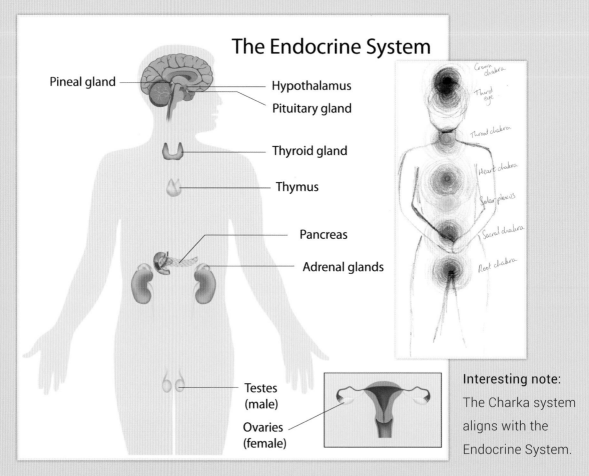

The Endocrine System

Pineal gland

Hypothalamus

Pituitary gland

Thyroid gland

Thymus

Pancreas

Adrenal glands

Testes (male)

Ovaries (female)

Crown chakra

Third eye

Throat chakra

Heart chakra

Solar plexus

Sacral chakra

Root chakra

Interesting note:
The Charka system aligns with the Endocrine System.

✳ **Name an Asana that would stimulate the thyroid gland.**

Shoulder stand (*Salamba Sarvangasana*).

✳ The spinal twist targets specific organs. What are the functions of these organs and why is the spinal twist such an important posture for them?

Right side of body	Left side of body
Liver – right lobe: processes absorbed nutrients and makes bile.	**Liver – left lobe:** processes absorbed nutrients and makes bile.
Gall bladder: stores and concentrates bile made by the liver and squirts it into the small intestine during digestion.	**Spleen:** produces macrophages and lymphocytes to fight infection.
Pancreas: maintains the body's blood glucose (sugar) balance. Primary hormones of the pancreas include insulin and glucagon, and both regulate blood glucose. Diabetes is the most common disorder associated with the pancreas.	
Right kidney: processes blood, extracting wastes to produce urine.	**Left kidney:** processes blood, extracting wastes to produce urine.
Large intestines: absorbs water from food and disposes of waste. **Small intestines:** where most digestion and absorption of food takes place.	
Ascending colon: 25cm long comprised of strong muscles that move waste products upward and onward out of the body.	**Descending colon:** stores food that will be emptied into the rectum.

Ask Anne-Marie . . .

. . . about Sanskrit Terminology and Philosophy

Author's comment: The theory and philosophy of Yoga is based on Ancient Hindu texts and scriptures, and for this reason can seem very dry and academic, often complicated and sometimes hard to grasp!

This is a huge subject but these are just a few of the questions I get asked. I use both Sanskrit and English in all my classes and lectures. I cannot see the benefits of only teaching one or the other. Using both makes sense as you are learning a new language. Yoga classes should, in my opinion, use both. If you only practice Astanga Vinyasa Yoga and use Sanskrit for poses, the English will be alien. However if you only know the English then you are missing out on the Language of Yoga. Ballet classes are in French, never English!

My advice is always ask if you don't understand something, or want to know more. If your teacher can't help you then maybe look for one who has studied Yoga to some depth.

❋ What is Prakriti?

Prakriti is the primal motive force, Nature, the basic intelligence by which the universe exists. It is comprised of the Three *Gunas* and gives rise to the material world and all that is in it, including mind and matter.

The whole world is a mixture of these Three *Gunas*, or qualities, of *Prakriti*:

Sattva: purity and knowledge

Rajas: activity and motion

Tamas: inertia and laziness

Prakriti evolves from *Purusha*, the source of consciousness, the absolute ultimate reality, the witness of the mind, infinite, formless, unchanging *Atman*. Once the unlimited becomes limited by the mind it is no longer absolute because everything limited by the mind becomes finite. Mind and matter are the veiling power of the consciousness of spirit that creates the world. This veiling power is known as *Maya Shakti*.

✳ What is the Astral body?

In Yoga, the 'body' is a vehicle for the soul on its journey towards enlightenment, consisting of the gross, subtle and causal bodies. Known as the Physical, Astral and Causal bodies, they are evolved from *Prakriti* nature. The Physical body is composed of the five elements of matter, whereas the mind and senses are in the Astral body, which does not perish when the body dies.

Every living thing has an Astral body. This is connected to the Physical body by a subtle energy thread along which vital currents pass. When this cord is cut, the Physical body dies and the Astral Body departs.

It is composed of three layers:

1. **Pranic Sheath** (*Pranayama Kosha*): More subtle than the Food sheath, but similar in form, it is made up of 72,000 *nadis*, or astral tubes, through which *Prana*, or vital energy, flows. The Chakras are found in the Pranic sheath.

2. **Mental Sheath** (*Manamaya Kosha*): Comprising the automatic mind, as well as the instinctive and subconscious aspects, this is where we carry on the automatic functions of our daily lives. It is very jumpy by nature, as it is constantly bombarded by input from the five senses.

3. **Intellectual Sheath** (*Vijnanamaya Kosha*): The intellect controls and guides the automatic mind. Discrimination and decision-making take place here and pass down to the more gross sheaths.

It is interesting to note that we use the word 'gross' to describe a person who is not of pure mind or thought; 'He had gross habits', for instance. They may swear anytime without cause, talk in a dirty way about a person or about sexual matters and are often inappropriate in their actions.

❊ What is Shakti?

Shakti is the female energy and power of *Purusha*, the source of consciousness, the absolute ultimate reality, *Atman*, the soul, expressed in finite mind and matter. The active power of pure consciousness, *Shakti* is the Divine power, the Mother of the Universe that resides in a human's body in the Mooladhara Chakra at the base of the spine.

❊ What is Kundalini?

In the individual, *Prakriti Shakti* is manifested as *Kundalini*, or 'serpent power'. When *Kundalini* is at rest, or is active only in the Base Chakra, man has only finite experience. Once awakened, it moves upward through the *Sushumna* – the astral nerve tube to the Sahasrara Chakra – and unites with pure consciousness in the Sahasrara Chakra. This process of upward movement is the final union with consciousness, *Shiva*. It is the reverse of the genesis of the mind, which evolved from Oneness into a separate, ego-state.

Explain the Practice and Meaning of Hatha Yoga.

The purpose of Hatha Yoga is to locate and activate the chakras, thereby raising the *Kundalini* known as 'dominant spiritual power'. This in turn is believed to help remove energy blockages and diseases in the mind and body.

Hatha Yoga attempts to balance mind and body via physical postures and exercises, controlled breathing, and the calming of the mind through relaxation and meditation. *Asanas* teach poise, balance and strength and were originally practiced to improve the body's physical health and clear the mind in preparation for meditation in the pursuit of enlightenment.

Through the forging of a powerful depth of concentration and mastery of the body and mind, Hatha Yoga practices seek to still the mental waters and allow for apprehension of oneself as that which one always was, Brahman. Hatha Yoga is essentially a manual for scientifically taking one's body through stages of control to a point at which it is 'one-pointed' and it is said to take its practitioner to the peaks of Raja Yoga, meditation being the ultimate goal.

Hatha Yoga is still followed, in a manner consistent with tradition, throughout the Indian subcontinent. Both the Buddhists and Jains have kept the traditional guru-student relationship that exists without sanction from organised institutions, and which gave rise to all the great yogis who made way into international consciousness in the 20th century, by keeping the science alive.

In the essay 'Buddhism Meets Western Science', Gay Watson explains:

'Buddhism has always been concerned with feelings, emotions, sensations, and cognition. The Buddha points both to cognitive and emotional causes of suffering. The emotional cause is desire and its negative opposite, aversion. The cognitive cause is ignorance of the way things truly occur: that all things are unsatisfactory, impermanent, and without essential Self.'

Buddhism is atheist and not religious, as the teachings are based on control of the Self and about getting through life with as little emotional pain as possible, and that can only be achieved by controlling the senses. Hatha Yoga is of the same path, to be able to sit in meditation without the pain of the body!

What are the Sanskrit names and translations of the basic Yoga postures that we use in a Sun Power Yoga class?

* *Savasana*: Corpse pose
* *Tadasana*: Mountain pose
* *Surya Namaskar*: Sun Salutation series
* *Virabhadrasana I & II*: Warrior I & II
* *Trikonasana*: Triangle pose
* *Natarajasana*: Dancer pose
* *Kakasana*: Crow pose
* *Hasta Padasana*: Standing hand to foot pose
* *Ardha Matsyendrasana*: Half Lord of the Fishes/twist
* *Badha Konasana*: Tailor pose
* *Janu Sirsasana*: Head to knee pose/one leg
* *Pachimottanasana*: The west pose/ head to knee, both legs
* *Salabasana*: Locust pose, warming the back of the body
* *Dharunasana*: Bow pose
* *Ustrasana*: Camel pose back bend
* *Salamba Sirsasana*: Supported Headstand
* *Balasana*: Child's pose
* *Sarvangasana*: All body pose, the shoulder stand
* *Halasana*: Plough pose
* *Setu Bandhasana*: Bridge pose
* *Chakrasana*: Full wheel pose
* *Matsyasana*: Fish pose

Note that *Asana* means 'steady pose'.

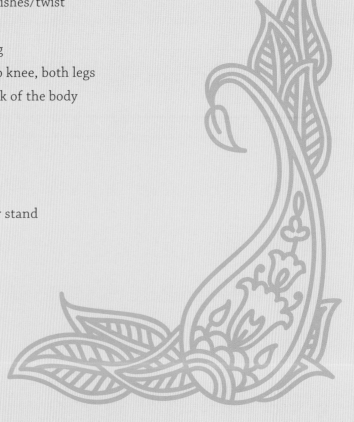

✳ What is Prana?

Prana is life force, *Qi* or *Chi* depending on the name you are used to calling this vital force.

Breath is the outward manifestation of *Prana*, the vital force or energy that flows through the physical body but is actually in the Astral body. By exercising control over the breath, you can learn to control the subtle energies within the body, and ultimately gain full control of the mind.

Prana usually circulates in five directions in the body, performing different functions. These five 'winds' of *Prana* are called *Vayus*:

Prana Vayu: moves from the diaphragm to the basin of the throat. It is seated in the heart and regulates breathing, heart rate, circulation, and speech.

Apana Vayu: flows downward from the navel to the feet. It controls urination, defecation, giving birth, menstrual flow, ejaculation, and creative work.

Samana Vayu: occupies the space from the navel to the diaphragm. It flows back and forth like a pendulum, regulating digestion and assimilation, and balancing the *Prana* and *Apana Vayus*.

Udana Vayu: flows from the base of the throat to the top of the head. It regulates coughing, choking, hiccoughing, and swallowing.

Vyana Vayu: flows in all directions, carrying *Prana* to each cell of the body.

Breathing with awareness, in addition to bringing a greater amount of oxygen to the body, also brings a greater amount of *Prana*. It is therefore with awareness that you can direct the breath to go wherever oxygen or energy is lacking, so filling in the gaps in energy.

Physical Benefits of Correct Breathing

* Provides sufficient oxygen for the correct and efficient functioning of every cell. Without sufficient oxygen the cells cannot metabolise food properly. Nutrients, including precious vitamins and minerals, are wasted.
* Allows the body to rid itself of all the noxious gaseous by-products of metabolism, especially carbon dioxide.

Mental Benefits of Correct Breathing

* Improves concentration and greater clarity of thought.
* Increases ability to deal with complex situations without suffering from stress.
* Retains emotional control and equilibrium.
* Improves physical control and coordination.

❋ What is Maya?

Maya is the concept of duality in a non-dualistic Universe. It is the mind's material world in which all things appear separate. When we are born we forget we are part of the whole conscious universe or that we are part of a complete 'oneness'. *Maya* continues the illusion, as it were.

❋ What is its Sanskrit meaning?

Maya means 'illusion' and is sometimes described as the 'Veil of Illusions'.

❋ Explain in your own words the concept of Maya?

Maya is the grand misperception that all that we see and experience, including our thoughts, are separate, divisible parts of a universe of multiplicity. Our experience of the universe and our own Self is therefore filtered through our limited sensory input, that is the cause of our fears, desires and the sense of 'I', the separate Self. It is our reaction to the world, in believing ourselves to being all alone, self-contained, vulnerable and finite.

❋ Give a personal example of how you think Maya reveals itself.

Very often, when I've been driving I have reacted negatively (even aggressively) to other drivers or the traffic conditions. For example, if running behind schedule it seems as if traffic lights change to red, other drivers go slowly, and there are hold ups where there were none last week, all because I need to be somewhere. I take these circumstances personally, as if they were all organised to frustrate me. The truth is that any frustration I might feel is all created by my own imagination, my own reaction to the circumstances. It is an illusion, *Maya*, based on my distorted interpretation of what I experience around me. I only see a limited, tiny view of the whole picture and yet deem it to be the truth, a 'truth' that declares 'life should not be this way'.

It is my mind that is distorting reality, through my thoughts. I always have an opportunity for an inner smile to emerge.

❋ What is The Sea of Samskara?

As a Yoga and Hindu concept, it could be said that we are all adrift in the Sea of *Samskara*, like driftwood, being carried by the tides and forces of our past actions and, because we are largely unaware of our sub-conscious intentions, we are not really navigating to our true destination at all.

❋ What is the Sanskrit meaning?

Samskara means imprints, grooves, or impressions.

❋ Do not confuse this with Samsara, which is a Buddhist concept. Give the meanings of both *Samskara* and *Samsara*.

Samskara are manifestations of the subtle imprints left on our consciousness by past actions, whereas *Samsara* is the endless cycle of birth and rebirth that continues until we find liberation (*moksha, nirvana*) through enlightenment.

Can you explain the concept of Samskara in simple words?

Samskara are the impressions of our past thoughts, actions and beliefs, in this life or previous lives. These manifest subtly in our unconscious/conscious minds as the habits, tendencies and characteristics that can govern or influence our behaviour, choices and decisions. Powerful stuff!

What does Sadhana mean?

'The first stage of *Sadhana* is to choose a practice. Even the most simple *Sadhana* will be challenging to the newcomer. Consider the *Sadhana* of lighting a candle every night, then immediately blowing it out. Nothing more or nothing less. Do this for ninety days. You will observe the mind coming up with every reason why you shouldn't do it and every excuse why you missed a few (or many) nights. Yet by accepting it as a *Sadhana*, you make a choice to do it and it becomes a Spiritual practice.

The second aspect of *Sadhana* relates to regularity; doing something at set periods. This typically would be at the same time in the same place everyday. Yet it doesn't have to be everyday; it could be every other day or every Tuesday and Thursday, as long as it is regular. Doing practice irregularly is not *Sadhana*.'

Saying that, choice and regularity are not the only aspects of *Sadhana*. If they were, simply dressing every day would be a *Sadhana*. We choose what clothes to wear and we do it. Dressing could be a *Sadhana*, yet it is just a mechanical action done every day. Thus, the final key to a successful *Sadhana* is conscious intention. This is where the power is generated, and more still, when the intention becomes an aspiration.

Explain a Sadhaka

A *Sadhaka* is a spiritual aspirant, a seeker of the truth.

What is an aspirant?

One who aspires to something and in this case it is a spiritual life-path.

✳ So what is a Sadhu?

A *Sadhu* is an ascetic or holy man, usually keeping to Hindu tradition, also known as a Sage.

In 2014 an all-female *Akhada*: group of *Sadhus*, was formed. It is believed to be the first such group in India!

✳ I see that 'Satsang' is part of many Yoga ashrams and centres. What is it?

Satsang is a gathering of like-minded people, where scriptures are delivered and knowledgeable persons like a Swami or Guru give a discourse. There will also be *Kirtan*, spiritual songs sung, which are both uplifting and unifying. Songs of Praise in a church on a Sunday is the same.

✳ What is Arati?

Arati is performed at the end of *Satsang*. It is the ceremonial waving of light, such as a candle flame, accompanied by chanting. Light is very important in spiritual practices as it represents the dispelling of darkness/ignorance and the path to light/enlightenment and knowledge.

✳ What are Srutis?

Scriptures, which are heard, not simply read by you alone, as in *Satsang* for instance.

✳ What is a Swami?

A *Swami* is an ascetic or yogi who has been initiated into the religious monastic order founded by some religious teacher. Swami Vishnu-devananda was a disciple of Sivananda of Rishikesh, for instance. The term '*Swami*' was originally used for the ones who were initiated into the Advaita Vedanta movement started by Adi Shankara. They wear orange or saffron as this is a sign of a *Sannyasin*, someone who has taken celibacy as part of the 'letting go' of a material life.

What is Japa?

This is the repetition of a mantra, a sacred sound such as *OM* or *Om Namah Shivaya*. *Japa* meditation uses *Mala* beads, a string of 108 beads and as each bead passes through the fingers a mantra is breathed in with one bead and out with the next bead.

What does the Sanskrit word Mala mean?

The word *Mala* means simply 'garland', a complete circle. *Malasana* is also a pose. It is a wide kneed squat with hands placed in prayer and elbows resting on the inner knees. The pose creates a circle.

I think that on a deeper level it means to get rid of anything that is gross, such as thoughts. Clearing the mind with each bead of the mala. Mind washing!

What is an Avatar?

An *Avatar* is an incarnation of a god in human form, such as Krishna.

Who is Arjuna?

Arjuna is the hero of the Baghavad Gita, who represents the student, a spiritual warrior or aspirant.

❄ I have heard 'Avidya' used in some lectures. What is it?

Avidya means ignorance, spiritual blindness and illusion.

❄ Who or what is Brahma, Vishnu and Shiva?

The 'Trimūrti', 'three forms', is a concept in Hinduism, 'in which the cosmic functions of creation, maintenance, and destruction are personified by the forms of Brahma the Creator, Vishnu the Preserver and Shiva the Destroyer or Transformer.' These three gods have been called 'the Hindu triad' or the 'Great Trinity'. Although this is Hindu theory it is also a part of Yoga theory and philosophy, as in such actions as *Anuloma Viloma Pranayama* for instance. On the inhale we are with Brahma the Creator, when we retain the breath, Vishnu the Preserver and when the breath is released, spent, empty, it is Shiva the Destroyer that we align with.

❄ Explain Brahmacharya

This is celibacy or control of sexual energy. This is one of the *Yama*'s (restraints) from Patanjali's Eight Limbs of Yoga, so a student who practices *Brahmacharya* is called a *Brahmachari*.

❄ Gurukula has been mentioned in books but what is it?

Gurukula is a system by which the student lives in the teacher's ashram and learns by observation and practice. Living the life of a Yogi.

❄ We say 'Shanti' at the end of class. What does it mean?

Shanti means 'Peace' and comes from the Hindi word *Shant*, meaning 'still'.

Knowledge is a never-ending endeavour.
There is not enough time in one life to learn all there is to learn.

Om Shanti Shanti Shanti Om

Your Knowledge Library

How to access what you have learned

It is a fact that we take millions of pictures everyday of all we see and do, and we imprint sound on our brain of what we hear and say. How and what we feel with our body is no different, and is called the emotional body, that has memory through our pain, joy and physical practice and is locked into our muscles – known as 'Muscle Memory'.

These memory pictures are stored in our brain and the actions are in the muscles of our bodies.

These pictures, sounds and tactile memories are in us forever. If we forget anything it is often due to the inability to access our collated knowledge base, or we are so stressed that what is not 'important' dropped off the radar. The expression 'too much on your plate' illustrates this well, with the image of food falling off of it!

All knowledge is filed away, much like a library or filing system – we put that information somewhere we can find it. The brain does the same in the neurons and creating new pathways.

The body stores movement memory in the cells of the muscles in the body. All cells, nerves and neurons don't forget anything as long as the brain is functioning correctly and is not damaged irreparably.

But...what happens if we don't believe we can store or access information we have been taught?

If we have tension in the muscular system, our blood flow is inhibited and therefore oxygen is not able to move through the body so well, as it's the blood that carries it. Organs, arteries and veins are then starved of a good oxygen supply.

Try thinking of the brain in the same way. In a stressful and anxious state, like before an exam or interview, we allow self-doubt to overpower our reason. What happens then is that we don't 'believe' we can remember anything. We draw a blank as our brain freezes up. Freezing will always relate to something getting stuck, stiff, or panic.

Relax the body and let the blood carry the oxygen freely.

Relax the mind and let your accumulated knowledge flow out of your mouth
into the ether, or out of your mind and onto those blank pages.

Free yourself from assumptions about your own capabilities.

Be in your own zone, devoid of judgment, criticism or weakness.

The power you have is infinite; you only need to say 'yes'
to own your own potential and for it to work for you.

Work smarter not harder!

Method of Loci: The Mind Palace

Locus: Latin for 'Place'; plural: Loci

'A locus is a set of points which satisfies a certain condition. As seen by the headlights (and taillights) for instance, a locus of points (the headlights or taillights) is the path traced out by the moving points under given conditions (following the road).'

Mnemonic; plural noun: mnemonics

'A system such as a pattern of letters, ideas, or associations which assists in remembering something'. From the Greek 'Mindful'.

The Method of Loci, also known as The Memory Palace, is a technique known by both the Ancient Greeks and Romans as a way of remembering things by revisiting a place and journeying back through that place, building, street or series of events, and accessing the things you want to remember. In basic terms, it is a method of memory enhancement, which uses visualisation to organise and recall information.

'When desiring to remember a set of items the subject "walks" through these loci in their imagination and commits an item to each one by forming an image between the item and any distinguishing feature of that locus. Retrieval of items is achieved by "walking" through the loci, allowing the latter to activate the desired items.'

So imagine walking through a building with pillars, each pillar has an object, an equation or a number series between them. Pillar one has something you want to remember, the next pillar something else. Using your imagination and visualisation you 'see' what you want to remember.

The best story I know about this Mind Palace technique is this:

A wealthy man was at a King's banquet in Ancient Greece, and there were many people around the long table. Suddenly there were eruptions and an earthquake ensued. As the building began to fall and the pillars collapsed, the guests were buried under the rubble.

The man was lucky enough to free himself, unlike his other dinner guests. When people came to help find the King and guests, and hoping to find them alive, they could see no one under all the rubble.

The man used his imagination and visualised the table they had been eating at. He walked back into the hall (in his mind) and recalled the people sitting around the table. He remembered the red-haired man to his left, the Persian prince to his right and recalled the other guests around the table. By doing this he was able to locate the guests under the rubble and save the King and retrieve the others either dead or alive.

This was named the Mind Palace. You can create your own mind palace using the above as a guide. When we make up rhymes with the letters of the first word, to help us memorise a list, we are creating a mnemonic.

Creating your own Mind Palace

1 Create and design your own building. Make a blue print. Decide what it looks like and if it's a modern futuristic building or of classical architecture. Think about the layout of the rooms, corridors and smaller rooms. These may be storage rooms and have smaller rooms within them. Think about the gardens around the palace and how they lead into the main structure.

2 Draw the Palace and colour it with your favourite palate. Make it exotic and full of diverse stimuli.

3 Create routes to specific memories, such as your past, schooling, life with parents, children. Place joy, hope and love in central halls and give them more than one way to get there. Mind Palaces are for your past life, your dreams, your aspirations as well as accumulated factual knowledge.

4 Be creative by using symbols to remember things. The images you put in your palace should, obviously, be as memorable as possible. Generally, images will be more memorable if they are absurd and out of the ordinary or if they are attached to some strong emotion or personal experience. The number 124 is not particularly memorable, but an image of a spear shaped like the number 1, going through a swan, which looks like the number 2, and splitting the swan into 4 pieces, is. Yes it's disturbing, but that's part of what makes it stick in your mind.

5 Use mnemonics. One example is, suppose you need to remember a great deal about music composition. As you enter your kitchen, you could see a little boy eating a piece of chocolate fudge, which would evoke the first-letter mnemonic 'Every Good Boy Deserves Fudge', which would in turn allow you to recall the order of notes on the lines in treble clef (EGBDF).

6   Explore your Palace. Walk around it and get to know it. Think about putting famous people like writers, artists or composers in very familiar places like on the toilet or in the kitchen!

7   Build new palaces. 'A memory palace can be reused over and over again if you need only commit things to memory for a short time. Just replace the existing contents with new ones, and you'll soon remember only the new ones. If you need to remember the contents of your palace for a long time, you can keep that palace as it is and create new ones in which to store other information as needed. If your house contains the phone numbers of everyone you know, you can walk to your workplace if you need to remember the order of a deck of cards.'

Further reading Dame Frances Amelia Yates (28 November 1899 – 29 September 1981) *The Art of Memory*.

Note to *Self*

Closing Prayer

Say nothing if your words are not

tinted with Love.

Make no moves if those moves are not

from the heart.

Touch no one if that touch is not

as light as the air.

Carry yourself with humility

and without fear.

Walk through life with grace and power but

never with arrogance.

Sing from your soul,

let your voice lift the heavens

and all that are in it.

It is our duty to enjoy life, it is a gift.

AMN

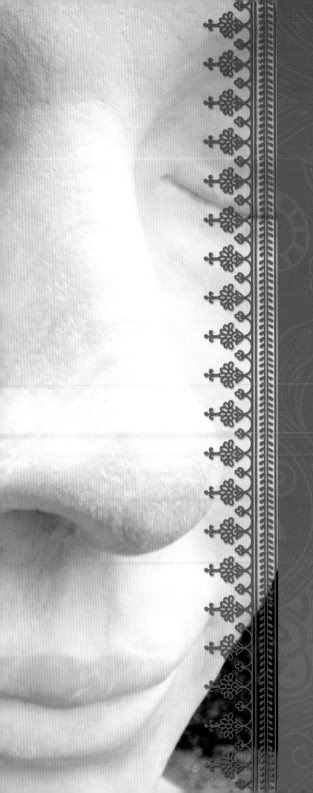

Often while meditating,
and with no warning,
I will suddenly feel
a smile illuminate my face
just like a warm sunrise and
I remember that the Buddha
has that same smile and ...

I think to myself,
what a Wonderful World

Louis Armstrong

SUN POWER YOGA

Excellence in Yoga Teacher Training

Accredited Yoga Teacher Training Intensive Courses

If this book has inspired you to teach, it is worth knowing that Yoga is more than a career, it is a lifestyle filled with opportunity and inspiration! Becoming a Yoga teacher is a wonderful way to live and give. It is a great working life too!

Our aim is to produce responsible teachers, with flair and a passionate understanding of the Nature of Yoga. We will help you to become knowledgeable, professional and, ultimately, an inspirational teacher.

Contact Anne-Marie and let's get your journey started.

+44 (0) 7730 680 221
www.sun-power-yoga.co.uk
yoga@sun-power-yoga.co.uk

Om Namaste

My Favourite Books... and other resources

❖ Anne-Marie playing drums with Toyah Wilcox and Maneaters, in the movie Jubilee, 1977 – www.youtube.com/watch?v=smj5O82wXiw

Theory

❖ *Yoga Sutras of Patanjali*, commentary by Sri Satyananda
❖ *Hatha Yoga Pradipika*, commentary by Swami Muktibodhananda
❖ *Baghavad Gita for Daily Living*, Eknath Easwaren
❖ *Paths to God, Living the Baghavad Gita*; Ram Dass
❖ *Essence of the Upanishads, A key to Indian Spirituality*, Eknath Easwaren
❖ *Bliss Divine*, Swami Sivananda
❖ *Reflections of the Self*, Swami Muktananda
❖ *Yantra, The Tantric Symbol of Cosmic Unity*, Madhu Khanna

Meditation and Mauna

❖ *Common sense Directions for an Uncommon Life*, Eknath Easwaren
❖ *Meditation and Mantras*, Swami Vishnu-devananda
❖ *Sister Wendy's Book of Meditation*, Sister Wendy
❖ *Silence Speaks*, Baba Hari Dass
❖ *The Prophet* , Kahil Gibran
❖ *Journey of Awakening, A meditators Guidebook*, Ram Dass

Incense for your practice & meditation

❖ I have found a wonderful range of quality incense from a local shop, Bagel and Griff, in Market Harborough Leicester. www.bagelandgriff.com

Breathing and Pranayama

❖ *Light on Pranayama*, B K S Iyengar
❖ *Breath the Essence of Yoga*, Sandra Sabatini

Mudras

❖ *Healing Mudras*, Sabrina Mesko
❖ DVD *Mudra Gestures*, Sabrina Mesko

Asana, Practice and Sanskrit names

❖ *Complete Illustrated Book of Yoga*, Swami Vishnu-devananda
❖ *The New Book of Yoga*, Sivananda Yoga Centre
❖ *Yoga Mala*, Pattabi Jois
❖ *Power Yoga* and *Beyond Power Yoga*, Beryl Bender Birch
❖ *Light on Yoga*, B K S Iyengar
❖ *Yoga for You*, Indra Devi
❖ *Visually Yoga*, Rapid Progress
❖ *The Yoga Bible*, Christine Brown
❖ 'Music for Sun Power Yoga', Spotify, iTunes

❖ Anne-Marie's DVDs *Yoga Divine, Yoga for Sport, Yoga Imagine This, Yoga for the Bigger Body, Yoga in your own zone: for Wheelchair users & ME sufferers*

Children's Yoga

❖ *Hatha Yoga for Kids – by Kids!*, the Children of Yogaville
❖ *Children's Book of Yoga*, Thia Luby
❖ *Yoga for Children*, Belle Gibbs

Chakras and Chanting

❖ *Chakra Mantras, Liberate your Spiritual Genius through Chanting*, Thomas Ashley-Farrand
❖ CDs with chanting, search www.sonarupa.co.uk
❖ *Opening to Spirit* , Caroline Shola Arewa
❖ *Way of Chakras*, Caroline Shola Arewa

Yoga for Hard Times

❖ *We're all Doing Time*, Bo Lossoff
❖ *The Depression Book*, Cheri Huber
❖ *Suffering is Optional*, Cheri Huber
❖ *There's Nothing Wrong with You*, Cheri Huber
❖ *Be the Person you want to Meet*, Cheri Huber
❖ www.cherihuber.com
❖ Cheri Huber: What You Practice is What You Have; youtube
❖ *The Power Of Now*, Eckhart Tolle
❖ *The New Earth*, Eckhart Tolle
❖ *Be Here Now*, Ram Dass
❖ *Still Here Now*, Ram Dass

Food and Mood

Nutrition and Vegetarian, Vegan cookbooks

❖ *Diet for a Small Planet*, Francois Moore Lappe
❖ *Beat Stress*, Lesley Kenton
❖ *A Girl and Her Greens: Hearty Meals from the Garden*, April Bloomfield
❖ *The Plantpower Way: Whole Food Plant-Based Recipes and Guidance for The Whole Family*, Rich Roll and Julie Piatt
❖ *Lord Krishna's Cuisine: the Art of Indian Vegetarian Cooking*, Yamuna Devi
❖ *Laurel's Kitchen*, Laurel Robertson and Carol Flinders
❖ Cranks Recipe Books
❖ *Plenty*, Yottam Ottolenghi
❖ *Healing Foods Cookbook: The Vegan Way to Wellness*, Jane Sen

Anatomy, Brain and Pregnancy

* *The World's Best Anatomical Charts*, Includes all body systems A must have!
* *Netter's Anatomy Coloring Book*, John T Hansen
* *The Atlas of Muscular Skeletal Anatomy*, Chris Jarmey
* *The Muscle Book*, Paul Blakey
* *The Emotional Life of your Brain*, Richard J Davidson
* *The Human Brain Book*, Rita Carter
* *The Art of Memory,* Dame Frances Amelia Yates
* *The Pregnant Body*, Dorling Kindersley
* *The Truth about Diet and Drugs in Pregnancy*, Gail and Tom Brener
* www.anatomytrains.com

Brain Games

* www.lumosity.com
* *Zen and the Brain*, James H Austin MD
* www.brainwave-meditation.net/down_load_youtube ...
* The Human Condition bookstore www.psychotherapy.com.au/shop/book-store/human-and-clinical-issue/emotions-guilt-shame-pride/the-emotional-brain.html

Self-help

* www.yocalm.com (streaming Yoga, meditation, visualisation, self-hipnosis, ambient music & visuals to your personal devices.)
* The Chopra Centre: www.chopra.com

Music

* Music for Yoga and other Joys
* Music for Sun Power Yoga
* Ben Leinbach
* Lisbet Scott
* Gary B (not Barlow)

Other website resources

* TED talks: www.ted.com/talks
* www.depressionalliance.org
* www.nhs.uk/conditions/Cognitive-behavioural-therapy
* www.samaritans.org
* www.ipgbook.com/keep-it-simple-books-publisher-KIS.php
* www.depressionalliance.org
* www.nhs.uk/conditions/Cognitive-behavioural-therapy
* www.samaritans.org
* www.ipgbook.com/keep-it-simple-books-publisher-KIS.php
* www.tantra-kundalini.com
* www.mandalaproject.org
* Mymuna Ali: www.veryyoga.co.uk
* Spectrum Yoga: www.spectrumturkey.co.uk

Index

Symbols

8 point pose 303, 313, 501

A

Aashirvaada 186
Abdominal Breathing 228
Abdominal Lock 499
Adho Mukha Svanasana 304, 504. *See also* Down dog
Advaita. *See* Vedanta
Agni 496, 502, 542
Ahimsa. *See* Eight Limbs of Yoga
Ajna. *See* Chakras
Alternate Nostril Breathing 236, 327. *See also* Anuloma Viloma
Amygdala 419, 421
Anahata. *See* Chakras
Ananda 68, 428
Anna Yoga 192
Anuloma Viloma 236, 327, 328, 329, 424, 498, 578. *See also* Alternate Nostril Breathing
Anxiety 406
Apana 278, 572
Apana Vayu. *See* Prana
Aparigraha. *See* Eight Limbs of Yoga
Arati 73, 576
Ardha Chakrasana 339. *See also* Half wheel pose
Ardha Chandrasana 489
Ardha Matsyendrasana 327, 333, 522, 523, 528, 570. *See also* Twist pose
Ardha Sarvangasana 338. *See also* Half shoulder stand
Asana. *See* Eight Limbs of Yoga
Asanas 74, 86, 175, 290, 412, 496, 500, 527, 569
Ashram 148
Astanga 36, 37, 58, 60, 108, 112, 501, 502, 566
Astanga Invocation 58
Astanga Namaskar 303, 501. *See also* 8 point pose
Astanga Vinyasa Yoga 36, 107, 566
Asteya. *See* Eight Limbs of Yoga
Astral body 238, 567, 572
    Intellectual Sheath 567
    Mental Sheath 567
    Pranic Sheath 567
Atharvaveda 63
Atman 60, 222, 276, 567

Autosuggestion 405
Avidya 578
Ayurveda 124

B

Back bends 530
Back problems 524
Badha Konasana 327, 333, 570. *See also* Cobbler pose
Balance 325, 342, 516
Balasana 327, 570. *See also* Child's pose
Bandhas 498
    Jalandhara Bandha 499
    Moola Bandha 499
    Uddiyana Bandha 499
Bhadrasana 530
Bhagavad Gita 108, 156, 158, 160, 194
Bhakti Yoga. *See* Four Paths of Yoga
Bhujanghasana 304, 336, 501, 534. *See also* Cobra pose
Bhutas 502
Blood circulation 541
Bow pose 327, 343, 570. *See also* Dharunasana
Brahma 87, 190, 196, 202, 205, 279, 282, 467, 578
Brahmacharya. *See* Eight Limbs of Yoga
Brain changes 418
Brain training 419
Breath-Awareness 226
Breath awareness meditation 432
Breathing 224, 572
Breathing techniques 494
    Abdominal/Diaphragmatic breathing 495
    Clavicular breathing 494
    Empowered thoracic breathing 494
    Paradoxical breathing 495
    Thoracic breathing 494
Bridge pose 336, 343, 570. *See also* Setu Bandhasana
Butterfly pose 530

C

Caduceus 234
Camel pose 343, 535, 570
Candle gazing 428
Central Nervous System 540
Chair pose 342, 551
Chakras 246, 529
    1 Mooladhara 248, 282, 284, 568

    2 Swadisthana 254, 284
    3 Manipura 258, 284
    4 Anahata 262, 284, 441
    5 Vishudda 230, 242, 266, 284, 495
    6 Ajna 270, 278, 408, 428, 430
    7 Sahasrara 190, 234, 249, 264, 276, 308, 568
Chakrasana 570
Chanting 111, 460, 596
Chaturanga 313, 502
Child's pose 327, 336, 337, 570. *See also* Balasana
Chin Lock 499
Cingulate gyrus 421
Cobbler pose 325, 327, 530. *See also* Badha Konasana
Cobra pose 304, 336, 501, 534, 535, 560. *See also* Bhujanghasana
Cognitive Behavioral Therapy 386
Coiled Serpent (The) 234
Complete Lord of the Fishes 527
Corpse pose 23, 144, 222, 327, 328, 339, 570. *See also* Savasana
Cosmic Dancer (The). *See* Nataraj
Crane pose 340
Crescent Moon pose 314
Crocodile pose 502. *See also* Chaturanga
Crown Chakra 262, 441
Crow pose 332, 570

D

Daily Practice 322
Dancer pose 327, 332, 570. *See also* Natarajasana
Danda 464
Deltoids 549
Depression 380, 391, 406
Dharana. *See* Eight Limbs of Yoga
Dharunasana 327, 570. *See also* Bow pose
Dhumavati Yantra. *See* Sacred Geometry
Dhyana. *See* Eight Limbs of Yoga
Diaphragm 563
Down dog 304, 313, 314, 340, 504, 506
Downward Facing Dog 504
Durga Yantra. *See* Sacred Geometry
Dvaita. *See* Vedanta
Dynamic Diaphragmatic Breathing 231

E

Eagle pose 83. *See also* Garudasana
Eight Limbs of Yoga 58, 107, 108, 112, 113, 121,
        290, 578
    1 Yama 113, 114, 288, 578
        Ahimsa 44, 100, 102, 114, 354, 368, 437
        Aparigraha 115
        Asteya 114
        Brahmacharya 115, 578
        Satya 60, 114, 190, 295
    2 Niyama 113, 116
        Ishvarapranidhana 117
        Santosha 116
        Saucha 116
        Svadhyaya 117
        Tapas 67, 116
    3 Asana 80, 117, 118, 194, 291, 318, 398, 424,
        500, 522, 524, 532, 564, 570
    4 Pranayama 112, 117, 119, 124, 224, 235,
        283, 290, 292, 424, 441, 499, 567, 578
    5 Pratyahara 120
    6 Dharana 120
    7 Dhyana 121
    8 Samadhi 108, 117, 121, 235
Endocrine system 263, 264, 529, 539, 564
Eugene Peterson. *See* Indra Devi
Evil Eye 209

F

Fasting 192, 194
Fish pose 327, 339, 342, 544, 570. *See
        also* Matsyasana
Food and Mood 139
Forward bends 530
Forward fold 302, 305, 315, 340, 501
Four Agreements 374
Four Paths of Yoga 109
    Bhakti Yoga 109, 111
    Jnana Yoga 109, 122, 123
    Karma Yoga 109, 163
    Raja Yoga 109, 112, 162, 290, 291
Full wheel pose 570

G

Gandhi, Mahatma 92, 107, 121, 166
Ganesha 203
Garudasana 83. *See also* Eagle pose
Gazing pose 315
Glutes 549
Gurukula 62, 166, 578
Gyaani 190

H

Halasana 338, 539, 570. *See also* Plough pose
Half Lord of the Fishes 333, 570
Half moon balance 489
Half shoulder stand 338. *See also* Ardha
        Sarvangasana
Half-Spinal Twist 528
Half wheel pose 339. *See also* Ardha Chakrasana
Hamsa. *See* Hand of Fatima
Hamstrings 549
Hand of Fatima 206
Harshad number 440
Hasta Padasana 570
Hatha Yoga 73, 80, 86, 106, 112, 124, 163, 164,
        224, 290, 569
Hatha Yoga Pradipika 106, 290
Headstand 538
Head to knee pose 325, 327, 556, 570. *See
        also* Janu Sirsasana
Heart 562
Heart Chakra 243, 258, 262, 441
Himsa 102
Hippocampus 421
Hypothalamus 421

I

Ida 234, 271, 281, 283, 284, 424
Incense 111, 175, 181, 286, 407, 410, 427
Inclined plane 533
Indra Devi 76
Intellectual Sheath. *See* Astral body
Inversion 194, 325, 326, 327, 341, 504, 538,
        541, 544
Inversions 538
Ishvarapranidhana. *See* Eight Limbs of Yoga
Isis 310
Iyengar 34, 36, 112, 235, 244, 249, 250, 258, 266,
        278, 527, 538

J

Jalandhara Bandha 499
Janu Sirsasana 327, 334, 531, 556, 570. *See
        also* Head to knee pose
Japa Meditation 436, 577
    Manasika Japa 437
    Vaikhari Japa 437
Jnana Yoga. *See* Four Paths of Yoga
Joints
    Ball and socket 556
    Pivot 558
    Synovial 558

K

Kakasana 332, 518, 519, 570
Kali Yantra. *See* Sacred Geometry
Kapalbhati 231, 328, 424, 496
Karma Yoga. *See* Four Paths of Yoga
Kevala Advaita. *See* Vedanta
Kirtan 111, 460, 464, 576
Knowledge Library 580
Kriya 101, 230, 290, 496
Kumbakhasana 303, 312, 501, 504. *See
        also* Plank pose
Kundalini 234
Kundalini Yoga 124, 235, 284
Kyphosis 560

L

Legs up the wall pose 327, 538, 539. *See
        also* Viparita Karani
Ligaments 553, 556, 558
Locust pose 325, 327, 342, 343, 560, 570. *See
        also* Salabasana
Lordosis 560
Lotus Feet 58
Lotus Flower 190
Low blood pressure 223, 545
Lunge 303, 304, 311, 314, 340, 512. *See
        also* Parsvakonasana
Lymphatic system 539

M

Mahabharata 156, 187
Mala beads 438, 440, 577
Mandala. *See* Sacred Geometry
Manipura. *See* Chakras
Mataji 72, 79
Matsyasana 327, 339, 544, 545, 546, 570. *See
        also* Fish pose
Mauna 153, 161, 162
    Mauna Vratham 154
Maya 90, 122, 567, 573, 574
Meditation 403, 412, 416, 424, 427, 428, 436,
        448. *See also* Japa Meditation; *See
        also* Breath Awareness Meditation; *See
        also* Tratak; *See also* Candle Gazing
Memory Palace 582
Men's health 508
Mental Clarity 194
Mental Sheath. *See* Astral body
Method of Loci 582
Mindfulness-based cognitive therapy 418
Mind Palace 582, 584

Moola Bandha 499
Mooladhara. *See* Chakras
Mountain pose 332, 501, 538, 560, 570
Mudras 237, 238, 427, 432, 498
    Chin Mudra 240, 427, 432
    Jnana Mudra 240
    Prana Mudra 243
    Shankh Mudra 242
    Tse Mudra 241
Muscles
    Deltoid 549
    Hamstring 549
    Isometric 556
    Isotonic 556
    Quadriceps 551
    Sternocleidomastoid 548
    Stretching 552, 555

N

Nada Yoga 124, 196
Nadi Centres 234
Nadis 196, 234, 281, 283, 424
Namaskaara 187
Namaste 182, 187, 302, 305, 312, 316
Nataraj 87
Natarajasana 327, 332, 570. *See also* Dancer
    pose
Navel Chakra 258
Neck problems 535
Niyama. *See* Eight Limbs of Yoga

O

OM 122, 129, 196, 436, 462, 577
Om Namah Shivaya 467

P

Pachimottanasana 327, 335, 531, 570. *See*
    also The West pose
Paripurna Matsyendrasana 527
Parsvakonasana 512. *See also* Lunge
Pigeon pose 340
Pineal gland 271, 272, 421, 422, 428, 430
Pingala 234, 271, 281, 283, 284, 424
Pituitary 421
Plank pose 303, 501, 504. *See*
    also Kumbakhasana
Plough pose 338, 538, 539, 570. *See*
    also Halasana
Pradakshina 176
Prakriti 566

Prana 572
    Vayus
        Apana Vayu
        Prana Vayu 572
        Samana Vayu
        Udana Vayu
        Vyana Vayu
Prana Vayu. *See* Prana
Pranayama. *See* Eight Limbs of Yoga
Pranic Sheath. *See* Astral body
Pratuthana 187
Pratyabivaadana 187
Pratyahara. *See* Eight Limbs of Yoga
Prayer 87
Prayer pose 302, 305, 342
Prostrate 186
Purusha 523
Purvottanasana 533

Q

Quadriceps 551

R

Rajas. *See* Three Gunas
Rajasic Food 132
Raja Yoga. *See* Four Paths of Yoga
Ramayana 156, 187
Reincarnation 94
Relaxation pose 325
Religion 85
Respiratory System 540
Reverse plank 533
Rigveda 63, 244
Rituals 173
Root Chakra 248
Root Lock 499
Rudra 214, 244

S

Sacral Chakra 254
Sacred Geometry 124, 131
    Mandala 124
    Sri Yantra 124
    Tantra 124, 248, 597
    Yantra 124
    Yantra Mandalas 130
        Dhumavati Yantra
        Durga Yantra
        Kali Yantra
Sacred Space 42, 48, 181, 427
Sadhaka 108, 163, 575
Sadhana 67, 163, 290, 575

Sahasrara. *See* Chakras
Sai Yoga 76
Salabasana 327, 570. *See also* Locust pose
Salamba Sarvangasana 564
Salamba Sirsasana 539. *See also* Supported
    Headstand
Samadhi 222. *See also* Eight Limbs of Yoga
Samana Vayu. *See* Prana
Samaveda 63
Samsara 102, 103, 574
Samskaras 103, 288, 489
Sankalpa 186
Sannyasin 67, 72, 80, 576
Sanskrit terminology & philosophy 566
Santosha. *See* Eight Limbs of Yoga
Sarvangasana 327, 338, 538, 539, 564, 570. *See*
    also Shoulder stand
Satsang 150, 576
Sattva. *See* Three Gunas
Satvic Food 132, 194
Satya 60, 114, 190, 295. *See* Eight Limbs of Yoga
Saucha. *See* Eight Limbs of Yoga
Savasana 23, 144, 222, 223, 328, 339, 570. *See*
    also Corpse pose
Scoliosis 560
Sea of Samsara 103
Sea of Samskara 574
Seated Yoga 371, 372
Setu Bandhasana 336, 570. *See also* Bridge pose
Shaashtaanga 187
Shakti 80, 129, 441, 567
Shanti 578
Shining Skull 231
Shiva 87, 196, 204, 205, 243, 244, 245, 278, 290,
    300, 441, 467, 568, 578
Shivam 190
Shoulder stand 327, 338, 538, 564. *See*
    also Sarvangasana
Sirsasana 327, 334, 531, 538, 539, 540, 541,
    556, 570
Sphynx pose 343
Sri Chakra. *See* Sri Yantra
Sri Yantra. *See* Sacred Geometry
Standing hand to foot pose 570
Sternocleidomastoid 548
Sthira 118
Stretching 322, 362, 489, 506, 513, 552, 554,
    555, 556
Sukha 60, 118
Sun Power Series 306, 327, 329

Sun Salutation 74, 500, 501, 502. *See also* Surya Namaskar

Supported Headstand. *See also* Salamba Sirsasana

Surya Namaskar 282, 298, 329, 500, 570. *See also* Sun Salutation

Sushumna 234, 249, 270, 277, 279, 281, 283, 284, 441, 568

Svadhyaya. *See* Eight Limbs of Yoga

Swadisthana. *See* Chakras

Swami 576

Swami Sivananda 25, 43, 66, 72, 80, 83, 109, 134, 148, 277, 283, 292

Swami Sivananda Radha 80

Swami Vishnudevananda 25, 36, 43, 68, 70, 72, 106, 148, 272, 282, 576

Symbols of Protection 201
    Cross 212
    Dream Catcher 211
    Evil Eye 209
    Ganesha 203
    Hand of Fatima 206
    Isis 214

Synovial joint 558

T

Table 533

Tadasana 302, 305, 310, 316, 501, 538

Tailor pose 333, 334, 530, 570

Talking Therapies 386

Tamas. *See* Three Gunas

Tamasic Food 132

Tantra. *See* Sacred Geometry

Tapas. *See* Eight Limbs of Yoga

Thalamus 421

The Feet of the Guru 57

The West pose 327, 335, 570. *See also* Pachimottanasana

Third Eye (The) 262, 270, 408, 428

Thousand Petalled Lotus 190, 234, 277, 308

Three Gunas 132, 240, 566
    Rajas 132, 235, 240, 566
    Sattva 132, 240, 566
    Satva 132, 240
    Tamas 132, 235, 240, 566

Three Locks
    Abdominal Lock 499
    Chin Lock 499
    Root Lock 499

Throat Chakra 266

Thyroid gland 242, 267, 564

Tratak 428

Tree pose 327, 340, 500, 520. *See also* Vrksasana

Triangle pose 129, 325, 327, 331, 341, 423, 513, 514. *See also* Trikonasana

Trikonasana 327, 331, 513, 556, 570. *See also* Triangle pose

Twist pose 325, 327, 340, 522, 550, 565. *See also* Ardha Matsyendrasana

U

Udana Vayu. *See* Prana

Uddiyana Bandha 494, 499

Ujjayi 118, 223, 230, 231, 328, 495, 496

Upanishads 123, 279, 282

Upasangrahan 187

Upavaasa 192

Up facing dog 313

Urdwha Mukha Svanasana 313

Ustrasana 535, 570. *See also* Camel pose

Utkatasana 551

Uttanasana 302, 305, 310, 501. *See also* Foreward fold

Utthita Trikonasana 556

V

Vaasanas 178

Varicose veins 541

Vayus. *See* Prana

Vedanta 36, 66, 67, 68, 74, 122, 123, 194, 306, 462, 576
    The Three Vedanta Schools 123
        1 Dvaita 123
        2 Advaita 123, 576
        3 Kevala Advaita 123

Vedas (The) 62, 123
    Atharvaveda 63
    Rigveda 63
    Samaveda 63
    Yajuveda 63

Vedic Chant 462

Veil of Illusion 90, 122, 573. *See also* Maya

Vertebrae 559

Victorious Breath 230

Viparita Karani 538, 539, 541. *See also* Legs up the wall pose

Virabhadrasana 327, 331, 500, 510, 512, 550, 570. *See also* Warrior pose

Vishnu 190, 196, 205, 237, 243, 467, 545, 578

Vishnu Mudra 237, 498

Vishudda. *See* Chakras

Visualisations 443

Vrksasana 327, 500, 520. *See also* Tree pose

Vyana Vayu. *See* Prana

W

Warrior pose 130, 325, 331, 508, 510, 512, 577. *See also* Virabhadrasana

Wheel pose 343

Y

Yajnas 164

Yajuveda 63

Yama. *See* Eight Limbs of Yoga

Yamas 100, 115

Yantra. *See* Sacred Geometry

Yoga for the Hands 238

Yoga Nidra 222, 405

Yoga of Sound. *See* Nada Yoga

Yoga of Synthesis 109

Yoga Philosophy 92, 240, 288

Yoga Shala 41, 181, 291

Yoga Sutras of Patanjali 107, 108, 112, 230

Yoga Theory 50, 99, 106

Yogic Breathing 228

Yogic Sleep 405

Youthful pose 532

Z

Zen Buddhist Meditation 391

Credits

Special thanks to our models and teachers included in this book: Graham Caley, Caroline Wickham, Aurelio, Ulla, Omy Nacri, Gary Newland, Jignesh Vaidya, Alva Malka, Germaine O'Shaughnessy, Helen Dight, Lorna Thompson, Mandy Vitols, Rachel Graham, Sharon Roberts, Tomasz Geborys, Brendan Murphy, Sylvia Reitzema, Paul Robertson, Theresa Khachik, Malcolm Sargent, Dmitri, Raphan Laye Kebet, Sammie Walker, Sophie Cox, Nidi Nanda, Ana Dos Santos, and the beautiful Avni Patel.

Any images not listed below belong to Anne-Marie Newland, Melissa Newland & Sam Hadcock.

page 5	www.sylviareitzema.co.uk	page 208	www.123rf.com/profile_evdoha
page 27	www.123rf.com/profile_anzemulec	page 210	www.123rf.com/profile_transiastock
page 21	www.123rf.com/profile_fotoaloja	page 213	www.123rf.com/profile_reddz
page 583	www.123rf.com/ profile_alessandro0770	page 216	1 www.123rf.com/profile_devilpup
page 585	www.123rf.com/profile_NejroN	page 216	2 www.123rf.com/profile_imagesbyhafizismail
page 45	www.123rf.com/profile_rolffimages	page 216	3 www.123rf.com/profile_tigger11th
page 49	www.123rf.com/profile_teraberb	page 216	4 www.123rf.com/profile_phaendin
page 52	www.123rf.com/profile_elenaray	page 216	5 www.123rf.com/profile_cienpies
page 63	www.123rf.com/profile_thefull360	page 216	6 www.123rf.com/profile_fergregory
page 71	www.123rf.com/profile_johannadeitmer	page 216	7 www.123rf.com/profile_nikkized
page 79	www.123rf.com/profile_plotnikov	page 216	8 www.123rf.com/profile_ashwin
page 56	www.123rf.com/profile_mack2happy	page 217	1 www.123rf.com/profile_sunnytime
page 87	www.123rf.com/profile_lenikovaleva	page 217	2 www.123rf.com/profile_soultkd
page 88	www.123rf.com/profile_roboriginal	page 217	3 www.123rf.com/profile_nikkized
page 91	www.123rf.com/profile_dmitriusyakovlev	page 217	4 www.123rf.com/profile_sumners
page 95	www.flickr.com/photos/111469876@N05/ www.facebook.com/talithakhachikphotography	page 217	5 www.123rf.com/profile_file404
		page 217	6 www.123rf.com/profile_plotnikov
page 98	www.123rf.com/profile_worradirek	page 217	7 www.123rf.com/profile_picturepartners
page 105	www.123rf.com/profile_elenaray	page 217	9 www.123rf.com/profile_nufunya
page 146	www.123rf.com/profile_sittipong	page 218	www.123rf.com/profile_elenaray
page 151	www.123rf.com/profile_arindambanerjee	page 232	Bob Spencer
page 167	www.123rf.com/profile_aodaodaod	page 234	www.123rf.com/profile_maximus256
page 168	www.123rf.com/profile_elenaray	page 239	www.123rf.com/profile_elenaray
page 172	www.123rf.com/profile_udra	page 240	www.sylviareitzema.co.uk
page 177	www.123rf.com/profile_tvirbickis	page 241	www.sylviareitzema.co.uk
page 179	www.123rf.com/profile_yuliang11	page 242	www.sylviareitzema.co.uk
page 180	www.123rf.com/profile_smithore	page 243	www.sylviareitzema.co.uk
page 184	www.123rf.com/profile_zurijeta	page 245	www.sylviareitzema.co.uk
page 198	3 www.123rf.com/profile_pinnacleanimates	page 247	Padmasana: www.123rf.com/profile_vanilladesign
page 198	4 www.123rf.com/profile_leshabu	page 247	Chakras: www.123rf.com/profile_sweet_caramel
page 198	5 www.123rf.com/profile_byheaven	page 253	www.123rf.com/profile_vitorta
page 198	6 www.123rf.com/profile_maadesigns	page 261	www.123rf.com/profile_elenaray
page 198	7 www.123rf.com/profile_velusariot	page 269	www.123rf.com/profile_feedough
page 198	8 www.123rf.com/profile_rvrobinson	page 279	www.123rf.com/profile_project1photography
page 198	10 www.123rf.com/profile_ujwalasiddh	page 284	www.123rf.com/profile_Eraxion
page 198	13 www.123rf.com/profile_annykos	page 287	www.123rf.com/profile_zhu_zhu
page 126	www.123rf.com/profile_goku347	page 289	Alex Hannam. *Leicester Mercury*
page 130	www.123rf.com/profile_tantrik71	page 296	www.123rf.com/profile_byheaven
page 197	Silvia Occhionorel	page 299	www.123rf.com/profile_elenaray
page 200	www.123rf.com/profile_fergregory	page 301	www.123rf.com/profile_irabel8
page 203	www.123rf.com/profile_posterize	page 302	Bob Spencer